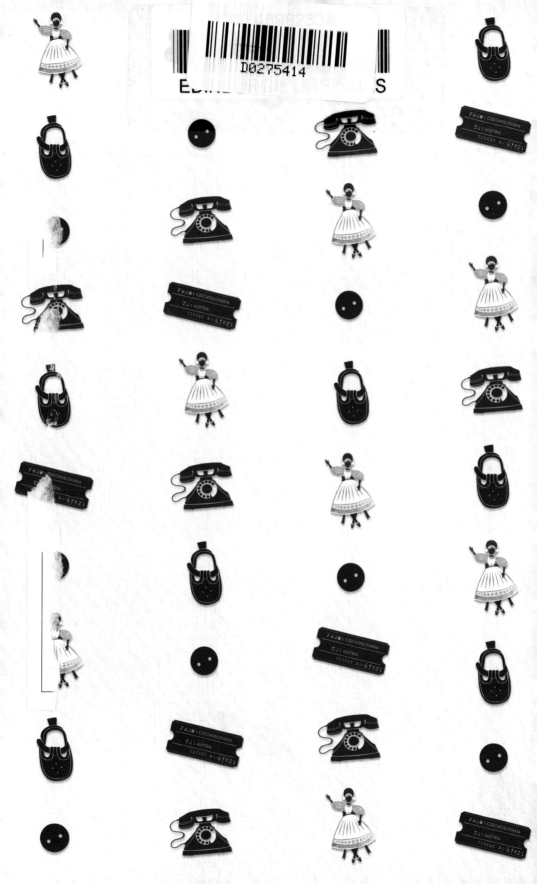

THE
MUSEUM
OF BROKEN
PROMISES

THE
MUSEUM
OF BROKEN
PROMISES

ENTER ITS DOORS, AND THE PAST WILL FIND YOU

ELIZABETH
BUCHAN

CORVUS

First published in Great Britain in 2019 by Corvus, an imprint of
Atlantic Books Ltd.

10 9 8 7 6 5 4 3 2 1

A CIP catalogue record for this book is available from the British Library.

Hardback ISBN: 978 1 78649 528 0
Trade paperback ISBN: 978 1 78649 530 3
E-book ISBN: 978 1 78649 529 7

Corvus
An imprint of Atlantic Books Ltd
Ormond House
26–27 Boswell Street
London
WC1N 3JZ

www.corvus-books.co.uk

For Annie and Duncan

'I gradually came to realize that there were two kinds of freedom, internal and external'

Ivan Klíma, *My Crazy Century*

Austria, 1986

$\mathcal{A}$ TWENTY-YEAR-OLD GIRL WITH A BANDAGED HAND waits on an Austrian station platform with a suitcase at her feet inside which is stuffed a rucksack but nothing else because it is only there for pretence.

The platform is grey and so badly maintained that plants scramble through the cracked asphalt. It is the same story on the track where the weeds sprout lustily between the sleepers.

Her eyes slot right and left, searching for a watcher. One of the grubby but sometimes desperate people who keep afloat by reporting on others. She is becoming an expert on those.

She strains to see into the distance. Small and isolated, the station is surrounded by woods. Ash and pine, and beautiful silver birches. Through a break in the trees, she sees a cluster of red roofs from the centre of which rises an onion-domed baroque church. So typical of Middle Europe, she thinks, the breath catching in her chest. Of free Europe.

A couple walks onto the platform. The woman is carrying an overnight bag and he a larger suitcase which he sets down. The woman is thin and dressed in a camel-coloured coat. He is stockier

1

and wears an Alpine hat with a feather in the hatband. They are prosperous and smug, and she hates them on sight. *They* can park their bottoms on the train seats and sit in perfect tranquillity all the way to Vienna.

The girl swings around in the direction from where the train will arrive. To the north and east is the border between Communist Czechoslovakia and the Austria where she now waits. Even though the rail route was established in the Hapsburgs' heyday and is well mapped, it is not going to be, and never would have been, a simple journey.

If the schedules run true to form (not something on which one counts in Czechoslovakia) the tank-like, grimy Soviet Bloc engine with its red star on the smokebox should be pulling into Gmünd, which is the exchange station for the engines and on the border between Czechoslovakia and Austria. Having made the same journey from Prague to Vienna a week earlier, she knows there is a special platform fenced off by a wall and barbed wire where the passport and custom control officials wait.

She is not Czech. Her ability to travel was not in question. Yet, on that train journey she realized she had been infected by the pathogen of repression. Sweaty palms. A constant urge to urinate. Checking, checking on her fellow passengers. Paranoia is promiscuous. It doesn't mind which philosophy it feeds on.

At Gmünd, the Czechoslovakian frontier bullies worked their way through the carriages as they will be doing at this moment. She and the other passengers sat in dead silence. On the platform, dogs and police checked the length of the train's chassis for 'deadheads' clinging to the underside.

When the all-clear signal sounded, the Czech engine decoupled. There was a bump as a shiny western one replaced it.

She remembers clutching her UK passport in her injured hand and trying not to think of the 'deadheads'. Instead she made herself concentrate on him – of when they first met and how it became what it is.

Then, as she is doing now, she thinks about love and what an extraordinary, incendiary thing it is and of how it consumes her. Of how her life has been transformed.

If she closes her eyes, she can summon him. His touch, his smell, his body.

The single bench on the platform by the waiting room is free and she sits down. Its wood is gnarled and splintering and guaranteed to ladder tights.

She lights up a cigarette.

Milos will have gone over and over the plan with Tomas. *It's the details that count.* She remembers Milos telling her about the escape plans. *Learn them.* The right seat, the right station, the right clothes… *You have to convince them that your journey is normal and you have been given permission to make it.*

A crate of champagne will have been sent to the watchtower.

It seldom fails, said Milos. Get them drunk.

Step by step. The architecture of an escape is painfully hazardous to construct because it involves trust.

Her heart beats faster. Don't think about failure.

It's madness to try and do a runner from the cross-over point at Gmünd. Suicidal. Everyone knows that. That's why this unremarkable station on the other side of the border is the one to go for and why she is here.

On arrive, he promised in his execrable French. 'I will.'

The autumn wind whips the tops of the trees. Her cigarette flares up and then dies. She grinds the butt with her boot and shivers.

The watchers. Who are they? Answer: everyone, including your grandmother. Once it is understood that an elderly woman with a string bag bulging with vegetables is as dangerous as the bully boy in the leather jacket, it becomes obvious that anyone can manipulate anyone. She also knows that, in more cases than she supposed, the watchers are as frightened as the subjects on whom they spy.

Waiting.

Waiting is an art form. Those who live in eastern Europe know its intimacies. The dry lips. The rapid heartbeat.

She shoves her cold hands into her pockets. In the left one she clutches the railway ticket she used to make her own getaway. *Prague, Brno, Gmünd…* She refuses to throw it away.

The elderly Volkswagen she has bought from a garage is parked up outside the station. God knows what condition the car is in but if it gets them to England it doesn't matter a toss. On the back seat is a loaf of bread, sausages, apples and beer.

'You'll have to marry me if you want to stay in England.'

'Do I now?'

Her stomach clenches with pain and she begins to shake.

She knows what she has done.

She knows.

She checks her watch. In the world she has just fled, there are many jokes about timetables being made of jelly. She's not laughing now.

Again, she checks her watch.

If all is well, the newly attached engine is easing its way to the border where the frontier police are poised to open the concrete barriers, leaving it free to gather speed towards Vienna.

If all is well.

4

She knew that the instructions would be precise. He must chop his hair short and wear a business suit – not his style at all. He must always keep his forged passport to hand.

'I hope your name won't be Wilhem,' she told him as they said goodbye. 'I refuse to love a Wilhelm. It should be Viktor for Victory.'

On the station bench, she prays that he is occupying the aisle seat – aisle seats are better positioned to make a break for it. In his briefcase should be a made-up schedule of business commitments for his four-day visit to Vienna and a forged docket for the hotel.

She squints into the distance. Smoke is billowing over the trees and, in the far distance, a train moves against a green backdrop. Gradually, it enlarges and bears down towards the station, wheels screeching on the rails as it reins in its momentum. A stink of anthracite and low-grade coal floats over the platforms.

What is love? What is her love? Profound, infinite, burning, tender... all those words.

Guilty?

Her hands clench.

The train has precipitous steps up to the carriages and the passengers are descending. A toddler is coaxed down. An elderly man clings to the rail and summons his courage.

The smug, prosperous couple further along the platform wait to board.

The wind shifts and the engine's steam throws a dense, white veil over the scene. A man in a pinstriped suit and black brogues steps down from the third carriage. His hat obscures his face but he has short hair and a red handkerchief tucked into his lapel pocket.

Gritty smoke blows into her eyes which are watering copiously.

Her heart beats a tattoo of relief.

Then...

The figure halts in front of her. 'Laure.'

The smoke clears. *Oh my God.*

Her insides are dissolving, her knees weakening. In a second or two, she is going to collapse onto the grey platform.

Petr holds out his hand.

Hers remain at her side. 'Where is Tomas? Tell me where he is.'

'I can't tell you that.'

'Is he alive?'

'I can't tell you that.'

He looks at her with a mix of pity and contempt. In a moment of clarity, she understands that Petr's feelings for her do not extend to ensuring her happiness. He has his life. He has his family. He has his politics.

She steps back, one foot feeling unsteadily behind the other. 'My God … you've betrayed him.'

He grabs her by her injured arm and she bites back a scream. '*I* betrayed him?' he says.

CHAPTER 1

Paris, today

*H*ER LIFE WAS NOT QUITE IN ORDER. WOULD POSSIBLY never be – but it wasn't bad. Accommodations had been made. She had the museum.

At 9 a.m., Laure folded back the shutters in Room 2 and looked out at a Paris revealed by the morning light. A bunch of pigeons strutted over the roof next-door uttering their pigeon racket.

In summer, the sun lightened the colours of the roof tiles. In autumn, they were slicked with rain and, in winter, frost sometimes ran a rim around their edges so that they resembled a Fabergé fantasy.

Little else changed over a year, which was precisely what Laure craved. She wanted to look out at the same vista, open the same shutters and turn to inspect the glass cabinets in which were enshrined the disquiet of those who sought resolution.

Those objects could be disturbing. Or poignant. Or funny. Almost always marked in their effect. It was not uncommon for a visitor to say they had experienced a sense of *déjà vu* when studying the display cabinets. Some confessed they had a feeling that there was someone else in the room other than the visitors. Some said that the objects appeared to exude a soul, with all its imprecision and mystery. Stopping to polish a small smudge on the glass of the cabinet nearest to the door, she walked into the next room. The day had begun.

Just before the lunch hour, a muffled cry sounded in the building.

Upstairs in the office, Laure, and her assistant, Nic Arnold, looked up from their desks. *One of those.* A touchstone moment when a dam broke in a visitor, releasing... well... many things.

She gestured to the door. 'You or me?' The cry was repeated and Laure made a decision. 'Both, I think.'

It was early autumn and the visitor numbers were dropping as they always did after the summer. Technically, it was a normal day. Yet, normal days could be deceptive. From them could erupt disquiet, even a violence of sorts. Certainly, violent emotions. The contents of Laure's unassuming, unshowy museum possessed a power to trigger them, particularly in those close to breaking point.

She picked up the first-aid pack. Nic picked up the clipboard. Together, they ran downstairs. If procedure was being observed, Chantal at the kiosk would be hastening upstairs ready to herd visitors away from the room in which the incident was taking place.

In Room 3, a man and a woman were fighting. Or rather, he was fending off an attack as she beat him on the face with the museum catalogue. Laure and Nic exchanged a glance. Nic put down his clipboard, stepped forwards and, as politely as possible in the circumstances, pulled the woman off the man.

Panting, the man stood back – disappointment and rage written all over his face. He touched his cheek where the edge of the catalogue had left a red mark. 'What do you think you're doing, Odile?'

'I wish I could kill you.' She was matter-of-fact which made what she said the more chilling. One hand clung to the belt threaded through her jeans which, Laure noted, had a large metal buckle. 'Perhaps I will one of these days.'

They were French. Not so surprising as this was Paris – but you could never predict in this museum (any museum?) what a visitor's nationality might be.

The woman's knees buckled, forcing Nic to tighten his grip. Laure whipped the chair, stationed by the wall for precisely these emergencies, under the woman and together they eased her down.

The first-aid pack had been designed to snap open easily and Laure produced a cup and a bottle of water. 'Would this help?' She was calm and measured. 'I'm forbidden to hand out medication but I can contact a doctor or the emergency services if you think you require them.'

Nic picked up the clipboard and wrote the time and date down in the boxes on the form headed 'Incidents'.

She held the plastic cup to the woman's lips who took a mouthful and pushed away Laure's arm. 'Thank you.'

Laure eased herself upright and addressed the man. 'Are you the person who we would deal with in an emergency?'

Tall. Wearing jeans and a corduroy jacket. Probably in his forties... 'If you're asking if I'm her husband, I am,' he answered. 'Yves Brun.'

Sour, too.

Nic noted it down. 'Is your wife unwell or was it something in the museum which has upset her?'

A shade crossed the man's features. 'I suspect it was something here.'

Even to an uninformed observer, and Laure and Nic were habituated to seven degrees of deception practised by the public, it was obvious Yves was skirting the truth.

Odile shivered. 'He knows what's wrong.'

Nic wrote that down too. Current regulations insisted on a precise record and he asked Yves for their telephone numbers.

Yves bent over his wife. 'Odile, you can't do this in public. It's becoming a problem.'

She gazed up at him and, without warning, spat at his feet. 'That sort of problem?'

'*Putain.*' He stepped back.

Again, Nic and Laure exchanged glances. The situation was likely to be more complicated than met the eye.

'The shoes...' Odile wiped her mouth. 'They belong to my daughter.'

Nic wrote: 'Room 3. Marital incident.'

Laure knew to what Odile was referring. At the front of the display cabinet was a rectangular box into which was meticulously folded a baby's layette. It included a cashmere shawl, two tiny vests, a pair of socks and distinctive green-and-white booties. The label read in French, English and Italian: 'My baby never made it into this world because of negligence'.

Laure placed herself so that she blocked the cabinet and its objects from Odile's sight. 'Do you wish me to summon help?'

The husband winced. 'No.'

'We all need help. The whole world needs help,' said Odile. 'And he's taken my daughter's things and put them here without my permission.'

'It's the medication,' said Yves. The anger had been superseded by a sadness, which Laure – who understood sadness – knew was unfeigned. 'She doesn't know any more.'

'Thank God,' said Odile. 'Who wants to know about being alive? Do you?' She swivelled around to look up at Laure. 'You don't look brimming with excitement.'

'Odile… may I call you Odile?' asked Laure. 'Those baby clothes were sent in by someone who lives in Italy. I have the records.' She waited for the information to sink in and added gently, 'The objects in here can affect one and it's possible to become muddled.'

'Don't patronize me.' Ignoring her husband, she opened her bag and drew out a blister pack of pills and squeezed a couple out into her hand. Yves exclaimed and turned away. 'Shut up,' she told him.

'When you left hospital you promised.' Yves stuffed his hands into his pockets.

'Oh yes, I promised.' She gagged over the pills but got them down. 'My baby… our baby… did make it into the world but only for a few hours. I had bought her the clothes,' she pointed to the cabinet. 'Exactly those. I never saw her in them.'

Deal with. Record. Facilitate. She and Nic knew the procedures well.

In the adjacent Room 4, Chantal had kettled off the visitors, who no doubt were riveted by her purple hair and many piercings, and asked them to remain there for five minutes. Shortly afterwards, Laure and Nic helped a shaky Odile down the stairs. Yves followed and reluctantly took his wife's other arm and he and Laure ushered her outside.

'Will you be all right?' she asked. He shrugged, and she added, 'I'm sorry.'

'What use is that?' said Odile, breaking free from her husband and making for the street. 'You can say sorry till your tongue drops out, it doesn't change things. It doesn't bring the dead back.'

Yves cast an apologetic glance at Laure and went after his wife.

Laure turned to go back in.

'You're Laure Carlyle, the curator, right?'

Laure was accosted by a tall, Nordically fair girl in dark glasses but her accent suggested she was an American from the South. Tennessee? Georgia?

Normally, the museum staff shielded her from the madder and more extreme petitioners. But the girl looked sane. And energetic. She also looked as though she wasn't acquainted with fear.

Buttonholing obviously came naturally to whoever this was for she continued, 'I'm a freelance journalist over in Paris working on stories. I heard about your museum and I would love to talk to you about it.' She searched in a black neoprene rucksack and thrust a card at Laure. 'I've just spent time here. It's special. It needs to be written about. *You* need to be written about.' She added, 'I do all the grunt work, so you needn't worry. You just have to talk.'

This was not unusual. The museum had gained footfall and traction in the guidebooks and the press. Journalists were intrigued by the concept and the location – oh, it's in *Paris*! There was a hum about it on social media. Even *Newsweek* had made an overture in an email: 'We will put you on the map'.

'I rarely give interviews.' Laure pocketed the card without looking at it.

'I googled you,' the girl said, and Laure bristled. As she always did. 'You gave an interview to an Italian magazine a few months ago. Might it be time for another?'

'No.'

'I have a big contact at *Vanity Fair*,' says the girl. 'It would be red meat for them.'

Carrot. Dangled.

This girl was on the make. Working her way into a career. She'll take risks, lie a little. Or, bend the truth. Laure had clashed with the type often. 'Please don't think this is unkind, but no.'

'Not unkind, but protective perhaps?' Far from taking the flat refusal, the girl remained polite, charming and persistent. 'This place needs to be known. It helps people?'

This was true. 'It does.'

'If I had set up this place, it would be because I have something in my past to exorcise. What do you reckon?'

The question was clumsily put, transparently ambitious, but smart.

'You'd be wrong.' Laure gave no hint of her dismay and made for the entrance. 'I have to get back to work.'

At the door, she looked back over her shoulder.

Chantal had returned to the entrance desk. She looked up at Laure. '*Quelle scène.*' She had the half-fascinated, half-appalled expression on her face that Laure had seen before. 'Nic reckons she was a bit mad.'

'Maybe.' Laure placed a foot on the first stair. 'Back to normal upstairs?'

'They all wanted to know who was killing whom and why.' Chantal's smile revealed very even teeth. 'It's made the visit for them. They'll tell everybody about it and we'll have double the numbers tomorrow.' She gestured to the revolving stand with the postcards. 'We never know what happens in the end.'

'No,' said Laure. 'But that's the point.'

'*Dommage.*' Chantal stuck her head on one side. 'You all right?'

Chantal's purple hair and piercings did an excellent job of disguising her motherly nature and she was hoping Laure would admit that she wasn't because it would give her permission to fuss over her boss.

'You're a treasure, Chantal, but I'm fine.'

'People…' She fiddled with one of her several ear studs. 'They think they can sound off anywhere.'

'No, they think they can sound off in here. And that's fine. Absolutely fine.'

Laure went upstairs to check over the rooms. Rooms 3 and 4 were crowded with visitors which always added an air of excitement. A large group of Japanese tourists wearing orange baseball hats were being shepherded through Rooms 6 and 7. Laure stepped aside to let them pass. Most of them ignored her and surged through the doorways, blind to anything but their determination to reach the end.

Room 5 was empty and the two videos on screens at either end of the room rolled on a continual loop. The first was of a walled garden. The first shots were of it under snow, with a frozen gallery of trees and bushes flanking a central lawn. The following shots were taken in spring and the starkness had been replaced by blossom and foliage. The summer brought frilled peonies and brazen dahlias in oranges and crimsons. The autumn shots were of berries and the laden apple trees at the far end of the garden.

The final view was of a garden that was no longer a garden. Instead of a flowerbed blazing with autumn colour and windfall apples servicing punch-drunk wasps, four houses had grown within the walls. Unimaginative creations with plate-glass windows of the variety beloved by out-for-a-quick-profit property developers. These were houses not constructed for beauty or pleasure but to make money. The label underneath this video read: 'My elder brother promised my parents never to sell the garden. Six months after their death, he did so for a large sum of money. I will never forgive him for destroying this piece of paradise.'

A couple of years ago, Laure gave a lecture to trainee curators, with an age range from early twenties to early forties, during which she described the second video in Room 5.

'The video is in black and white and shows a small room, furnished with a table and two chairs facing each other. There is no window in the shot. A black Bakelite phone, the squat old-fashioned type with a cumbersome dial and plaited cording, occupies the centre table. The cheap plastic chairs are embossed with cigarette burns, and the floor is of rough planking. There are no indications as to where the room might be.

'The shot is held steady on this *mise en scène* and the only sound to break the silence is the click of the camera.

'Without warning, the phone shrieks into the silence.'

She continued. 'The piece is powerful and disturbing, and the image of the telephone ringing appears to tap into a collective unease that many of us carry. I have watched it many times and, like most onlookers, still jump. Some of the visitors have been known to scream. On the feedback form which we ask visitors to fill in, one of the questions asks them to tell us which object had the most effect on them. A consistent majority pinpoint it.

'We've had letters about it asking if it's a horror film. Or a political one? Or is it just an installation?'

At this point, she ran the video for the audience.

'The answer is,' she concluded, looking at the row of expectant faces, 'the answer is that it combines all these elements which, I would argue, is the mark of a successful exhibit. You will, of course, question how it qualifies for the Museum of Broken Promises?'

There was a shuffle of expectation and the women – generally it was the women who took notes – in the audience took up their pens.

'I should add that this particular exhibit was sent in anonymously in the early days of the museum's life and you will understand why

15

when I read the label, which is in French, English and Czech. "From 1948–1989 in Communist Czechoslovakia we were promised employment, peaceful politics decent living standards and no corruption. This is what we got."'

By mid-afternoon, Laure was ensconced in the interview room with a cake tin from Room 1 on the table between her and the smiling woman who sat opposite.

'It's lovely to see you again, Myrna.'

'It's quite a journey from St Louis,' Myrna replied, 'but I had to see you. And to pick this up.'

The change in her was startling. Three years ago, middle-aged, newly divorced and drained, Myrna had sat in this room crying so hard that Laure fetched a second box of tissues. Today, she was no less faded or unobtrusive, but there had been a sea change: she was tougher-looking, full of humour, resolved on who and what she was. It was very attractive.

It had been another matter then. Deep and profound weeping, such as Myrna had indulged in, was one way of groping towards an explanation.

'My husband couldn't understand that I had another life inside my head,' she explained. 'When we got married, he promised that he would make it possible for me to paint but he didn't.' She gazed over Laure's shoulder. 'He went out of his way to make it almost impossible. Then I realized that he didn't want me to paint because it took attention away from him. He doesn't want me to paint because he loves me.'

It was always tempting to pronounce judgment. 'Never, ever do so', Laure instructed her team.

16

The cake tin was decorated with a series of cartouches, scenes from a domestic life, the first of which showed a woman cooking at a stove. Hovering above was the same woman with permed frizzy hair and a frilled blouse holding a paintbrush filling in a sky of lapis-lazuli blue.

Each of the cartouches repeated the device of Myrna performing her housewife routines, with the conceit of her alter ego hovering above to create a transcendent or magical scene. Open that tin, Laure remembered thinking, and out would sift broken desires along with the cakes over which Myrna had cried as she baked.

'It was not as though I was overambitious,' Myrna confessed through the tissues. 'I just need the peace to do my painting.' She struggled for composure. 'I've left my husband. The paintings on this tin tell you why.' Averting her eyes from the tin, she said, 'There's an angel cake inside. Pink and white with frosted icing. Enjoy. Please.' She got to her feet. 'I love him,' she said. 'But it's not enough.'

'I've come to take back the tin,' Myrna was now saying. 'He's begged for forgiveness. He tells me that he now understands. We're starting over.'

Possibly, Myrna's husband had arrived at a new understanding because the beautiful, glowing tin displayed in the museum had brought his wife a small fame and many commissions. No cynic (well, only a touch), Laure was delighted to acknowledge this winning fusion of love, forgiveness and... money.

'I'm so glad,' she told Myrna, and meant it.

'Would you like to meet him?' He's lurking in the street outside.' Myrna shot Laure a conspiratorial look. 'Didn't have the balls, if you know what I mean.'

This was a day in the life of the Museum of Broken Promises.

CHAPTER 2

*S*HE NEVER ATE BREAKFAST AT HOME BUT, IF THERE WAS time, Laure brewed strong black coffee.

Her apartment on the second floor of a former warehouse was typical of a modern Parisian conversion: small (some said cramped), the windows were plate glass and the doors MDF. The kitchen only just accommodated a modest oven and fridge and, if the table flap was up, it was a squeeze to get to the sink.

Apart from the stacked, labelled boxes in the second, tiny cupboard of a bedroom occupying what space there was in it, furniture and trimmings were kept to a notable minimum. Sometimes, there was a vase of flowers, a coat cast onto a chair, a French novel in a yellow dust jacket but, usually, the effect was extreme minimalism.

Finding anywhere to live in Paris was a nightmare and a flat, however small, was a flat. Admittedly somewhat joyless, the anonymity of the place suited her plus it was only a short walk to work.

In the courtyard below, Madame Poirier, the *concierge*, conducted one of her conversations punctuated with explosive syllables. 'It's against regulations, *monsieur*,' she was saying.

Which ones this time? Laure wondered. (Madame Poirier's regulations came and went.) Which *monsieur* was she bullying? In truth, Madame never shut up, but, like the ugly doors and windows, she was part of a set-up into which Laure had inserted herself. The quasi-bullying, the tiptoeing around the regulations, the irritations were anchors. They were the ingredients of the life she had chosen.

Having washed up the coffee pot, she put it out to dry on a tea towel spread out over the drainer and checked that the one sharp kitchen knife was back in the drawer. Not content, she reopened the drawer and stuck a cork onto the tip of the knife, just to be sure. Sharp knives made her uneasy.

She rarely cooked or entertained and possessed only four pieces of good furniture, including the sofa. But hardly anyone ever slumped down into it for a late-night drink or to read the Sunday papers. Sometimes her English friends – including Jane back home in Brympton – commented on how unlived-in it felt.

Charlie, her younger brother, was more forthright. 'You could at least unpack the boxes, Laure.'

'They're fine as it is. I want it light, free from clutter.'

'Most normal people have something. A photo, some books, the chair Granny gave them. You might as well live in an egg box.'

Laure eyed him. Charlie was not much of a home-bird either and their mutual amusement held more than a tinge of irony. 'Pot and kettle?'

'The very ones.'

If it was a *modus vivendi* which struck the English as odd, the French saw nothing peculiar about it. They were not curious as to how Laure chose to live and, if they wished to eat a meal together, they met at a restaurant.

Listening to the news with half an ear, she drank her coffee and dried her hair. The *meteo* predicted 26 degrees at midday and she hoped no higher because her hair would suffer. *Dommage.* She gave it a final blast from the dryer, threaded drop pearl earrings into her ears and inspected her nail varnish, an exciting dark red that required upkeep. But, the colour of riot and sex, it was worth it.

She tilted her head at the image in the mirror.

What she saw in it told her that her efforts had paid off. She had sometimes listened to other women saying how much they hated their looks but she felt that she had been through too much to allow herself to indulge in that. It hobbled the mind. She swept a finger over her cheek. Her skin, of which she was proud, was still clear and youthful-looking. Once upon a time, in another country, Tomas told her that her skin reminded him of mother-of-pearl. Her final act was to apply sun-protection cream before picking up her laptop and handbag and letting herself out of the front door.

Emerging into the street, she turned canalwards, glancing right and left and scanning the buildings. It was the old habit of 'dry-cleaning', the art of shaking off surveillance, that she had never discarded. Or rather, it refused to discard her. She set off and her mobile piped 'Night Owl'. It was Xavier, her ex-husband. '*Oui, mon brave.*'

'*Ma belle.*'

Neither greeting meant anything much. It was the language and tone they had mutually agreed to adopt since parting several years previously. Xavier had remarried and had had the son for which he had longed. So civilized had been the divorce that Marie, the new wife, invited Laure over to dinner from time to time. Possibly to keep an eye on her predecessor?

'If we had loved each other more,' Xavier once remarked, 'meeting would be a problem, but it's not.'

'Strange to think how cut and shut it is now,' she remembered replying.

'Strange but true. Yet not uncomfortable, I think?'

'No, darling Xavier, not uncomfortable at all.'

They had stared at each other. Laure could not help thinking, as she sometimes did, that his kindly, worldly regard enshrined the accusation: your heart is arid.

Traffic sounded in her ear and she deduced Xavier was in the street. A decade of marriage inevitably meant that this and that intelligence about your spouse stuck in the memory and there was a fair bet that he was wearing taupe chinos and the same black jacket he had cherished for years. His hair would be brushed back and, ten to one, he would be squinting into the distance because he was too vain to wear his glasses.

'It's one of the days I miss you, Laure. And your lovely gooseberry-coloured eyes.'

She smiled. 'Me too, Xavier.' Regret for the failed marriage surfaced more frequently than she owned up to. Xavier had his quirks, but he was a principled man and often very funny. 'But you have a wife.'

'So I do.'

Knowing that Xavier was still fond of her warmed Laure, picking her way around the rubbish on the street. 'You will always be half a Brit,' he once said. 'However good your French and however long you live here. You need a champion.'

Rubbish. Laure was more French or, to be accurate, more Parisian than Xavier gave her credit for. '*J'aime deux choses seulement… vous et la plus belle ville du monde*,' she replied. It was a line from an old and sentimental poem, but it pinpointed her giving of her heart to the city.

Xavier's point about championing her was the one that held the real bite. If they had championed each other a little more during their marriage, the outcome might have been different. For that, she blamed herself. Mostly.

Despite the banter, Xavier never wasted his phone calls. 'Spotted an article in *Figaro* about the Louvre lobbying to gather the Museum of Broken Promises into its embrace. Its spokesman argues that the day of the private museum is over. They reckon you and they would be terrific in bed together.'

'Apparently.' She gave a tiny sigh.

'Pushing the metaphor: the Louvre is a disgusting old roué and you're but a child bride. It's the old thing. Money talks and those who have it talk away. How would it fit in with Nos Arts en France?'

Nos Arts en France was a semi-government body that issued grants for cultural enterprises. Laure had been warned that they were tricky but had found her dealings with them to be straightforward.

'The board of Nos Arts will assess the situation and let me know whether they wish to continue funding the museum. If they do, nothing will change and I'll be happy.'

'Nos Arts have been generous to you.'

'We could not have survived without them.'

Xavier became serious. 'Do you mind if you're taken over?'

She looked up in a sky lashed with trails of whipped cream. 'I shall fight tooth and nail.'

'*Chérie*, you might not have any choice.' He sounded regretful. 'You have become powerful but not that kind of powerful.'

It wasn't the first time Laure had encountered a threat – theoretical or otherwise – and she had learnt to deal with them by splitting herself into compartments.

There was the Laure whose experiences in the past helped her to negotiate the dusty, complicated structures of public governance without too much bother.

Then there was the Laure who burned to make her museum work precisely because the past still lived in her and who could be cast down by the bureaucratic grind.

'On a happier note,' she said, 'Maison de Grasse is going to be our patron.'

It was Xavier's turn to be taken aback, and the audible click of his tongue was an expression of admiration for a coup. 'Nice.'

Having started life as a small, exclusive perfume house, Maison de Grasse had grown into a multi-national that supplied scents for a huge range of goods from household cleaners, which would be unusable without them, to candles and room sprays. They still created and manufactured the most exclusive perfumes, of course. Many of the larger French companies offset tax liabilities by becoming patrons of a museum. Maison de Grasse was following suit in concluding that it would be a prudent blend of fiscal planning and largesse to support a slightly alternative arts project. For Laure, there were sweeteners promised in the form of publicity for the museum and advertising support.

'Nice,' Xavier repeated.

A man totally absorbed by the screen on his phone banged into Laure. She dropped hers and the conversation went dead.

'Sorry, sorry,' said the man. 'I didn't see you.'

Crystal clear.

Many of Laure's older memories were anguished and fudged, but what she recorded on first setting eyes on Canal Saint-Martin and the streets spidering out from the ribbon of water were just that: crystal clear.

Ten years ago, it had been run down in places and it was stupid to wander there at night alone. But, here was the thing: the *quartier* clung to its seductions. Her searches revealed that, in its past, it had seethed with life (some of it pretty low), with sex (bartered or otherwise) and it possessed a unique louche elegance. It was an area that proclaimed to the visitor: I possess an impeccable pedigree, and many of my old buildings have survived revolutions and the destructions of Baron Haussmann. Or something like that. The wording often changed in her head but the gist was the same.

The poor and homeless liked it. As did its long-stayers. So did Laure on the run from her divorce. Listening to the slap of water against the sides of the canal was to feel grounded into the city's inner life. Likewise, traversing one of the cast-iron footbridges spanning the grey-green, rubbish-speckled water, or tracing the topography of streets with their occasional sinister feel, and she was passionately protective about the just-hanging-on-to-a-living shops and cafes.

That had been then. Recently, an ice-cream shop selling every hue and flavour known to humanity, and an expensive clothes boutique, had arrived, plus a *chocolaterie* and a *salon de beauté*. Possibly, her museum had helped the renaissance but now that she had become a true-blooded *canaliste*, she kept watch over rapacious developers. Unreconstructed it still may be, but the *quartier* commanded intense loyalty from those who lived there, in a way that modern, sanitized areas possibly did not. Even, as some partisan *canalistes* argued, the up-itself Left Bank.

The smell of the water was familiar and inescapable as she emerged out of the street and onto the canal bank. Flattish.

Brackish and, since it was early autumn, carrying a hint of decay. (She had first noticed how water could smell that hot summer in Prague when she and Tomas had idled along the river.) An empty *bateau mouche* slid through the water eastwards, leaving a backwash of flotsam of orange peel, a plastic bottle and the remains of a hamburger.

In the Rue de la Grange aux Belles, Madame Becque was folding back the shutters of her grocery shop. Recently, she and her husband had painted the woodwork a bright blue and dyed their poodles' coats a lighter blue to harmonize, which added immeasurably to the gaiety of nations. The favoured bar on the corner that served late-night brandies was putting up the shutters for a few hours' rest. A homeless man sat cross-legged outside it. As she went past, Laure dropped a euro into his cup.

Further up the street, a scruffy, litter-strewn patch of earth was sandwiched between two buildings. Laure stopped. 'Kočka,' she called. Czech for 'cat', it was not an imaginative choice, but it was the one that had come into her head when she first spotted the little stray a couple of weeks ago.

Tail dragging behind her, a tabby emerged from the shadow cast by the wall. Tiny-boned. Almost emaciated. Exhausted from the business of staying alive and beyond frail. Laure touched the small triangular face and ran a finger down her backbone, gently rubbing the spinal bumps and flat bone before the tail. It was a moment of communion. Of comfort. Of a small trusting exchange between animal and human.

Should she be worried that she was not doing Kočka any favours by feeding her? An argument ran that said that a homeless stray would be better off dead. Death was not the worst thing to happen. Death could be welcomed.

It was then she noticed that under the starved belly poked pink, swollen nipples.

Her throat tightened. *Kittens.*

Kočka was waiting unsentimentally (unlike Laure) for her benefactor to service her hunger. Laure emptied the expensive cat food stuffed with vitamins into the fruit punnet she had brought along and watched the cat fall on it.

Bending down, Laure caught the faintest of purrs but, otherwise, she was ignored. Pleased about the purr, she told Kočka, 'No promises.'

She continued north up the Rue de la Grange aux Belles.

When she had first set foot in the street, she was a woman whose decree absolute had just slid onto the lawyer's desk. It had been a hard-frosted winter's day. Her shoes were flimsy, and her frozen feet had refused to cooperate. As they grew damper, they made a flapping sound on the pavement.

She had caught sight of a girl in a red coat and pile of coffee grounds on the pavement. A bad-tempered exchange emanated from the Asian supermarket. A dog barked. The cold was neither kind nor exhilarating and grey, bad-tempered snow flurries threatened.

Exploring the *quartier* was to experience a jumble of impressions. It was only later, much later, these initial images assembled like a jigsaw to construct her personal landscape: the shutters, the noise of the dinky machines which cleaned the streets each morning, the ironwork on the older houses and, in her stone niche, a statue of the Virgin whose bovine eyes appeared to skewer passers-by.

She had been so certain that pessimism was a condition of life and the slightest setback tipped her thoughts out of the box in which she struggled to confine them. Not helped by her broken marriage,

27

she was dogged by a sense of failure. By that she meant: the past was too big to cope with. Apparently, according to quantum physics, the atom does not follow one path in order to exit a maze. It goes down every path all at the same time, which was a fine description of what Laure was doing. Running down every path without knowing why, falling at every obstacle, finding her face in the mud.

It had taken her roughly thirty seconds to identify as interesting the flat-fronted, three-storey house at the further end of the street. A good proportion of its roof tiles were slipping from their moorings and the paintwork had bubbled and flaked. She watched the first few flakes of snow sift down over its roof while she absorbed its worn-at-the-edges presentation, the fact that it had obviously survived for a couple of hundred years, that it did not care a tinker's cuss whether she, Laure, was a failure or not. Having absorbed that, the suggestion winged through her mind that the life inside the – no-doubt – moth-eaten rooms could be creative and serene.

Crucially, it was for sale.

She had no money. No expertise. Nothing except an idea that arrived as she gazed at the house from the opposite side of the street and clenched first her right foot then her left in an effort to drive circulation into her feet.

After arranging access to the house, she allowed herself plenty of time to walk through it. She examined its sash windows and tapped the floorboards, she trudged up the too-narrow staircase, poked her head into antiquated lavatories and ascended to the attics. She sniffed neglect, decay and trouble and winced at the reluctant squeal of a swollen door and the scatter of mice up above.

The atmosphere suggested past struggles to live and to thrive, some disastrous, some triumphant. She wished for no more turbulence in her life. None, ever. As she paced the freezing, despairing rooms, she asked herself: would it be better to avoid such a place?

Redemption was more than a word. It was a nirvana. It was a state of grace perpetually shuffling away from her. But maybe she could source it in bricks and mortar?

In the cold, her toes had felt as stiff as clothes pegs. Yet, as she listened in to the orchestration of the house's creaks and shifts, the answer became clear.

Today, its paintwork was new, its stucco repaired, the roof fixed and a sign hung over the entrance which read: *Musée* and, underneath in French and English: 'Museum of Broken Promises'.

The second line read: 'Curator, Laure Carlyle'.

CHAPTER 3

*T*HE OFFICE AT THE TOP OF THE HOUSE WAS TINY. Originally, perhaps, the maidservant's quarters, who might have considered it palatial but, for Laure, it presented an increasing problem of how to pack in the administrative needs of the museum.

A solution had been to paint the walls, plus the even smaller room next door that was used for interviews, an Imperial Chinese yellow which resulted (God knew how) in making them appear more spacious. Another tactic was to demand a draconian level of tidiness.

It was nine o'clock. Nic was already at his desk. In post for the past eighteen months, he was English, bilingual, unattached, ambitious to make his way in arts administration and part of the generation who had taken it as read they could up sticks to live in Europe and think nothing of it. 'It's been easy to move around,' he said. 'It's what a lot of us do.'

Of course, Generation Nic did. For them, Europe had been an extension of home territory. And she had felt the same.

He lifted a hand in greeting. 'Knock, knock.'

'Who's there?'

'Robin.'

'Robin who?

'Robin the piggy bank again.'

They were playing the game of who could nick the worst joke from the internet.

She thought of Nos Arts en France and crossed her fingers. 'What if I told you that you don't get any better?'

Nic's eyes widened. 'But I've learnt everything I know from you.' He waggled his fingers. 'Tell me I've become indispensable.'

'You have,' she replied truthfully.

Still only in his late twenties, he possessed an unusual capacity to read people. To observe Nic negotiate his way out of a tricky encounter was an object lesson in life skills. If pushed, she would admit she learnt from him and was grateful for it. Love could, and did, take one by surprise but – and this had come as a surprise too – so did affection.

'Have I got shaving foam on my chin?' he asked.

'No, why?'

'You're staring at me.'

She smiled. 'That's because I like you.'

'Someone has to.'

Nic tapped into what the museum was about. He understood the objects had things to say. When she had first ushered him through the rooms, she had watched that understanding dawn on him.

The inaugural coffee of the day had been transferred by Nic to a thermos and placed on her desk along with Laure's schedule. She sat down, placed her bag under the desk and tapped in 'Vet, Canal Saint-Martin' into Google. Seconds later, she was on the phone and making an appointment.

'Didn't know you had a cat,' said Nic.

'I don't.'

He sent her a look. 'The schedule needs your OK.'

She glanced over it. An interview with a freelance journalist was slotted for mid-morning. 'Oh God.'

Clever Nic had become expert in managing Laure's reactions. 'I arranged it so it's done with before lunch. It will all be over by the time you tuck into your *frites*.'

'*Frites!*' She glanced up. He was smiling. She grinned reluctantly. 'Who?'

'She says she's got top contacts who would look at her pitch.'

Laure rolled her eyes. 'In a previous life, I must have sinned greatly.'

At his nicest, Nic could be flexible. Other times, he was up there with Caligula and Stalin. 'This one shouldn't be too bad and you must do it. She sounds good on the phone and I've checked her out. She's had pieces in the *New York Times* magazine, among others.' He added, 'She's young. Working her way up.'

'They're the worst.'

'Are they now?' He observed her expression. 'Spoken as the woman who refuses to reveal if she prefers marmalade or jam at breakfast.'

She gave a self-conscious little laugh. 'Maybe.'

Xavier always told her it was pathological.

On previous occasions, Nic had said it was understandable but… he would never voice it, but by 'understandable', he meant short-sighted.

'If you take a chance, a big piece in a major publication will benefit the museum.' Nic had resorted to deviousness and worked the arguments up an ascending scale. 'Those up-themselves museum directors would have to take note of you, Laure.'

'I don't mind if they do or they don't.'

'Think Gianni from Rome.'

'He was unique.' Gianni Rovere, the Italian journalist, had been good-mannered, humorous, and did Laure the courtesy of reflecting on her answers before going on to the next question.

'Some might see this as a negative place,' he had observed towards the end of the interview.

'No,' said Laure. 'The museum offers a space to begin again.'

Nic's final thrust: 'The directors of Maison de Grasse will love it. It's the sort of exposure that will convince them they made the correct decision.'

He had the best interests of the museum at heart and she trusted him. 'If I agree, will that do until Christmas?'

When Nic smiled, the sun came out.

Mid-morning, he ushered the journalist into the office. Laure looked up and frowned. 'Oh,' she said. 'We've met.' She picked up the card given to her by the girl that she had dropped into her filing tray. 'May Williams?'

Minus the sunglasses, May Williams could be seen to possess startlingly blue-grey eyes – one glance from which appeared to send Nic into a trance. Today she was dressed in skinny jeans, a tight T-shirt and fashionable trainers but looked nervous. 'I really, really want to write about the museum.' On closer inspection, faint shadows were traced under the startling eyes. 'Could be an important piece.'

Her seriousness was disarming and went some way to cancel out Laure's irritation at the tactics to get the interview. She glanced up at Nic who pulled himself together and said, 'Coffee, I think.'

The girl produced a sheaf of papers from the black rucksack. 'I thought you would like to look at what I've done.' Her tone was matter-of-fact but the hand with its bitten nails told another story as she fanned out the papers in front of Laure. 'I promise you it's not shoddy work.'

Laure skimmed through a couple. What she saw suggested a whip-smart intelligence and incendiary writing.

Oh God, she thought. I don't want her on the case.

When the coffee arrived, May sniffed it and her eyes closed for a second. She drank a mouthful and a rime of milk appeared on her upper lip. 'I've fallen in love with French coffee.'

'If you like, I'll take you to some of the best places to try out,' said Nic.

May smiled at him.

It occurred to May that Nic had not lied when he reassured Laure that he had checked this girl out. More had been discussed on the phone than the interview.

'I'll show you around,' Laure said, 'and you can get the feel of the place before you do the interview.' May sprang to her feet and picked up the coffee cup. 'Leave the coffee, please. We have to take great care not to have accidents.'

'Sure.' May drained the mug and patted her top lip. Her body appeared to assemble into brisker lines. 'Shall we go?'

Laure motioned them downstairs to the kiosk where Chantal was checking over the stock of souvenirs. She looked up from her tablet. 'We need more fridge magnets with the handcuffs on them,' she said in French. 'Can't get enough. This is the last one.' She held it up. The magnet was stamped with a picture of fluffy tiger-skin handcuffs with the legend underneath: 'They promised heaven.'

Laure translated and May laughed. Laure ushered her into the first room and she observed, 'You're bilingual, right? How come?'

'My mother's French. My father, English.'

May said little as Laure took her on the museum tour except to enquire how many rooms there were. 'Three on this floor, four upstairs making seven altogether, plus the offices. It is difficult as the rooms are different sizes and we are always pressed for space. The largest must have been a reception room and the smallest we think was probably a powder closet. Most of the floors are still original. You can tell by the width of the floorboards.' She continued. 'You will know from when you were here the other day that you start here and progress through three rooms following the *sens de visite* arrows. Then up the back staircase. Through those rooms and back down the main staircase, which is tricky as it's narrow. But it can't be helped.'

May circled around. 'It's very quaint and atmospheric, perhaps disturbing but definitely quaint.'

'The objects represent something other than "quaint", said Laure tartly.

May stopped dead. 'Oh, Lord. I have this rule to sit on the folksy words from home but that one sneaked past.' There was a suggestion of panic. 'I don't mean to make the museum sound hokey.'

'Home?'

'Alabama.' She grimaced. 'Mint juleps, pie, Jim Crow.' She gestured with both hands. 'Craziness. Suffering. Heat. All that.'

May Williams had been glad to escape. 'So, a refugee?'

May made a non-committal noise and peered into the main display case. 'A railway ticket? What's the language?'

A second elapsed before Laure replied. 'Czech.'

'Ah, yes, I think it was photographed for the interview you did with the Italian? It made a noise in the Czech Republic, who are a bit antsy about being reminded of the bad days under the commies.'

Laure turned away. 'I believe it did.'

In the second room there were three display cabinets. May pointed to the first. 'I wanted to ask you. What's with the match-box?'

36

'If you look closely there's a milk tooth. Seven-year-old Jamie brought it in.'

'A child?'

'Do you know many children? I don't but, it turns out, they're fierce guardians of promises and know immediately when they've been broken. Jamie's father had promised him that he would be left money by the Tooth Fairy when his baby teeth dropped out. It was fine for the first two teeth but, by the third, Jamie's father had gone and the Tooth Fairy with him.'

May made to place her hand on the glass but thought better of it. 'Couldn't Jamie's mother have left the money?'

'I suspect she wanted to show her ex-husband up. She brought Jamie in and he gave me the matchbox and told me the Tooth Fairy was a big liar.' Jamie's little face had been wounded and furious in equal measure. 'He was talking about his father.'

'So little Jamie's distress and sadness are on display.'

Laure ushered May into the next room. 'Interesting how a small boy found a way of dealing with it.'

'Or the mother.'

Alerted by the acid inflection of 'mother', she asked, 'Do your parents approve of what you do?'

'What my father likes is bourbon. Lashings of it. Ask my dinosaur mother, who's a good woman, by the way, but she just doesn't happen to like her daughter... ask her what she hates most in the world she would treat you to the spiel about unmarried women paying astronomical rent to live in a box with cooking and plumbing smells in the Sodom of New York while waiting for the big break.' May stared past Laure to a cabinet with a look that suggested difficult and complicated emotions. 'She said it would be a hiding to nothing. It would be hard. And it was.'

'I'm sure it was hard. But you made contacts. Obviously. Good contacts.'

May's face cleared. 'I did. It was one way of getting back at a mother born a hundred and fifty years ago but who happens to live now and whose pet hates are crazy liberals and feminists.' Her eyes lit up. 'That's a long ways around of saying, she's not like you.'

Laure had a startled micro-second to absorb that she was bracketed with May's mother. Laugh or cry? 'Right.'

'Oh, Lord…' Realizing she may have blundered, May Williams rattled around her journalistic armoury and produced a compliment. 'I know you're the sort of woman who'll wear tight jumpers and eye shadow when you're ninety.'

Laure found herself smiling. 'Good.'

'No children of your own?'

'No.'

The unspoken question hovered. The unspoken answer sat on Laure's tongue: I denied myself children. Not consciously, perhaps, but somehow it was never the right person, the right time, the right state of mind.

The two women continued onwards.

A few minutes later, May asked, 'So why Czech?'

'I lived there for a long summer.'

'And that's a broken promise?'

'Actually, yes, as it turned out. It was.'

In the smaller room, the tall, lanky May resembled a confined animal. 'How do you theme the display?'

'Big question and it took us a lot of time to work out what was the most effective. In the end, we stuck to the relationship of the objects. Household stuff, say. Clothing. It doesn't always work. But displaying the objects chronologically proved too difficult to control as we had to keep changing the rooms around.'

May snapped shut her notebook. 'Sure.'

'We've got a new patron and we're discussing refurbishment.' She led May towards the staircase, keeping the subject of conversation in her court. 'Museum display is changing. Revolutionized, actually. Museums are becoming tactile places. Fun places. Unpredictable places. We have to keep up with the big guys.'

She led her into the final room. May pointed to the 'Number 7' written in gold lettering above the door lintel. 'Seven. The special number.' Her forehead wrinkled. 'Of the first prime numbers, seven is the most interesting? At least, I think so. You can't multiply or divide it within the group.'

'Maths isn't my strong point.'

The question sneaked in. 'Then it must be difficult to deal with the museum's finances?'

'Did I say that?'

May let that drop and took a run at the next question. 'What you leave out is as important as what you include, right?'

The light from the restored sash window fell over May's hair, picking out its strands of white blonde and gold. An innocent question? Probably. Permitting May to write a profile of Laure was to cede power. May would dig. Laure glanced out of the window. Dealing with the fear of what lay hidden in the wrinkles of her psyche was an old, exhausting battle which she hadn't won. 'Yes,' she answered. 'What you leave out *is* important.'

May swivelled. 'What do you think you're doing with these objects?

A hint of scepticism? 'It's a closure process.'

'For whom? Someone might look at this and think "what a load of old tat".'

'Feel free to do so. Giving an object to this museum is a way of dealing with something that's gone wrong in your life.' Laure pointed to a sensationally ugly multi-coloured vase dominating the smaller display case. 'As a society, we're in danger of forgetting the importance of ritual.'

'If you say so.' May focused on the vase with a look of disbelief.

Laure found herself grinning. The confection of fantasy, yearning, rage and deep disappointment penned up behind the glass of the display cabinets was hard, if not impossible, to quantify at the best of times and the vase certainly didn't look up to the job.

'It's so awful I can't take my eyes off it,' May confessed.

'On bad days, we pray to the god of breakages but somehow he doesn't hear us.' She added hastily, 'Don't quote me.'

May transferred her attention to a framed silhouette hanging between the windows. It was rough and ready and the scissor marks on the black paper were crude. Its subject – a slight man with hair swept back and a Roman nose – held a guitar. 'He looks great. Is he still around?'

Laure stood behind May. 'No.'

'What happened to him?'

'Well…'

May ran a hand over her hair, her fingers tangling in its mass at her neckline. She pulsed with energy, nerves, and a quirky vulnerability. Had Laure been like that? Yes, she had – and it was a good thought.

Usually when asked, Laure replied, *I don't know who he is.* This time the words edged out of her. 'I don't know where he is. I wish I did.'

40

*

May Williams would be analysing that response. Of course.

The idea sat uneasily at the back of Laure's mind as she went about the rest of the day. A finger with a sharp nail had been poked through her shell and, when that happened, it unsettled her.

On the Rue de la Grange aux Belles, Monsieur Becque was conducting his late-afternoon sale of the produce. For a couple of euros, Laure was invited to snaffle an Alphonse mango on the turn, four tomatoes and an aubergine. Not bad. She paid up, exchanged greetings and continued on her way.

It was a warm autumn evening, the kind in which Europe specialized and Parisians had been enticed onto the streets. Although the daylight was only just beginning to fade, windows were lit up and drinkers clustered in the bars and cafes, bright with illumination. Girls were bare-armed and, frequently, bare-backed. Older women wore high heels and leather skirts, the men chinos and bomber jackets. Groups of them flowed towards the canals and their exchanges blended together on the evening air. Quite a few were ensconced on benches, heads bent over their phones.

Laure set her face against the tide and turned northwards up the street towards the Maison de Retraite on the corner of Rue Martat and Rue Louis Capet. On this evening where life of every sort accosted the eye, she was about to visit someone on the brink of death.

Like the museum, the Maison was one of the older houses in the Saint-Martin *quartier*. It had long, narrow windows, walls of brickwork and stone and machicolations that hinted of a medieval past. It was a familiar sight but Laure had never been inside. On being invited to enter, she stepped into a narrow and gloomy corridor so cloistral in flavour that it didn't seem suitable for elderly

41

inhabitants. Yet local gossip had it that it was a good place to spend your last days. 'They're kind in there.' 'They understand about being old…'

At the reception, she was met by the slightly dishevelled and out-of-breath *directeur*, Madame Maupin, who looked to be a hands-on person. So it transpired. 'Apologies, *madame*, I've been helping a new resident settle in. He wasn't happy with the position of his bed and we had to move it around until he was.' She held out her hand. 'It is good of you to come. I hope you did not mind us contacting you?'

'No. Not at all. I rely on people contacting me.'

Madame Maupin spotted a mark on her skirt, exclaimed and rubbed at it. 'Madame Raoul does not have long; she had heard of what the museum does and wanted to make a donation. I guessed it was better to go to the horse's mouth.' That particular idiom was never so effective in French but Laure took the point. 'She's been hoping to make it to her hundredth birthday. But you never know what God has in store.'

'No, indeed,' replied Laure and trusted she did not sound as wry as she felt.

Madame Maupin ushered Laure into the lift that took them up to the top floor. Despite the smaller windows, the light was brighter on this floor and a slice of sunlight poked in through the south-facing casements.

Madame Raoul's room was small and narrow. A hospital bed had only just been squeezed in but the medicines, clock, rosary and Bible were laid out with surgical precision on a white cloth on the top of a chest of drawers. A chair was slotted in beside the door.

At Laure's entrance, the woman propped up in the bed with multiple pillows turned her head. Madame Maupin bent over her – and kindness flowed through the curve of her body. 'There's no need for *politesse*, madame.' She stroked the corner of the pillow. 'Just say what you wish.'

Laure took up a position on the other side of the bed. Madame Raoul focused on the *directeur*. 'The pillowcase, madame.' The voice was faint. 'Will you fetch it?'

Madame Maupin opened the top drawer of the chest and extracted a package wrapped in tissue paper that she laid on Madame Raoul's chest who indicated that she should unwrap it. It was a square lace-edged pillowcase decorated with white-work embroidery. A tang of lavender, and the mustiness of old unused linen, so often smelt in *brocante* shops, mingled with the smell of medicines and old lady.

Madame Raoul lifted a skeletal hand and pointed at the pillowcase. 'I made this,' she said, 'when I was seventeen and about to be married.' Between sentences she paused to take in a breath. 'We were taught by our mothers and they were taught by their mothers. Where I came from it was the tradition. Every girl had to do it. It was a symbol of our role as wives and mothers.'

Laure touched the linen with a fingertip. 'It's exquisite.'

'Madame Maupin, you won't like what I'm going to say.' Madame Raoul looked up and the two women exchanged a look. '*Chère* madame, I don't wish to upset you.'

'In that case, I've other things to do.' Madame Maupin drew the chair up to the bed and indicated that Laure should sit down. 'You will find it easier to listen if you're comfortable. When you've finished, please ring the bell.'

Laure sat down, and her face was now almost on the same level as Madame Raoul's. '*Restez tranquille,* madame. If we agree it has a place in the museum I can see exactly where it would go. Tell me about it.'

43

Madame Raoul's chest heaved. Laure put her bag on the floor and folded her hands in her lap. If this exchange was to be peaceful, she knew she must remain still and watchful.

The indrawn breath was laboured. 'Being a woman is to be God's beast of burden.'

Laure sat up. She had been expecting pieties, not iconoclasm.

'You're a professional woman and you will know. I was a farm girl who had no choice. Aren't you ever forced to the conclusion that, in creating woman, He played the biggest joke?' She was visibly struggling to breathe and Laure laid her hand gently on her shoulder. 'The work of a God who's a sadist.'

'Does that mean that you do not believe?' Laure glanced at the paraphernalia of faith arranged on the chest of drawers.

There was a long sigh. 'It keeps them happy. My hatred of God is too much for them. I understand. It's hard for them.' Her eyelids drooped wearily. 'We were raised with faith, hung like a key around our necks. I believed it. God was the Father and I was taught that my purpose was to obey Him and my husband.'

Laure waited.

'Faith is a lie, madame.'

Madame Raoul's faith? Or all faiths that came in many forms, including political ones?

'God took two of my babies. Not content with Lucie, he had Jean as well. God wanted everything that was precious to me and made sure that He got it.'

'Your husband?'

Madame Raoul fingered the pillowcase. 'If you could look… if you could see, beneath my skin are bruises and scars given to me by the man who promised to love and honour me.'

The effort to make sense was enormous and she fell into a doze.

Laure looked up to the window and the darkening sky outside. It went without saying that the dying must be allowed to vent doubt and distress. They must be given licence to ask the questions that, perhaps, they were not permitted, or did not have the strength, to express during their lives.

Madame Raoul woke as suddenly as she had slept and fixed on Laure's face. 'Nothing in life was as promised,' she said. 'I ask you to take the pillowcase as an example of how women are betrayed.'

'Not all, surely?' Laure said gently. 'But some.' Madame Raoul frowned and Laure continued. 'Madame Raoul, we've only just met each other but I don't like to think of you so bitter. Is there nothing I can say to help?'

Madame Raoul turned her head away. 'Don't worry. Now I've said what I've wanted to say, I will be good and peaceful. I won't worry them.'

Madame Raoul's initials and those of her husband created a flowing bas relief. Folding the tissue paper around it, Laure said, 'It looks almost untouched.'

The dying woman took several painful-sounding breaths. 'If you look closely enough, there are bloodstains.'

'Whose?'

'Mine. From the sewing. I could never wash them out.'

Walking home, Laure reflected that the bloodstains, tiny as they must be, told the real story of Madame Raoul's pillowcase and not the perfection of the snipped, conquered and embellished linen.

In the apartment, Laure ran a tepid shower, dried and got dressed in a sleeveless dress, twisted her hair up and took a cab to the Marais where she was meeting friends for dinner at the Lapin Blanc. In the cab she decided the pillowcase should be framed in a plain wood frame and hung in Room 7.

Early the next morning before she had left for work, her mobile shrilled. It was Madame Maupin. 'Just to let you know that Madame Raoul died peacefully in the night.'

'I'm sorry. She was an unusual woman. Did she have any family at all? I need to know for the museum records. For when we return the pillowcase.'

'None at all,' was the answer. 'I'm afraid she was in prison for many years and her family disowned her.'

Laure was reluctant – very reluctant – to ask the question. 'In prison for what?'

She heard the sigh at the other end of the phone. 'For murder. Madame Raoul killed her husband.'

CHAPTER 4

*M*AY HAD DONE HER STUFF AND CONFIRMATION THAT *Vanity Fair* had commissioned an in-depth feature arrived the following week. After wrangling, it was agreed that she would shadow Laure for three days and would sit in on interviews provided she had signed a document undertaking to preserve confidentiality of the donors.

She rang in to check over the dates and Laure said, 'I'll put you on to Nic for the details.'

'Oh, *good.*'

Out of the corner of her eye, she watched an animated Nic take the transferred call.

Sharp at the agreed time, May turned up in a tight pair of jeans and a black satin bomber jacket embroidered with red dahlias and the black neoprene rucksack. She held a tray of takeaway coffees and offered it to Nic. 'Americano with a dash of milk, right?'

'Right.' Nic's smile contained a helpless quality.

May turned to Laure. 'Flat white?'

Laure laughed and pointed to the jacket. 'You're supposed to be unobtrusive.'

'Of course.' May took off her jacket and stuffed in into the rucksack. 'OK?'

Extraordinarily enough, when May dropped into a chair in the interview room, she appeared – God knew how – to shrink into the wall.

Nic ushered in Joseph Broad who faced Laure across a small desk. He was thirtyish, of mixed race, undeniably handsome, and he looked wretched. His expression was one with which she had grown familiar. This was a man who was not at peace with himself.

In the office next door Nic was on the phone and visitors to the museum were coming and going up and down the stairs. In the interview room, however, it was calm and quiet, which was the plan.

'I don't know why I'm here.' He corrected himself. 'Yes, I do.'

The struggle for disclosure was also familiar to Laure. 'Beginning at the beginning helps both of us,' she said gently. 'Take your time. I'm here to listen.'

Joseph Broad drew out an expensive-looking wallet and extracted a railway ticket from it. The manner in which he held it suggested that the ticket burnt him and he dropped it onto the table. 'As you know, my name is Joseph Broad but it should be Joseph Murry.'

Out of the corner of her eye, Laure saw May settle further into the chair, her hair colour almost lost against the yellow walls.

'Murry is the name of my birth mother who I tracked down.'

Laure sat with her hands in her lap, waiting. Joseph Broad looked down at his feet and then up at Laure.

'She lives in a rundown area near Nottingham. In a tower block. I went to look before I made contact. It shocked me as to how bad it was. No one should have to live like that. The contrast between our lives was dreadful.' He gestured to the wallet.

The wallet, the Brooks Brothers shirt, the upmarket city shoes all told their own story.

She waited as he collected himself. Trial and error had taught her that silence was powerful and acted like a sponge to draw out the sting. Often those who donated imagined, in deciding on this big step, that whatever it was driving them had been harnessed and brought under control. They knew what they were going to say. They had it down pat. They rehearsed it before they came. They knew how they felt.

Except, they did not. When it came to the point, very often the reservoirs of pain and anguish broke their banks and swamped their good intentions.

Laure smiled encouragement at Joseph Broad.

'I made contact,' he said. 'We talked on the phone. She told me that at the time she felt it was impossible to keep me. Her circumstances were rock bottom and she thought I would have the chance of a better life if she gave me away.'

His distress impelled him to his feet and over to the small window – a reaction which he might have been surprised to learn was a common one.

May's sneeze fractured the silence. 'Sorry, sorry.' She found a tissue and blew her nose.

'Do you know Paris?' Laure asked Joseph.

'I've done the sights.' Joseph returned to the chair. 'I'm here for business a lot but mainly see the inside of the hotel.'

'Do you mind leaving your story in a strange city?'

'Should I?'

'It's a question worth asking.' Laure opened the file on Joseph Broad which Nic had prepared. 'It might tie in with why you want to leave a donation and why you decided to look for her.'

Joseph Broad's lips turned a shade paler. 'It was a feeling. OK, I had a dream where I was minus my legs. I'd had a heavy night but the feeling bugged me for weeks afterwards. When I mentioned it to my partner, Paula, she said it was because I've no roots.' He attempted to laugh. 'I said that was cod psychology.'

Laure asked gently, 'Can I use a cliché? Just because you're paranoid does not mean they're not out to get you. Paula might be correct.'

Joseph took ten seconds to process the suggestion. 'I was adopted at six weeks and lived in Surrey with some nice, good people. I was well treated and I loved them but, always, always I felt this despair and I never knew why. They're dead now but, since they died, I've had this urge to find out who I am. I paid a researcher to do the preliminaries and he located my mother and the agency who put me out for adoption. Via the agency, I made contact and we spoke on the phone.'

'It was OK?'

'It was OK.'

Joseph wasn't telling the truth which was, probably, too difficult to handle at this point and it was not for Laure to probe. May extracted her laptop from the rucksack and Laure shot her a warning look.

'The ticket?'

His shoulders tensed. 'She promised to meet me in London. I offered to send a car but she wasn't having any of it. We agreed she would come by train and I sent her the ticket for London.' He edged the ticket towards Laure. 'This is the return bit. First Class.'

Both Laure and May remained quite still. The finale to this story was predictable – and breathed sadness.

'She promised she would come. She did *promise*.' His gaze slid past Laure. 'I can't get over how pleased she sounded when I first made contact. She told me that you never stopped thinking about a baby that you gave away. She told me that my name wasn't Joseph but Barney after my grandfather. I told her that she could call me Barney.'

A hush held the room.

'And what did you tell her?'

His lips moved but no sound came out. He tried again, the words slipping and sliding away from him. 'I told her that I longed to know her.'

Laure looked down at the file. Her mastery of the art of remaining unmoved by another's distress was still not perfected.

Joe looked first out of the window. Then at the floor. Then at the well-kept hands grasped tightly in his lap. 'I waited for three trains to come in. Nothing.' His eyes glistened. 'You would have thought...' A pause. 'Wouldn't she be curious to see what she had given away?'

May coughed. Laure frowned at her.

She rearranged the papers in Joseph Broad's file. 'I've talked to many people doing this...' she gestured to the file, 'and I know from—' She cut herself off. 'I've come to understand that guilt and regret are the most difficult of burdens to carry. You need courage to deal with them and sometimes people just can't summon sufficient amounts. They've been too hurt. Or worn down. I'm not a professional psychotherapist, merely an observer, but I would urge you to consider if your mother needs more time.'

'She may.' He paused. 'I don't.' Between the two utterances, his features hardened into anger.

Laure made up her mind. 'Three things. We offer you the chance to place the object in the cabinet. Some donors find that part of the procedure important. Secondly, we ask you to provide a description as to why it is here. Thirdly, you must specify what you'd like done with an object after its time here is up.'

He leant across the desk. 'Please write: "I am your son and you failed to meet me." And put it where you wish. I'm leaving this evening.'

'Are you sure?'

The previous suggestion of tears that she had spotted earlier had left a tiny slug's trail at the corners of his eyes. 'I'm as sure of it as anything.'

The 'it' encompassed what Joseph obviously considered a failure and he was the sort unused to failure. His anger and confusion were demonstrably painful to him and painful to witness. At her observation post, May shifted uneasily.

Joseph pushed the ticket across to Laure. She picked it up. It contained none of the imperfectly masked emotion of its donor.

Nic returned from escorting Joseph Broad downstairs and reported that he had slotted a hefty offering into the donation box before leaving.

'Poor guy,' said May. 'But it did him good coming here. Don't you think?' Neither Nic nor Laure replied. She looked from one to the other. 'Are there moments when it gets to you and the positive energy runs out?' Not that Laure had doubted it from the first meeting, but May was shrewd.

Nic looked up and his gaze locked with May's, and it was he who replied. 'From time to time.'

Laure slotted the railway ticket into a plastic wallet and labelled it 'Joseph Broad/Murry' with the date.

May was poised over the keyboard of her laptop. 'Do you have much feedback?'

'Yes, we have. A lot.' Nic got in first. 'I can show you if you like.'

Feedback was preserved faithfully in the archives. Many had written in. 'Visiting the museum has cleansed me', wrote one. 'I am now able to face myself', wrote another.

Before she left that evening, Laure made her customary evening round, walking from room to room to check that all was well and in situ.

Her brother Charlie teased that she had the Florence Nightingale chromosome.

Maybe.

Knowing oneself was such a huge task, mostly uphill. Never finished.

'Good answer,' Charlie had said. 'But you – and I – are more piecemeal than many we know.'

Apart from the bursts of laughter coming from the office upstairs where Nic and May had holed up, there was only the clock's tick and the click of her heels on the floorboards to break the post-visitor hush.

Irresolute for once, she hovered in the doorway of Room 3. Where to place Joseph Broad's railway ticket? Beside the doll with the smashed-in face? Alongside the milk tooth in the matchbox? They were all connected, as May had been quick to pick up. The convergence between Jamie's anger and Joseph's childhood despair fed directly into a shared experience of adult treachery to children.

Room 3's floor was particularly uneven and it had been necessary to prop up one leg of the cabinet containing the framed Czechoslovakian railway ticket. The notice underneath gave the date, where it was issued and its destination. The label read in English, French and Czech: 'A railway ticket for the route used by people leaving Czechoslovakia for Austria in the 1980s. This was an escape route favoured by those fleeing from the regime. Many did not make it.'

In the early days of the museum, some visitors were curious to know its history and Laure told stories of eastern European dissidents who had been caught by the dogs or the guards at the crossing point into Austria – narratives of flight, fear and uncertainty. When asked how that particular ticket represented a broken promise, she replied, 'I'm not allowed to give details', which only increased speculation.

As the museum developed and filled up with objects, interest in the ticket waned but she clung on to it long after she should have done.

Having unlocked the cabinet, she reached for the frame of unpolished wood which she had chosen because Tomas had loved the forest.

She held it against her chest.

CHAPTER 5

Prague, 1986

*M*Y GOD, IT'S A GREY PLACE, THOUGHT LAURE ON FIRST
sighting the city through the windows of the limousine sent to
pick up the Kobes family from the airport. Unlike the rainbow
Paris which she knew well. Or the green and brown Yorkshire of
her childhood.

Over the succeeding days, she revised her opinion. There *was*
colour if you sought it out. It streaked through the baroque stones
of Hradčany, the enormous castle complex hunching over the city,
which she could see from her employers' apartment in the Malá
Strana (the Strangers' quarter), directly beneath it. Later on, she
became familiar with the sly summer sparkle of the Vltava river
dividing the Malá Strana from the confusing matrix of streets in
the Staré Město (the Old Town) and was treated to the swathe of
summer green up on the Letná Plain.

It wasn't a sexy city like Paris. Yet, there was something deep and
mysterious about it that even the summer sun could not penetrate.
Resting at its heart was a history of changing faiths, of persecution,
of demons and music. It was a haunting place and a haunted place,
its past littered with ironies.

Take the sentence in the book *Prague on a Shoestring*, with which she had armed herself. 'Once the capital of the Holy Roman Empire, Prague is a Protestant capital with a magnificent Catholic cathedral.'

Petr Kobes, her employer, told her that the Czechs called their city *matička Praha*, 'little mother Prague', but, he added with the smile that charmed her, it was as well to be aware that one of its most famous writers, Kafka, had written: 'this little mother has claws'.

In the Staré Město, a couple of drunks were propped up against a door with studded nails. Further down the street, another slumped on a bench, an empty bottle of Becherovka rolling mournfully on the ground beside him.

You could smell the booze as you passed. Nothing new there, she thought. Any day of the week there were drunks back home. 'The English are hopeless with drink', her wonderful, if a tiny bit superior, French mother had said more than once. They have drunks in Paris, too, Laure reminded her. Her mother had an answer for that one. 'Parisians are better at it.'

This bunch looked especially depressed. Not one of the grey-looking men and women gave her so much as a glance as she passed by them with the children. In that minatory lecture on Prague, Petr warned her to take care. 'The drunks will rip your fingernails out if they think they can sell them for Slivovice.'

Same old, same old, she thought and grasped Jan and Maria's hands even more tightly.

Yet it wasn't same old. Most things were strange and that was the point. Encountering the new, and absorbing it, was intended to help her negotiate the shock of her father's dying. Having collapsed halfway through the first year at university, she knew she was a mess and her mother packed her off to Paris. 'My city will heal you,' she said. 'You can return to university later.'

Laure resisted. Before her father's death, she hadn't the slightest notion of what 'grief' meant. What it entailed. How it worked. Nothing of its intimacies. Nothing of its obstinate capacity to drag a person down. She wanted, and needed, to dump that grief on her mother, to let her take responsibility for it. Her mother was wiser. 'You'll be amazed what going away can do,' she said as she cradled the weeping Laure. 'Because you're so sad you will be receptive to the experience in a way that's different to when you're happy.' She stroked Laure's hair. 'Think about that.'

'Where are we going?' asked Jan.

'To the Old Town Square.' Laure touched his shoulder. 'I hope we're going the right way.'

Her mother had been right. The point about Prague was that it wasn't home where it was permissible to collapse. Nor was Paris home, where she had first joined the Kobes family. Being in exile *was* a therapy.

In the Paris of her childhood visits, Laure had never felt a second's homesickness or alienation. Nothing had changed when she walked off the ferry, caught the train, and stepped down onto a platform in the Gare du Nord, invariably littered with cigarette butts. Nowhere smelt like Paris and, inhaling it down to the bottom of her lungs, she felt the darkness of the past few months begin to shift and lighten. Three weeks later, she was on her way to Prague with the Kobes family.

It was hot here. Hotter than she was used to. The continental climate. Very hot summers, very cold winters – she exhumed a remnant from geography lessons. To her surprise, it suited Laure. She liked the radiation from iron railings, the heat spreading over her skin and the damp patch welling between her shoulder blades. She liked that the deep, sharp blue of the sky showcased a brassy sun which reminded her of the book on medieval paintings displayed in the local library by Miss Boyt, the optimist. 'I will never give up trying to civilize you,' she informed the sixth formers. 'So, you might as well give in. Especially you, Laure Carlyle. What with your French mother and all that, you should be aware of these things.'

Miss Boyt's logic escaped Laure. Nevertheless, from time to time, she rifled through the books and picked up a fact or two and she was increasingly pleased that she had.

Here she was.

If the heat suited Laure, it did not suit her charges, ten-year-old Maria and the eleven-year-old Jan. Both children were sticky, uncomfortable and making their displeasure felt. However, there was no point in returning to the Kobes' apartment as Eva had instructed them not to return before five o'clock. A certain detachment from her children seemed to be Eva's *modus vivendi*. Used to her own mother's all-embracing parenting, Laure asked herself if this was quite normal.

She had not made up her mind. Yes, managing the two children was far from the easy ride she had blithely assumed but it was a *quid pro quo* situation. She tilted her face up to the sun. There were unexpected compensations for it had never occurred to her that children were fun. Nor that she would feel so protective of them.

'Oh, *Mees* Laure, our mother likes you to take us to bars ...' Jan had turned out to be an excellent tease and she had to keep her wits sharpened. Marie was a soberer child who needed to think about things and was easily hurt. Close in age and, thus, competitors, she and her brother were at the stage where they did not get on.

Unsurprisingly, Laure's French was approaching faultless (and the Kobes children spoke mostly French) but handling the Czech language and currency was going to be tricky. She bent over and adjusted Maria's sunhat and said, 'Let's find an ice cream. But you will have to ask for it, Jan.'

The trio had tramped across the Charles Bridge which spanned the river between the Malá Strana and the Staré Město, stopping now and again to look at the statues, many of which were still damaged from the Second World War. Below, a grey-green Vltava flowed seawards. Apparently, said the reliable *Prague on a Shoestring*, in the fourteenth century, a saint had been thrown into the river from this bridge. For his beliefs, no doubt, even as he promised loyalty to King Wenceslas who had ordered the execution. Personally, Laure echoed her father's robust political views: it never did to put one's trust in princes.

From the bridge a street led directly towards the Staré Město square where, she was relieved to see, there were a few shops. Venturing into a couple, she found dark interiors and sparse stock. In the third, a notice hanging on the wall read in large black type: 'Workers of the World Unite'. A smell of disinfectant in the fourth wafted over them from a back room.

There was no ice cream to be had.

The children were turning less cooperative by the second and Laure speculated what sort of country was it that had no ice cream during a blazing summer. Was it that ice cream was capitalist? Or did Czechoslovakians not care for it?

An odd set of rules apparently applied. The chief being: if there was demand, let's not supply it.

Maria tugged at Laure's hand and wailed with heat and weariness. Jan spoke up for both. 'Laure, we want to go home.'

She was pretty sure Jan meant the comfortable apartment near Neuilly, Paris, in which the Kobes were housed by Petr's firm. Not the apartment close to St Nicholas Church in the Malá Strana where the family were established for the summer.

The Kobes were Czech. *Not Slovak* – Eva had made a point of the national difference when conducting the interview with Laure over the phone – and had been living in Paris for the past five years. 'My husband works for a pharmaceutical company and travels all over France. I need help with the children, particularly as we are planning to spend much of the summer in Prague.' She spoke so rapidly that Laure had trouble following her. 'We will return to Paris in the autumn.' She paused and added something which Laure found odd. 'We *must* return to Paris in the autumn.'

Eva was precise in her requirements which included fluent French. The details of terms and conditions of employment were laid out in a letter of contract which arrived on headed writing paper. 'Petr Kobes. Director of Exports, Potio Pharma.' They included the specification: 'no nail varnish'.

No nail varnish it was.

Eva was blonde, faded and given to brooding and long periods of silence. Since returning to Prague, she had also appeared distracted and distressed. Laure had no precedent on which to pin it down other than to say that she couldn't help feeling that Eva was concentrating on something far removed from the everyday but which did not lie within the remit of her experience. So far.

Eva's husband was the opposite to his wife. He was tall with flat, good-looking features, eloquent brown eyes, wore his French clothes elegantly, sported an expensive haircut and used aftershave. He had good manners and seemed genuinely pleased that she was working for the family.

'In Paris, we are communists in a capitalist country,' Eva explained, speaking very rapidly as she sometimes did. 'And have to be careful. But when we go to Prague *you* must be careful. You will be the foreigner. We've had to get special permission to allow you to accompany us.'

If the treatment of the Kobes on arrival at Prague airport was anything to go by, Petr was a player in his country. It didn't take her more than a few minutes to deduce that some communists were more equal than others. The family had been ushered past the arrival queue to a special exit where a glossy black car awaited. As Laure climbed in and sat back on the leather seats, she noticed that the steering wheel looked like it was made from ivory.

None of these recollections were helping her to obtain ice cream.

'*J'ai envie d'une glace…*' said Jan.

'*Pipi…*' whispered Maria clutching at Laure.

'Hold on and I'll try and find somewhere.'

One side of the square was taken up with a row of old buildings behind which was a church whose spires rose up with fairy-tale crenulations. The sight took Laure's breath away and she longed to be on her own to take it in.

Imagine walking through the cool interior and, like the prince in search of Sleeping Beauty, climbing up into the towers.

Maria began to wail in earnest and she bent over to wipe the hot little face. 'Don't worry, we'll find somewhere for you to go.'

She shepherded the children over to the monument dominating the square, which she knew from the late-night reading (*Prague on a Shoestring* was becoming a bible) was a memorial to Jan Huss.

The monument was big. Too big, she thought. And in need of restoration. 'It was a symbol of defiance against repressive regimes.' Or so said this new bible. Whatever it was, the people sitting on its

61

step behaved oddly. A relay appeared to be under way. One person would sit down, remain stationary for a minute or so, and jump up. He or she was then replaced and the process was repeated, as if they were observing a hidden rota.

She made Jan and Maria sit on its steps while she figured out what to do and checked the time. Only three o'clock. In desperation, and with some difficulty, she bought a packet of boiled sweets from the nearest shop and, hoping they would divert them, doled them out to the children. They were oddly coloured and tasted of nothing much.

'Look,' said Jan, pointing to an arched doorway, guarded by a full-sized wooden witch figure with a beaked nose, over which a wooden notice had been nailed. Painted onto it was a puppet in a Pierrot costume and the word: *Marionety*.

With a sigh of relief, Laure asked, 'Do you two like puppets?'

Fifteen minutes later, having emerged from the negotiations at the ticket booth, and taken poor Maria to the lavatory, all three were ensconced with a dozen or so other children and adults.

Originally, the room with seating for seventy or so must have been part of a private house and traces of former grandeur in the cornicing were evident. Benches had been set out for the audience in front of a raised stage protected by a pair of curtains of virulent yellow onto which a hammer and sickle had been painted.

The walls were hung with wide strips of black material. In the spaces in between were several black-paper silhouettes pasted down onto white paper. One was of a girl with a pony tail. Another was of a male head with swept-back hair. Another showed an enchanting cut-out scene with a coach and horses dashing through a starlight night. Another was of a demon with staring eyes rearing up in front of a girl whose hair flowed down her back like a waterfall.

It was even hotter inside the room, the sort of thick heat that made you super aware of your body. A door leading into a garden had been propped open as wide as it would go.

Maria and Jan had lapsed into silence. To Laure's surprise, Maria slid her hand into hers. Laure stroked her fingers. 'Not long now,' she said.

Dressed in black from head to foot with her hair hidden by a bandeau, a girl drew a curtain across the door and the lights dimmed. Backstage, a couple of recorders struck up with a folk tune. Maria's fingers clenched in Laure's.

The stage curtains winched back, revealing a black backdrop lit by a single overhead light. The children in the audience rustled like wheat in the wind.

After a few minutes, Laure realized that she was watching a version of *Sleeping Beauty*. In this one, the Good Fairy was dressed in dungarees and a peasant scarf. The Bad Fairy was male, wore a pinstriped suit and a papier mâché bowler hat.

Jan giggled at the sight. 'Funny.'

As the story developed, Laure spotted an emerging agenda. The king and queen were demanding aristocrats, the courtiers were stupid and lazy, and Princess Aurore was spoilt and treated her nurse shockingly. Still, her scream when she pricked her finger was very convincing. Convicted of neglect, her parents were led off to prison before the courtiers fell asleep.

If the story had veered from the traditional, the puppetry was superb. After her initial resistance to having the story so altered, Laure gave in and laughed and gasped aloud with the best of them.

Having learnt her lesson, she made sure the children visited the lavatory in the interval. When they returned, their original seats had been taken and the only spaces left were beside the open door leading outside. Before she could stop him, Jan bolted through it and she followed.

The garden, such as it was, was a modest rectangle wedged between larger ones on either side. It admitted only partial sunlight but someone with green fingers tended it. Plants had been trained up the wall. Scarlet pelargoniums and ornamental grasses had been planted in a pair of rusting dustbins. A clematis grew in and out of the railing dividing the rectangle from the neighbouring garden. At its centre was a stone sun-dial, a beautiful object which looked antique, set on a pillar carved with stone flowers. The bench ranged against the back wall had been colonized by a male figure perched on its arm, smoking a cigarette.

Laure barely registered him as she was busy cajoling Jan back into his seat. When the lights had dimmed, however, he returned inside – and, then, she did sit up and take notice. Wearing a striped linen waistcoat with bone buttons that had seen better days, he was young, shambolic, sexy.

He indicated the seat next to her. 'OK?'

She nodded and turned away to deal with Jan who was poking his sister. 'Stop it.' In her confusion, she had lapsed into English and she noticed that the stranger gave a sharp look. She corrected herself. '*Arrête.*'

Act Two began with a peasant family toiling in a cornfield, singing a cheerful song. Mother and Father were unremarkable in sand-coloured dungarees. In contrast, their son had lustrous dark hair and eyes, a sensitive-looking mouth, blue trousers and a red-checked shirt.

The family were joined by villagers who – unlike the lazy courtiers – threw themselves into the toiling. The man in the waistcoat leant over and whispered to Laure in fluent but accented English. 'If you would like to know, they're singing about how joyful it is to work.'

'That's excellent,' she whispered back, 'but what's that to do with *Sleeping Beauty*?'

The dark made this exchange oddly intimate.

'It makes the point they're not corrupt aristocrats. The parents are also telling how fortunate they are because their handsome son helps them out and keeps them cheerful.'

Was this a joke? The Kobes had warned about this sort of thing. Best not to take chances, she decided, glancing at her charges. Maria was chewing her hair and Jan was watching the stage with rapt attention. Since she had arrived in the country, she was ever more conscious of being ignorant, but she *did* know enough to know that she had to be careful.

There was a lull on stage and the curtains swished shut but the lights remained off.

He eased closer to Laure and she breathed in tobacco, fresh male sweat and a hint of lavender. 'He believes in the power of collective work,' he said, 'and in the goodness of the State.'

She would have liked to have replied, *oh, that fairy tale*, but stopped herself.

He tapped his foot and she felt an energy pulse her way. 'Don't worry, it's the music that matters, not the lyrics.'

His English was *very* good.

'I'm Tomas,' he said into her ear.

She could feel the warmth of his body, feel his breath on her cheek.

'I'm Laure,' she replied before she could stop herself.

A silence fell, as if each was turning over this new information in their minds.

Maria's nose was running, and Laure searched her bag for a handkerchief. 'Isn't this fun?' she said in French.

The proximity of their two bodies was unnerving.

'Terrible-coloured curtains.' She said the first thing that came into her head.

He shifted away. 'Beggars can't choose in this country.'

A gap appeared between them and, to her surprise, Laure minded.

'Sorry.' Out of the corner of her eye, she looked Tomas over. In addition to the waistcoat, he was wearing a battered pair of jeans and a cheesecloth shirt.

'No need.' He flashed her a smile and, suddenly, she was drawn into a complicity.

Laure drew Maria close. She needed to put her arms around someone – a child, a lover – and to feel them as they would feel her. To hold someone, or to be held, was proof of being alive. For too long she had felt herself to be a mute, cold thing.

Maria's head fell back against Laure's chest.

'Here,' said Tomas. 'You can stretch her out across our laps.'

The curtains pulled back. Jan sat up. Offstage the recorder played a marching tune as the handsome peasant son embarked on his search to find the princess, which included making friends with a black bear who helped him hack through the hedge of thorns. Eventually, he discovered a comatose Princess Aurora. Strings swaying, wooden knee joints buckling, he bent over to kiss her awake. A child in front of them bellowed in delight. Maria sat up.

A memory pushed to the front of her mind, so unwelcome that she closed her eyes. It was of Rob Dance dressed from head to foot in black, sitting in his studio at Brympton. She could summon every detail: tins of tobacco shedding their guts over the floor, Rizlas on every surface, and photos pinned up like scales on the walls.

First love had to be got over, and as quickly as possible. Laure had read that somewhere and agreed. But it hadn't felt quick.

At the touch of the peasant-prince, Aurora woke up and their marionette shadows merged on the backdrop behind them.

Despite the heat in the room, Laure was in a cold sweat. Rob had taken her virginity. Very rapid. Very indifferent. Almost dutiful. Afterwards, feeling cheated of the sensations about which she had so often speculated, she had wriggled back into her jeans and watched him buckle his belt. 'You have to leave', he said. 'See you.'

At the finale, Tomas eased Marie gently upright and she bounced on the bench with delight. Children and adults were applauding noisily and so did Laure. 'I'm glad you approve of the company,' said Tomas, brushing back damp hair from his forehead. 'It's destined for great things.' He peered at Laure and his smile widened. 'I can truthfully tell them that we play to an international audience.'

'Any time you like,' she replied. 'I can be French or English.'

He put his head on one side and took a good look at her. 'Sexy French or sensible English. I'll have to think about which,' he said. 'And I'll let you know.'

She couldn't help the grin that stretched across her mouth.

He held up an arm that had a half-sucked boiled sweet stuck to it. 'What's *that*?'

'Oh God, I'm so sorry. One of the children must have spat it out.' She grabbed the handkerchief, wrapped up the sweet in a corner and dabbed at his arm with the rest. 'There wasn't any ice cream,' she said, by way of explanation, which he appeared to understand.

The puppeteers, two men and the girl in black, took their bow. The latter saw Tomas and beckoned. He got to his feet and Laure saw that he was only just taller than she was, and very slight. Fragile even.

Joining the company in front of the stage, he linked hands with them and all four took a bow, with the applause still sounding.

She told herself later that it was purely by chance that he turned his head and caught her eye.

The square in the Malá Strana was dominated by the eighteenth-century church of St Nicholas, built by the Jesuits as part of the fight-back against the spread of Protestantism, so said the 'bible'. Judging by its size, its massive green dome and interior ornamentation, it was a mighty fight-back in glittering gold, pilasters, frescos and sinuous arches.

St Nicholas divided the square that sloped upwards towards the castle. A former palace took up the entire west side, and a series of broad arcades the south side. The Kobes' apartment was tucked into a galleried courtyard leading in from the street, and took up two storeys of light, airy rooms.

What struck her when she first arrived were the beautiful and elaborate parquet floors, which were speckled and crazed with sun damage. Someone should have protected them. The next thing she noticed were the cracks in some of the walls, which, in one or two places, looked alarming.

In the bedroom she had been assigned under the eaves, the sun had done its worst and the floor beneath the window was bleached white in places. But the view out of her window enchanted her – rooftops, odd bits of the Charles Bridge and, beyond it, the towers and spires of the old town.

Tonight, she and the Kobes were eating supper together, which they did from time to time. They were in the dining room with an alternative view facing up towards the church and the crouching castle above it. They sat in hideous plastic chairs and ate Eva's pasta off porcelain plates and drank lemonade out of Bohemian glass.

Eva had piled up Laure's plate and she was finding it hard to get through it. She put down her fork. 'Is it always so hot in Prague?'

'No,' said Eva. Her voice shook in a strange manner.

'In the summer, yes.' Petr threw his wife a look.

Laure's gaze wandered to the peeling plaster cartouche above the double doorway. It must have been an original and showed a stag fighting with a bear. 'This is a lovely apartment. Do you know who used to live here?'

Petr forked up sticky meat sauce. 'Why do you wish to know?'

The words were uttered pleasantly enough but there was an undercurrent. Of what? She wasn't sure. Laure felt herself colour up. 'Just curious.'

Eva patted her hair which was twisted into an unsuccessful bun. She was looking a lot less smart than she had in Paris. 'A family lived here for many generations, but they vanished during the war. Lots of people did. They left without taking any of their possessions. Afterwards, Potio Pharma acquired this and other places because they thought it would be a good home for its workers.' She turned to Petr. 'And so it is, isn't it, darling?'

'That's right,' said Petr, his gaze levelled directly on Laure's face. She had a feeling that she was being reassessed, clinically and unemotionally, which was unpleasant. Then he smiled in his friendly fashion and everything changed. 'How were the children today?'

'I took them to a marionette theatre in the Old Town Square. It was good. *Sleeping Beauty*.'

Eva drank a mouthful of water. 'Is that the company which that group, Anatomie, is involved with?'

'Possibly.'

'Anatomie?' asked Laure.

'A rock group. They're well known in the country,' said Petr. 'Eva went to see them perform and came back in love with the lead singer.'

'Petr, I did no such thing.'

Petr's grin lit up his eyes. 'Yes, you did.'

Eva seemed alarmed. 'Be careful what you say.'

Laure must have looked puzzled and Petr helped her out. 'Rock stars are considered deviants and subversives. It's unwise to get mixed up with them.'

Eva looked out of the window. Then she began to laugh, an unpleasant, even unhinged, sound.

'Eva, you're tired.' He leapt to his feet. 'Why don't you go and have a bath?'

'I don't want one.'

'I insist,' he said, ushering his wife out of the room.

Having washed up, Laure went to her room to read. She could hear the murmur of her employers' conversation in their bedroom opposite. At one point, there were raised voices and feet padding down the corridor. Then, she could she could have sworn she heard Eva cry out. Wooden doors were not exactly soundproof. She wondered if Eva was wearing one of the French nightdresses that made up part of her tasks to launder and which were so much more sophisticated than anything that either Laure or her mother possessed.

A little later, needing the bathroom, she let herself out into the corridor. The door to Petr and Eva's room was ajar and, like it or not, she found herself peering through to the bed framed in the doorway.

Her nightdress streaked with blood, Eva was lying on her side with Petr bent over her. He had imprisoned her wrists and Eva was resisting. Not very effectively.

He shifted position and Laure saw that his hands were covered in blood too.

Was this a sex game? She had no knowledge on which to call. No experience. Was Petr beating his wife up or trying to rape her? And the blood?

Whatever it was, it was horrible. Saliva rushed into her mouth and she swallowed frantically.

Was Petr murdering Eva?

Who could she call for help?

Frozen by horror, she was unable to move. Then, it was over. Eva quietened, began to sob and muttered words in Czech. Petr released her and stood upright.

The treacherous floorboards creaked as Laure slid past. Over Eva's bare, white shoulder, Petr encountered Laure's appalled gaze as he bent to kiss his wife.

She stuttered. 'Is everything all right? Can I get help?'

'No,' said Petr, walking over to the door. 'It's over now. Eva will sleep.' He seemed exhausted and infinitely sad. 'It's not what you think.'

'But the blood?'

'Nothing for you to worry about. Perhaps one day I can explain. But not now.' He held out his bloody hands. 'I'm very sorry about this.'

'My God, what *is* this?'

She read confusion and distress in his eyes, and her own softened. 'Can I help?'

'You're quite safe,' he said. 'I promise.'

71

She fled down the corridor. On her return, the door had been closed. She went to bed and lay flat. *Prague on a Shoestring* would not be offering enlightenment and she directed her energies into trying not to think about the dreadful and complicated things that went on behind that door.

CHAPTER 6

Paris, present day

LAURE WAS OUTLINING TO MAY WILLIAMS THE PLANS FOR the lunch to celebrate the collaboration between the museum and the Maison de Grasse when the first of the day's interviewees was ushered in.

She was a woman of forty or so, who had once been beautiful but had dieted herself into a pickled-looking skin. She had heavily made-up eyes with black rings engraved under them and professionally manicured hands. The preliminaries dispensed with, she produced a games board and a set of wooden chess pieces, which she set out with an ease that suggested second nature.

It was done in silence. Used to waiting, Laure took the time to observe a tell-tale downturn of the woman's mouth but also her expensive leather designer jacket.

When she had placed the last pawn in position and the two sides were ranged against the other, she began. 'You might not recognize me,' she said in heavily accented English, 'but my name is Adeline LeDuc.'

'I've heard of you,' said Laure.

May was already googling the name. 'You're a grandmaster at chess.'

'Yes.'

May read out, 'It's a title awarded for life. Currently, only three women hold it.'

'That is true, too,' said Adeline. She slipped into French. 'But it's not helpful to… rather, I try to avoid gender politics.'

Laure translated for May and indicated the chess pieces. 'That's a beautiful chess set.'

Adeline raised her gaze from the board. 'It's handmade to my specification.'

'May I?' Laure reached over and took up a king. The figure had cropped hair and armour and wore a tabard quartered with armorials bearings on which the British lion was evident. 'Am I imagining it or is this Henry V?' She picked up a second figure which was of a young man with a scarf wrapped a couple of times around his neck. 'Hamlet?' She gestured to the board. 'Characters from Shakespeare?'

'That's right.'

'A compliment to the English?'

'I think there's an argument for saying that Shakespeare is beyond nationality.'

Again, Laure translated for May who said, 'I agree.'

Laure held the Hamlet piece in the palm of her hand. On the board were the pawns: a flowing-haired Juliet, a diminutive Feste, a willowy Rosalind dressed *à la garçonne*. Here were the fools and heroes. The reckless and the asinine. The noble and the wastrel – the bundle of human characteristics and follies were represented by those figures. 'It's surprising how recognizable they are,' she commented.

'If you know Shakespeare,' intervened May in stumbling French.

'I commissioned it as a wedding present. The person who made these was a fine craftsman. He's dead now.' She sighed, a sound gusty with regret. 'He understood that each piece had to repay being handled. It was vital that they were beautifully made and beautifully balanced.' One manicured hand darted across the board and a white pawn was positioned for the fight. 'You might like to know I've just made a classic opening gambit.' She waited for Laure to translate. 'I've won with it on a couple of occasions.'

May was fascinated. 'So, if you had to counter it how would you do it?'

In response, Adeline LeDuc moved the black pawn to face the white. 'That's put those two out of action and given me the advantage to move the bishop.'

As happened in some of these museum encounters, there were discoveries. 'Madame LeDuc, tell us why you wish to donate such a beautiful thing?'

May muttered, 'To be or not to be and – presumably – it wasn't?'

Laure sent her a look.

'My husband was also a major chess player,' said Adeline. 'We had it set up in our bedroom. Sometimes, in the night, if one or other us were puzzling over a problem in a game we would get up and work it out on the board.' She touched the second king, Macbeth holding a dagger. 'We thought it would work. At the beginning, we promised each other that we would not mind if one or another won more tournaments and made more money. It didn't turn out like that. I kept winning games but lost the marriage. Pierre tried. We both tried. He hid his jealousy and I made light of my winnings. Sometimes, I concealed them from him. Once, I deliberately fluffed a major tournament.'

Laure translated.

'Men,' offered up May.

Adeline LeDuc understood and shook her head. 'Too easy.' May coloured up. 'It could have been the other way around. If Pierre had been the one to become a grandmaster, I might well have been bitterly jealous. Having married people competing on the same turf is not good.' The expression in the eyes was bleak. 'He failed to honour the promise.'

Laure nodded. 'I understand.'

Adeline took up the Macbeth piece – the black king – and used it to square up to the white king, Henry V. 'I would like it to be in a place where people could see how special it is. I can't play with it ever again and my ex-husband refuses to touch it.' She tapped Macbeth. 'That's checkmate.'

'Neat,' said May.

'Madame,' Laure stood up, 'it has been a pleasure to meet you and to discuss the chess pieces. My colleagues and I will consider the space available...'

Perhaps because Laure had signalled the end of the interview, Adeline LeDuc's benignity slid from her. 'My husband should learn.' She gathered up the chess pieces and shut the board with a snap. 'I see that I don't impress you,' she said to Laure, demonstrating what kind of adversary she might be across the chessboard.

Having handed Adeline over to Nic, Laure returned to the interview room. May was staring out of the window, her laptop open. 'How about this?' She read out from her notes. '"So many things have been offered up in the museum, apart from the objects. Fragments from lives that have not gone according to plan which are presented in anger, in resignation, in despair but, sometimes, with relief and a lightening of spirit."' She looked up and what she read in Laure's expression obviously puzzled her. 'You're not going to take the chess pieces, are you?'

'No.'

'Darned if I know why not.'

Laure crossed over to the window and May joined her. Together they looked out over the Parisian roofscape, gloriously fretted in the sunlight. 'If you enter competitions you're in them to win. That's the nature of the beast, yes?'

May did her hand-in-hair gesture. 'Haven't got you.'

'As competitors, they have a duty to try and win and, if they were competing in the same competitions, one of them was always going to be in the ascendant. The promise they made to each other wasn't realizable from the start. It wasn't really a promise. It was a way of allowing the marriage to happen. They must have known that.' Reluctantly, Laure turned away from the view. 'With such limited space, I have to make difficult decisions. The chess set has to be one of them.'

On the way downstairs, May stopped and asked, 'Henry V conquered the French, right?'

'Best not to mention it while you're in France,' replied Laure. 'But, yes, he did, temporarily.'

'So, apart from anything else, the chess set represents inconvenient history?'

'If you like.'

'Hmm,' she said, and proceeded to surprise Laure. 'Glossing over history is a fool's game. It comes back to bite you in the foot.'

Laure ran down the remaining stairs. 'But it can stop one going mad.'

May locked on to Laure like a heat-seeking missile. 'Then you know what's it's like to go mad? Or to have a breakdown?'

'Did I say that? It was an observation, that's all.'

At the finish of her evening inspection, Laure emptied the Donation Box, recorded the tally onto the online spreadsheet, shut down the computer in the sales kiosk and went upstairs. Here she leant against the door frame and watched as Nic and May swapped travel anecdotes.

Nic was lounging by the window, a lean brown arm on the sill. May was in his chair looking up at him.

'I bet you didn't.' Her smile was radiant.

Laure crossed over to Nic's desk. 'Is he telling you how he conquered Everest single-handed?'

'Something like.' May did not take her eyes off Nic. 'Should I believe him?'

'Depends how much you enjoy fairy tales,' replied Laure affectionately.

'I have to work with this person,' said Nick. 'My life is hard.'

Laure picked up the volume of Philip Larkin poems which had been in Room 1 and due for return. Its inscription 'man hands on misery to man' had been taken from the volume and embellished by an enraged husband who had struck out the first 'man' and substituted 'woman'.

May got to her feet. 'I shouldn't be here. But I wanted to ask how long objects have in the museum?'

Laure retrieved her bag from under the desk. 'Some have been here since the beginning but it's usually three years or so. Having a turnover encourages visitors to return to check out what's new. Each object is catalogued on paper and the computer. If we're discarding, we get in touch with the donor and ask them how they wish us to dispose of it.'

Once outside in the street, she felt so tired that she phoned her dinner date to cancel.

'Simon, I'm done. I'm so sorry. Could we rearrange?'

'I'm here to be mucked about with.'

'Sorry.'

A lawyer working for Nos Arts en France, Simon had turned into a friend. They had first met over the negotiations for the modest grant from Nos Arts. Later, an anonymous sponsorship deal had been offered which was to be administered by Nos Arts and Simon agreed to take it on. Initially, the deal had been reviewed on an annual basis and then – out of the blue sky – suddenly extended to a generous five-year funding contract. Additionally puzzling were the terms of the sponsorship which specified that Laure, her trustees or her team were not allowed to ask as to who the sponsor was.

Why? she had wanted to know. Why should I be so lucky? Simon replied that there were many things on earth and in heaven that could not be explained and this was one of them. He also told her to take the money and run.

One of those rare people who managed to be both discreet and a gossip at the same time, Simon never divulged even a hint of the process by which the decision was arrived at. 'I'm a professional,' he said, with the uneven smile which she had grown to love. 'Anyway, it keeps you interested in me.' Simon was faithfully married to Valerie with three children but liked to pretend that he wasn't.

'Simon, I love you very much. Please kiss Valerie for me and my goddaughter.'

The Rue de la Grange aux Belles was busy. Night softened the city's harsher outlines as daytime city smells segued into evening ones of roasted garlic, turmeric, perfume of all kinds, cigarette smoke.

She walked slowly, eyes searching through the litter of papers and takeaway boxes for a sign of life. She passed the manhole halfway down the street and was hit by a smell of old, confined water and rotting things.

She was increasingly anxious about Kočka.

By the time Laure reached the triangle of earth where she usually encountered her, she was experiencing something akin to dread. If Kočka had moved on, dragging her difficult, painful life behind her, then did she have a future? A living thing that was so unloved and untended went against nature and she castigated herself for not doing anything about it sooner.

But Kočka was there, in her usual place, stretched out over the lumpy, concrete-infested earth. At Laure's approach, she raised her head. The large eyes were clouded and she was panting. Beside her lay three new-born kittens, two still inside the caul. None of them moved and Laure knew they had not made it.

Laure reached for the bottle of water in her bag and squirted a little into Kočka's mouth. She seemed grateful and licked it feebly. Laure got hold of her mobile and dialled the vet with whom she had earlier made the appointment. An answerphone kicked in and she was instructed that if it was an emergency she must go to the nearest animal hospital.

Laure took off her cardigan, laid Kočka on it and wrapped her up in it. Wincing, she took up the still damp kittens, placed them carefully in her bag and summoned a taxi.

The animal hospital was full with a record number of injured and abandoned animals. 'One of humanity's periodic fits of inhumanity,' commented the vet when Laure lifted Kočka onto the examination table and unwrapped her kittens.

She must have smelt them for she turned her head and uttered a soft distressed cry. The vet stooped over her and made a thorough examination, palpating her still swollen abdomen and checking for tears and bleeding. 'She wasn't in good enough condition to get them through.' He cocked an eye at Laure's now ruined cardigan. 'Sorry about that.'

'So am I,' she said. 'It was expensive.'

She stood and watched, breathing in the smells of frightened animals overlaid with disinfectant that pervaded the room as he gave Kočka the works – vitamin shots, antibiotics and a drug to stop her lactating. Once, he looked up from Kočka's prone body and said, 'This is going to cost you a fortune.' Finally, he laid the dead kittens on the table beside her. 'She must be allowed to mourn.'

They watched as the frail, wounded, disadvantaged Kočka nuzzled each one in turn.

'I'm afraid you're going to have to take her,' the vet said eventually. 'We have no room.'

'I can't do that.' Those oh-so orderly arrangements of her life upended. Allowing in the music and fire and grief of a past? She looked down at the little cat who was trying to say farewell to her kittens. She grasped the edge of the instrument trolley and struggled to explain through the lump in her throat. 'There're rules where I live.'

The vet indicated she should leave off hugging the trolley. 'Hygiene,' he said, not unsympathetically.

An expert in these situations, he handed her a tissue. 'In my experience, most animals live where there are so-called rules. Kočka cannot be put back on the streets. Else why did you bring her in? When she is better and we are less pressed then something might be able to be done.' He allowed a second or two to elapse. 'We might have to put her down.'

She stared at the vet. It was obvious he had been in this situation before, and kind and skilful as he was, he knew how not to blink.

A noisier than usual row was in full swing in the Poirier apartment. Even so, smuggling the cardboard carrier containing Kočka past Madame Poirier's sentry post took nerve and ingenuity. The old skills she had learnt in Prague kicked in. *Move at normal speed. Do not look round.* Tiny Kočka was weightier than she looked but Laure didn't falter on the stairs.

Inside the apartment, Laure placed the carrier on the floor and went through into the bedroom. The hair dryer was on the bed where she had flung it this morning and so, too, was the scattered make-up on the shelf by the mirror.

At the back of the cupboard where she kept her linen, she found a worn swimming towel. This she spread over an armchair in the sitting area. Inside the carrier, Kočka was crying and she lifted her out of it and placed her on the chair.

The vet had warned her that what was an, essentially, feral cat would not respect an interior and might be spooked by being enclosed but she was probably too weak and doped-up to react. Laure hunkered down beside her, stroked the small head and, one by one, fed her the cat biscuits that the vet had given her.

After a while, Kočka slept, the rise and fall of her breath barely rippling her torso that was both swollen and emaciated. Unwilling to move, Laure settled herself on the floor beside the chair and reached for her laptop. Figures. Plans. Projections. With the movement of a finger, these slipped over the screen and vanished. She didn't take in any of them.

If Kočka was peaceful, Laure was not. Leaning over, she extracted the frame with the railway ticket from her bag which she had brought home. (It was hers to take.)

She reprised May's questions.

'So why Czech?'

'I lived there for a long summer.'

'And that's a broken promise?'

'Actually, yes, as it turned out. It was.'

She sat for a long time with the frame propped on her knee. Tomas refused to contemplate leaving the country until it became clear that he had no option. 'I fight through the music,' he said during one of their many discussions in the early days when they drank beer in the sun or wandered along the river. 'The patriot stays. Anyway, what would happen if they caught me?'

She knew enough to answer. 'Prison.'

He picked up a lock of Laure's hair. 'You've just proved you're a Westerner from a soft, liberal culture. If I'm caught they will screw information out of me however hard I try to resist. I cannot put others in danger.'

'Screw?' She had made a joke of it.

It wasn't funny. It would never have been funny. 'All right, get it out of me.'

In Communist Prague there was one life playing out on the surface while another parallel one with its own language and myths was hidden from view.

He shouldn't have done but Tomas's friend, Milos, had told her about the escape routes. By then they knew each other well enough.

Drive the Trabant to Hungary and attempt to get over the border. *The guard dogs were notorious.*

Get to Berlin, organize a contact from the West to come over with fake documents and do an exchange in the so-called Hall of Tears, the Tränenpalast, where the *Ossis* and *Wessis* were forced to say goodbye to each other. *Very high risk and only recommended for German speakers.*

Get out by train from Prague to Austria. *The Vienna option.*

Whoever it was on the run was instructed to go to the restaurant at the southern end of Wenceslas Square owned by Milos's father, to walk through the tables and to let himself out of the back entrance. Next, they were to head for the telephone booth at the bottom of the street. If a piece of string was tied around the receiver, they were to dial the number they had been given and wait for the code word. (If no string, they were to abort.) Next, they were to make their way to the safe house used by dissidents on the move (rumour had it that it was run by the British) and once they had given the correct code word, they would be given new papers and a bicycle to get to the station.

Results were fifty–fifty.

But that time, someone released the information, maliciously or carelessly or innocently, and the carefully constructed chain fell apart. Where and by whom? Milos? Lucia, the Boadicea-like fighter for regime change? The nameless contact who was to supply the code word?

Fatigue gritted her eyes and her limbs were heavy with exhaustion. Even so, she knew it would be one of those nights when she didn't sleep much. (They used to send Xavier crazy.)

Kočka woke several times, mewling and restless. On sentry duty on the floor, Laure calmed her as best she could. Towards dawn, she lost consciousness.

Tomas was playing the piano. This puzzled Laure because his instrument of choice was the guitar.

His hair was cropped uncharacteristically short and she noticed a strip of white skin above the sunburn on his neck.

'The keys are too stiff,' he was saying in his good, but accented, English. 'I have to work doubly hard.'

He was playing Beethoven's 'Ode to Joy' which was not his music at all either. 'I know it's a cliché for the West,' he said, swivelling to look at her. 'But not for us.' He turned back to the keyboard. 'For us, the end of the war is a long way off.' He played more. 'Music is the best kind of warrior and will have to do the fighting.'

It filled her ears with sublime sound.

'My God,' she heard herself say. 'I've waited for you for so long.'

'*On arrive.*' His French was nowhere as good as his English and he would have struggled in Paris. '*On arrive.* I promise.'

I have been awakened, she thought. I am dizzy, enraptured, without boundaries. I never dreamt that being in love meant to be exultant and at ease at one and the same time.

Watching him at the keyboard drove the breath from her body.

The notes became choppier as she swam up towards consciousness.

So immersive and deep was the dream that it took Laure some time to reorientate herself, and, at first, Kočka's face peering down at her from the chair made no sense.

She struggled upright. Kočka would need the cat-litter tray and she lifted the still limp body from the chair and set her down in the tray that had been added to the staggering bill paid to the vet.

Kočka protested but seemed to get the idea. Laure turned away. Even cats required privacy.

CHAPTER 7

$\mathcal{A}$T THE MUSEUM THE CALLS CAME THICK AND FAST, mainly to do with the Maison de Grasse partnership.

While she waited for Laure's attention, May perched on Nic's desk and the two of them talked. From over the phone, Laure observed their interaction, swapping jokes, allusions, teases. Something told her, and she was unsure why, that they were seeking sanctuary in each other.

Nic laid his hand on May's arm and May's blue-grey eyes flew to Nic's and they fell silent. A pang went through Laure. She, too, had experienced those wordless, electric exchanges that sent shocks through the body and soul.

The calls continued late until lunchtime. 'I'm sorry,' Laure finally put the phone down. 'I must check on my sick cat.'

Nic did not take his eyes off May. 'You denied having a cat when I asked.'

'I didn't then.'

May suggested she walk over to Laure's apartment with her from where she had arranged to continue on to her next interview with a dress designer in the Marais. 'So exciting. I'm spending the afternoon in a Parisian garret.'

Nic shot Laure a look that she interpreted as a warning. At the first opportunity, she took him aside. 'What are you telling me?'

She had never seen anyone looked so shell-shocked as the normally cool Nic. 'Look, she's pretty ruthless when it comes to work.' Laure knew she should put him out of his misery but watching the tussle between his loyalties was irresistible. 'But, at heart, she's lovely.'

This was as pitiful a case as Laure had ever seen and she *almost* felt sorry for the helpless Nic. Her lips twitched. 'Shall I tell her that?'

'*No.*' Having clocked she was teasing, he added, 'I just wanted to be sure that you knew that she can be… forensic.'

She peered hard at Nic and reminded herself that it was Nic, not herself, who was diving into swirling, lust-saturated waters. But she did know about the astonishingly visceral responses, the anticipation mixed with breathlessness and, in the best sense, about desire. Reflecting so, she felt that old beat of regret. Yet, grief and secrets were part of the deal in life and she had taught herself to get on with it. She smiled at him. 'And you should be careful, too.'

Together Laure and May walked down to the canal before turning into Laure's street. Laure asked about May's assignments and May explained she would be doing pieces on the dressmaker who took her inspiration from Morocco and a new flea market that had opened nearby in Bastille. Excitement and professional hunger pulsed from her – and Laure heard an echo of her younger self talking, talking, as rapid and as intense as she had been.

'Who sent you to Paris?'

May stopped to scrape clogged leaves from her pink and black trainers. 'No one. Saved up and took a chance.'

'That was brave.'

'Or desperate.'

'To get away from your mother?'

'The parrot on my shoulder, yes.' She was edgy. 'I wanted a life. I wanted a career.'

For once, the street noises were at a minimum. The autumn sun was at its most glorious and Laure inhaled an odour of dry leaves, bakery, water and the faintest suggestion of spices.

'You love Paris,' observed May.

'Yes.'

'A little? A lot?'

'Paris has become part of me.'

'Was Prague the same? Or Berlin?'

Laure forced herself not to stop mid-stride. 'Did I ever mention Prague or Berlin?'

'Not in so many words.' May skirted around a tent erected on the canal bank with a camping gas ring leaning drunkenly beside it. 'I've done some homework. You had a boss who was a big commie chief? Right?'

'No comment.'

May said: 'I know you hate talking about yourself, Laure, but this isn't big intrusive stuff. Just background. I hope… I know … the article will be useful if I get it right. For both of us.' Her gaze darted from trees, to the canal, to bridges… taking it all in. 'It could be good. Really good. I feel it.'

'Hang on,' said Laure. She retraced her steps to the tent, bent down and righted the gas ring. 'They have so little,' she explained on re-joining May.

May tried again. 'Did the British know you worked for a communist?'

Laure swung round. 'You're stepping over the mark,' she said. 'That's *not* your business.'

'Except that history can't be rewritten and it's out there.'

May had a point. 'You're right,' Laure conceded.

May looked only a trifle smug. 'Thank you.' She paused. 'I hope we can be honest with each other.'

Did May mean it? In the apartment, a still weak Kočka was spread over the swimming towel on the sofa, much as Laure had left her. As Laure and May came into the room, she lifted her head and her pupils enlarged. Laure sat down beside her and stroked the swoop of fur between her eyes which, to her surprise, Kočka permitted.

'This is ridiculous,' she said, pity and protectiveness churning inside her. 'What am I going to do with you?'

May extracted a recording machine from her things.

Kočka closed her eyes.

'I can't keep her.'

'Why not?'

Laure explained. May, who had seen the point of Kočka at once, wedged herself down on the sofa beside her and touched the tip of her paw. Kočka accepted this tribute. 'If she's a feral cat, shouldn't she be frightened of people?'

Laure fetched a tray with glasses and offered May an apple juice. 'I think she might have belonged to someone at some point. She seems to understand about being indoors and I don't have too much of a fight getting a pill down her.'

May eyed up Kočka. 'How the hell do you get a pill down a cat?'

'Get it into their mouth and make them sneeze.'

'Stupid me. Why didn't I think of it?' Her drawl deepened. 'Laure, I've read some cuttings. Some of them aren't so flattering.'

May was probably referring to a spiky profile in *Madame Figaro*. Their chief feature writer had not bought the idea of the museum, maintaining it was a waste of public resources. Representations of personal disaster that were not works of art per se should not, he maintained at some length, be subsidized with the taxpayers' money which came via Nos Arts de France.

For the first time, she had seen Nic angry. Why, oh why, he accused Laure, weren't you more emollient?

Notebook settled on her knee, May exuded good will and professionalism. The effect was calming. *She* was charming. But, as Laure knew from experience, it was no guarantee.

Laure took the initiative. 'You mentioned this was your first time in Paris? It can be an overwhelming experience. I used to come here as a child, then as a twenty-year-old, working as an au pair. I remember feeling faint for a lot of the time because everything was so overwhelming.'

'It took me a day to prise open my jet-lagged eyes and then you couldn't stop me.' May crossed long tightly denimed legs. 'I came to Paris on the off-chance that I could get some things going. It's been great. Helped by being shown where to get the mind-blowing coffee. Now, I'm in it. Totally. What a city. I come from Birmingham, Alabama, which is way down the US food chain – don't quote me – and has its share of the past to tussle with. But Paris is something else. Paris is layered in it. Everywhere you go, it's in your face. Revolution, snap. Napoleon, snap. Dior, snap.'

Laure understood.

'You look every inch the Parisienne now.' May gestured at Laure's leather jacket. 'Every darn inch. Bet it cost a fortune.'

Laure recollected the time she had spent tracking down the boutiques she liked, the shoe shops, the hairdresser. 'Thank you.'

May's finger hovered over Kočka's paw. 'You were born in 1966. Right?'

Laure's recent visit to the optometrist and the prescription issued for reading glasses had come as a jolt. 'Yes.' She sat down in the chair opposite May. 'What do you want to ask me?'

'You tell me. Give me the opening and we'll take it from there.'

Laure checked her watch. Was there a chance of getting away with only half an hour? She pointed to Kočka. 'As you've found out, I've lived in two cities where it would have been beyond most people's means to take in a feral cat.'

May flicked on the recording machine. 'Prague and Berlin.'

The words arrived, surprisingly easily. 'In 1986 I found myself in Prague for several months, just before the fall of the communist government. My father died suddenly, and I couldn't cope at university. At that age, death doesn't seem possible. It was a double blow. I was going to muck up my exams and my French mother arranged for me to take a year out in Paris as an au pair. As it turned out, my employers were Czech and that's how I got to Prague.'

May pushed the recorder a shade closer to Laure.

'I joined the foreign office and, after the Wall was demolished, I worked in Berlin for the British Embassy in a minor capacity. Which I liked too, even though it was grim at times.'

'A minor capacity,' said May, sounding thoughtful. 'I can't see you in a minor capacity.' She paused. '*Were* you a spy? At the time, they were crawling all over the city.'

Laure said with a cold, quiet disdain, 'I thought this was an adult interview.'

May flinched visibly and shifted in her seat, which made Laure suspect that she was more rookie and at sea than she had supposed. Even so, when questioning, the trick was: *to bait the hook to suit the fish*. Maybe that was May's schtick to give her leverage with the awkward questions?

May rallied. 'Needs asking though? Wasn't Berlin an odd choice?'

'You go where you're posted. But I left the service when I was offered a very well-paid job as an interpreter in Paris.' The half-truth slid off her tongue.

'So, you developed a taste for living abroad. Or, preferred it.'

'I did.'

'Have you ever been back to Prague or Berlin?'

'No.'

'Any particular reason?'

Laure shrugged. 'Hasn't been convenient.'

'Or, you didn't wish to.'

Again, Laure shrugged.

May asked if she could use the bathroom and Laure pointed down the passage. May took her time but when she returned, she asked, 'How did it all begin?'

She meant the museum.

How?

'Where do ideas come from? Who knows?'

Divorce, sleeplessness, childlessness, weariness of working as an interpreter all played a part. But the reasons why they pushed Laure to action at that moment were too deeply buried for her to be exact. All she knew was they had rubbed against each other – wire wool on an encrusted fire grate – and produced a shiny idea.

She concentrated on the practical details. 'Once I had the idea and found the house, I buttonholed the bank and borrowed as much as I could, bought it and restored it. I hired a publicity agent to create a buzz about the museum and I applied to Nos Arts de France for funding which I was granted on an annual basis. Not so very remarkable. Just business.'

May took down notes. 'Can you give numbers?'

'Sorry, confidential. I never knew from one year to the next if money was forthcoming. We had five years of steadily improving footfall which was so good and kept me going. Then, Nos Arts informed me that an anonymous sponsor wished to take on the funding for a further five years and what's more he or she was giving enough money to pay for the entire operation.'

Simon had rung to tell her. 'What's your magic, girl? Whatever it is, I'll have some of it.' He waited until her cries of 'it can't be true' had died away before saying, 'This is a big achievement, Laure. Few have managed it.'

Describing the moment could not possibly convey the satisfaction, the sense that something had, after all, arrived at completion. 'It was quite a day when you're told there's a staggering sum on which to call. We had got there. It was working.'

May scented blood. 'You've no idea who it might be? Or why they did it?'

'We've hit a moment of change, I think. The museum is seen as fresh and anti-establishment. It offers an invitation to many who would normally feel excluded, who perhaps don't go to museums. It can step over boundaries that other museums have to observe.'

'Except *you* monitor the acquisitions.'

'I do everything in my power to keep an open mind. There're things in the museum that would never see the light of day in the established institutions. Nor would their stories.'

'Fair enough.' May fiddled with her recorder. 'And the Maison de Grasse?'

'That will dovetail well. The firm services the mass market—'

'Those masses that can afford their quite pricey products,' May opened up her notebook and tapped into it. 'Paying... yes, fifty euros for a scented candle as it's advertised here is probably not top of the list for most.'

'But their floor cleaner is,' countered Laure. 'The trustees tell me they are delighted by the association. Remember, they're not doing the funding, but providing patronage.'

'What did you *feel* when it all took off?'

'Very good.'

'Just good? Weren't you over the moon? Praising Jesus?'

Her lips twitched. 'Nic and I needed a large glass of wine. OK, three.'

She remembered the feeling of release – sweet and addictive – and that, at last, something had gone right in her life. Looking back, it was the moment when she pivoted away from pessimism towards the self with whom she liked to live.

'Good,' May looked up. 'I'm beginning to see you.' The uncertain expression was gone – a reminder to Laure to be careful. 'Are we getting somewhere?'

'You make it sound like a psychotherapy session. It's not. This is an interview, nothing more.'

May checked the recording device. 'Is it lonely being the curator?'

Tomas, Milos, all of them, had warned Laure to keep her mouth shut. To ask questions was to invite suspicion, they said, let alone answering them. *Be stupid, always be stupid.* Once learned as a survival strategy, it had stayed with Laure.

May raised an eyebrow. 'Is it?' 'Being spied on is like having your skin peeled away,' she had once observed to Tomas.

He had taken her in his arms, stroked her hair and said, 'Never get used to it. Otherwise we're dead.'

'Being head of anything is lonely,' Laure replied. 'It's the nature of the beast.'

Sometimes Laure imagined her experiences were stamped on her exterior – like a birthmark, or a scar from an old injury. As for her interior? The scars went deep there: cutting down into her mind and thoughts.

'What's the point of the museum?' May settled back into her seat. 'You can take as long as you like.'

It was now well past lunchtime. 'I'll get us something to eat,' Laure said. 'Then we can discuss.'

From the fridge, she took out some slices of melon and Parma ham and arranged them on two plates. 'It's not much,' she said, emerging from the kitchen, a plate in each hand, and came to a dead halt. 'What are you doing?'

May was over by the table under the window where she appeared to be taking photos of the papers piled on it.

Laure set the plates down. '*May?*'

She swung round and coloured up. 'I hope you don't mind. I was taking a photo of your picture. It's so beautiful with the sea and the driftwood.' She pointed unconvincingly to the framed photograph of a beach in the west of Scotland littered with rocks and driftwood on the wall above the table.

Laure's rage sprang into life – and it was almost pleasurable, as if she had given herself permission to let go. 'No, you weren't.' She made to grab the phone, but May stepped to one side and shielded it against her chest.

'You were snooping.'

'I'm sorry,' said May.

What did Laure expect? Her guard had been lowered, which had been unwise. May could never be anything else but someone who was doing her job.

'I thought I would learn something about you.' May tightened her grip on her phone. 'You're very difficult to get through to.'

'And what makes you think you have the right to do what you have just done?'

'No right.' Her voice slithered over the words. 'Only the desire to write truthfully.'

'Get out.'

May stood her ground. 'Laure, I'm not a spy.'

'You know *nothing* about being a spy.'

Quick as a flash came the retort, 'And you do?'

May did not, and could not, know about *that* universe. The colourless years. The watching, the uncertainty. The voluntary venture into grey, incomplete moral territory from which there was no return. It was an enterprise, sometimes a fearsome one, that left no one unmarked. 'Give me your phone.' May flinched at Laure's tone. 'Now. And the password.'

'You can't take my phone.'

'Yes, I can. And I will.' There was no mistaking Laure's anger and May handed it over. Laure tapped in the numbers and deleted the photograph of the medical insurance forms that had been on the top of the pile of papers. 'Were you also snooping when you went to the bathroom?'

May owned up at once. 'I looked into the room with the boxes. I'm sorry. But I was fascinated by the labels. "Prague", "Berlin". I would love to talk those over with you. I know they're important in your story.' She kneaded one hand against the other. 'I noticed the Czech railway ticket in the frame.'

'What are you suggesting?'

'Not that you've stolen it.'

'I should bloody think not.' As the museum's curator, she had handled worse situations – and this should be no different. 'You have abused our arrangement.'

May gnawed an already bitten fingernail and did not move. 'I apologize, Laure. It was wrong of me. Very.'

May was clearly panicked. Losing this assignment would not be good for either but May would be the real loser.

'How can you write so acutely and act so stupidly?'

'It has to be done sometimes,' she said. 'It's not good. But it achieves good.' The uncertain expression was back. 'By good, I mean clarity.'

'Leave. Now.'

What a performance May was putting on, she thought. A good theatrical one.

'*Go*. And don't come back.'

'The papers were there. You were in the kitchen. I wanted to find out more about you.' May assembled her defence. 'If the papers were really important you would not have left them lying around.'

'If you mean I hadn't anticipated inviting someone without principles or morals into my flat, then no.'

The grey-blue eyes were now huge rock pools of distress and contrition.

'Please,' said May, all pretence apparently ripped away. 'This will be a big feature. It was my idea and I went after it.' She added in a low voice, 'I need it.'

The air in the flat felt stale, despairing. Laure walked across to the window and pushed it further open. She held an advantage. May knew it wasn't only the killing of the interview that had made her plead for it. Killing the interview meant that May would probably have to say goodbye to Nic.

She kept her back turned on May. 'I bloody hope the dos and don'ts of my medical insurance were worth it.'

'Actually, they were very boring.'

One never got used to being spied on. Never and, almost certainly, May would know nothing of that. There were techniques to combat it and scrutinizing someone from top to toe worked well when it was advisable to disconcert a watcher. Laure turned around and allowed her gaze travel up the long legs, the skinny hips and white lace T-shirt up to the clever, almost beautiful but not quite, features and the mass of fair hair – raking over the combination of the confident and vulnerable that May presented.

'You're very determined,' she said.

'Yes. I am.'

'I wonder how much?' said Laure, more to herself than May. 'How much is your determination made up of skulduggery?'

May lifted the hand holding the phone in a gesture of surrender. 'It's fine to hate me.'

'Just so there's no mistake, I repeat that the ticket in the frame belongs to me.'

'Of course.'

Laure handed over May's phone. May took it, picked up her rucksack and went.

Kočka got up, stretched and resettled.

Laure sat down beside her, held out a hand and was annoyed to see that it was shaking.

It didn't always happen, thank God, and it had got better as she grew older. But, from time to time, it took only a small invasion of her private world, a rattled-up routine, for her to be back running through the streets, heart frantic beneath her ribcage. Running once again from the grey men and leather-jacketed goons who watched and preyed and pounced.

Those flashing images had their effect. Countering them was hard, even years later, but she had learnt to force herself to turn her mind around.

So… it was healing to remember being with Tomas down by the Vltava, almost delirious with happiness. He had drawn her close and she inhaled the aphrodisiacal scent of male sweat and tobacco. He bent over to kiss her and it seemed to Laure that what was flowing through her veins was liquid joy.

Then her disobedient thoughts swooped down on the old, unanswered nagging questions.

Did Tomas ever make it to the railway station? Had he ever held his railway ticket to freedom, even for a few seconds? What would have been worse? To reach the train, only to be dragged off? Or never even getting within spitting distance of it?

She shifted position. Time to concentrate on something else. On Kočka. What was Laure doing taking her on? (Semi-feral. Expensive. Needy.) She touched the fur between Kočka's ears, absorbing through her fingertip the whisper of eggshell bone beneath it. To take her in, to love Kočka, was to invite vulnerability, possibly distress.

It would be complicated. Laure had little spare time to deal with Kočka and, unless she killed Madame Poirier (no hardship) and replaced her with a sympathetic concierge, she would be forced to move. Her guarded, compartmentalized routines would be thrown into flux. A small creature's demands would invade her calm.

In the morning, it would be simple enough to bundle Kočka into the cardboard carrier, to take her back to the vet and to let them deal with her.

Kočka stirred, adjusting a paw that sat at an angle, which suggested it had been damaged in the past. Its fragility was unbearable. It made her feel… what? Uncomfortable. Broken.

May had accused her of being difficult to get through to.

True. She was observing life through a pane of glass. That was how she wished it. You must not live with ghosts, she told herself. It is time to forget them.

Laure's personal history coloured much of her attitude. But not entirely. No one could look at the planet today, riddled as it was with violence, rotten regimes and persecution, and feel good about it.

The sounds of Paris filtered in through the window.

Laure gently arranged Kočka's tail and a familiar ache folded itself over her heart.

CHAPTER 8

$\mathcal{T}$HE FOLLOWING MORNING, MAY WALKED INTO THE OFFICE and planted herself in front of Laure's desk. Laure looked up. 'I don't wish to talk to you.'

May looked seriously sleep-deprived. 'I'm so sorry. Please, will you forgive me?'

'Why on earth would I?'

She clasped her hands behind her back. 'You have no reason but I'm asking for another chance.' Doggedness. 'Except that I could, and would, do a good job for you.'

Laure did not reply and there was an unpleasant pause.

Nic had been in the interview room and put his head around the door. 'The Maison de G wants to finalize the menu. Can you talk?' He vanished.

A lunch to celebrate the collaboration between the museum and the Maison de Grasse had been slated for later in the month, a date carefully chosen so as not to clash with the run-up to Christmas.

Laure took the call which lasted a few minutes. May hovered, restless and distressed. When the call finished, Laure stood up. 'Yesterday you asked me about Prague and Berlin.'

'I did.'

'I don't expect you to understand. They were beautiful places but, when I lived in them, also terrible. Full of unresolved bitterness and fracture. The sort that eats up the soul.' Her gaze slid from May's bitten nails to her own statement red ones. 'I refuse to let Paris be like that.'

May looked as though she might grab Laure's hand. 'I understand. I come from the south. Remember?'

'Don't ever do anything like that again.'

There was a dried spot of blood on May's chewed thumb. 'I'll do my best.' She ran a hand through her hair, smoothing it back into severity. As if, thought Laure, that was going to help. 'I'm truly sorry.'

Slice May open and the word 'contrition' would apparently run through her like a stick of rock. Laure smothered a smile. 'Put it this way, I won't be contacting your mother.'

May's mouth twisted. 'My nickname is Night Bug. It's not affectionate. I give you permission to call me the same if you want.'

She sounded calm enough but there was a coded emotion locked into the information and it crossed Laure's mind that May's mother did not have a clue how to handle her unusual daughter.

'OK.' She signalled a resumption of equal relations. 'Let's discuss the celebration lunch.'

May rallied. 'I hope there will be goodie bags with diamonds and a mountain of flowers. Butterflies?'

'Don't lose sight of the objective,' said Laure, drily.

The phone rang incessantly and Nic was kept busy compiling the list of would-be donors. Mid-morning, Chantal brought up the post and deposited five packages on the table.

'Is this average?' asked May.

Laure checked the statistics on screen. 'Submissions are up again,' she said. 'It's been going up every month.'

'Interesting. Is it because promises are more easily broken? Or are harder to keep?'

Nic was conducting an animated telephone conversation in French with a man who wished to donate a sack of manure in memory of the wife who had just dumped him, and was having a hard time persuading him it would not be acceptable.

It was Laure who answered. 'Partly it's because people have changed. We've become different.' May shot her a look. 'Haven't we now given ourselves permission to admit to betrayal? As a generation, I mean. Admit to our sadness?'

'Really?' said May. 'Haven't humans always given vent? One way or another?'

'Wait till autumn proper.' Nic finished the call. 'When summer's lease has run out then it'll get worse.'

At a stroke, the atmosphere lightened.

May looked from one to the other. 'Is he always this cheerful?'

'When summer's lease runs out,' said Laure, 'Nic gets worse.'

The parcels on the desk awaited attention. Laure gestured to May. 'Do you want to do the honours?'

The first one contained the board game Diplomacy, and the second a long narrow box which, when opened, revealed a swathe of tissue paper with a copy of a British magazine.

Laure read aloud from the covering letter.

Dear Curator, will you accept this for the museum?
When you have read the enclosed, I'm sure you'll agree
it deserves to be displayed. I am an ordinary man but I
liked to think that I understood people but I was wrong. I
hadn't a clue. These events have left me gob-smacked and
I won't be getting over them in a hurry.

105

She peeled back the tissue paper to reveal a bridal veil and continued.

> *Having thought about it obsessively, I've concluded that I can't adequately describe my feelings and this will have to do instead.*
>
> *In brief, I got married early this year but the marriage only lasted two months. That was bad enough. Worse, is the lack of explanation. Every time I ask my soon-to-be ex-wife what went wrong and why, she refuses to answer me. A couple of weeks ago, a friend showed me this piece that had been published in the magazine. (See sticker.) What has this to do with the breakdown of the marriage? If you read it, it will become clear.*

'Can I read it?' May asked.

Laure looked down at the veil – foamy white and hopeful-looking. Protecting privacy up to a point, and being kind, was a first principle and, like it or not, May was a predator. Yet, the piece was published and in the public domain.

'Laure, you *can* trust me.'

Who fooled who? Yet, mouth set in rueful lines, semi-duplicitous and rash, May could not be dismissed. She was quick, she was intelligent and brave enough to go venturing into the world to make her way. Those were things worth encouraging.

'Correct,' she replied gently. 'You're a journalist who needs a story.'

'Quite right. It's the eternal battle. How to be human and do my work.' Her gaze sought out Nic's. 'But deep down in my candy-floss

106

soul I do manage to have proper feelings.' They exchanged a tiny smile.

Laure pushed the magazine over to May who skimmed through the pages showcasing high fashion, fusion recipes and what was what in retinol creams. She found the article and began to read it out loud.

This was an office where French and English accents dominated. Her Southern drawl, dropping letters, emphasizing vowels, issued from different linguistic geography hinting of other worlds.

The veil was chosen by Jenna and me. We had talked on the phone for hours over which one to go for and, because I wanted to hear her voice, I spun it out. Why not? I was about to lose her. She was about to vanish into the two-up, two-down life complete with a set of cutlery, place mats and a lawn mower.

I asked her a question: didn't she think a veil too old-fashioned and submissive?

'That's the idea, Rosie.' She was unbothered and that hurt, too. (Actually, everything in this business hurt.) 'Ned and I are going to give each other our lives.' She laughed. 'Ned's fed up at the moment, but I tell him that, if we can pass this hurdle, it'll be plain sailing.'

When I heard that, I understood the urge to commit murder. I also imagined how, having murdered, one must feel beautifully empty.

We arranged to meet at the bridal boutique to choose the wretched veil. It was a tiny place, dominated by a rack that stretched from wall to wall onto which were crammed dresses in every shade of white and with every permutation of tuck and ruffle that you could imagine. It was like looking at a shelf of different meringues, some of which it must be said had shed their freshness.

The assistant laced Jenna into her dress and clicked her tongue. 'You've lost weight.' She jerked the laces tighter on the bodice. 'Quite normal.'

The dress was spectacular. Plain, tight-sleeved, flowing, made from the lightest of tulles, it perfectly suited her colouring and figure.

She tried on the first veil which turned out to be the wrong white against her skin. The second was too short and perky.

The assistant threw a third one over her head. 'There,' she said.

Its hem drifted to the floor around the still, white figure and I saw a ghost. Of the past. I saw, too, the future. It wasn't one I wished to think about.

'Wonderful,' said the assistant and gave a stupid little clap.

It was.

We avoided each other's gaze. I kept my eyes fixed on the assistant who was poking and prinking away. Jenna pinched a fold of it between her fingers, as if to draw every frisson of sensation from its texture.

What are you doing? I stopped myself from crying out. Why are you doing this when you have me?

It was impossible to forget the poisonous wave that had crashed onto me the day Jenna told me it was over and she was going to marry Ned. Impossible. Jenna cried at my reaction and I became hysterical, which frightened her. She begged me to let her go. After hours of torment, I gave in. 'Go,' I told her. 'I never want to speak to you again.'

That didn't last for long.

My own reflection lurked in the mirror behind Jenna's. My dress was hanging in the flat. It was of the palest grey and a bouquet of blush pink roses had been chosen to go with it. As chief bridesmaid, I would bring up the rear of the procession.

What was I thinking?

The assistant was divesting her of the veil and the dress. I registered Jenna's too-loose engagement ring and a bra strap that was beginning to fray. Those were details for me to notice, not him, and I hugged them to me fiercely.

Jealousy is a vile thing. On one hand, I relished its savagery but, equally, I hated being in its grip because it denied me control. I went to see someone about it. Yatter, yatter. The only thing he did (apart from issuing the bill) was to nod and say nothing. The consequence? Everything I did was infected by it.

The assistant retired to the till, which was discreetly hidden behind another curtain – anything to do with money in these sickly emporiums was always disguised. Jenna got dressed in her jeans and T-shirt. I reached over to help and she flinched away. 'Don't.'

She was crying.

'You should be happy,' I hissed at her.

She bent over to lace up her trainers. 'What have I done, Rosie?'

'You're a fraud and I should be shouting it from the rooftops.'

'Go on, then.'

She refused to look at me.

At that moment, the penny dropped. Jenna wanted me to tell her groom that she did not love him. She wanted me to do the dirty work.

She didn't say it… oh no, she wasn't going to say it… but I knew.

Yes, I knew Jenna was a coward who would be happy to ruin her life, Ned's life and mine because she dared not to say anything.

Guess what I did?

'A variant on the traditional love triangle, then,' said May, returning to the letter. '"When she wore this veil, my wife promised to love me but she lied. She loved someone else and that someone was her bridesmaid who wrote this disgusting rubbish."' She folded it up and replaced it in the envelope. 'Has the museum ever been sued for libel?'

'It's always a possibility but we work closely with the lawyers.' Laure lifted the veil out of the box. Delicate and almost weightless, it was spume drifting over her outstretched arms. On examination, what was clearly a bite mark – pink and lipsticky – revealed itself at the hem.

'Whoa,' said May. 'Can I take a photo?'

'No.'

May peered at it. 'How full of rage and hatred must you be to bite a wedding veil?'

Nic sounded shell-shocked. 'I'm not surprised he used a green marker.'

At the museum entrance, Jean-Paul manned the ticket counter. Laure introduced him to May and explained that Jean-Paul was halfway through a curating degree and came in to the museum for practical experience. He and Chantal did alternate weeks. 'The *stagiaires* as they are called, are unpaid, but we fund their expenses.'

Jean-Paul's expression was enigmatic.

May turned large eyes on him. 'Does curating have a future in France?'

'Yes, the government is supportive,' replied Jean-Luc.

May switched on the smile which could blind at a thousand paces. 'How lucky you are. Back home, we are forced to rely on rich individuals.'

A group of women, all wearing identical green plastic macs, filed in through the entrance and Jean-Luc's attention was diverted. Laure asked May if she wanted to see her install the bridal veil which she had earmarked for Room 2.

'I get it,' said May on entering and surveying the display. 'The theme is clothing.'

One wall of the room was taken up by a full-sized display case, approximately six foot by twelve.

There was a plain white T-shirt on which was printed 'Iron Maiden'. The positioning of the transfer, however, had been imprecise and the 'I' was lost under the armpit. At a quick glance the legend read: 'ron Maiden'.

'Ron Maiden?'

'I've a soft spot for him,' said Laure. 'He makes me laugh.'

'He sounds a loser.'

'Apparently he was.' Laure pointed to the label and May read out. 'He couldn't even get the T-shirt correct.'

Laure wrestled with the lock to the cabinet. 'Pass over the veil.'

Laure worked at arranging it and made sure that the bite mark was evident. May took a tour of the objects in the cases and halted in front of the cabinet by the door. 'A puppet?'

Laure tugged at the final fold of netting, arranged the label and backed out of the cabinet. Standing back, she assessed her handiwork. Draped and folded, the layers of white netting projected an intense aura. 'It's a marionette, actually.'

'What's the difference?'

'Marionettes always have strings and are manipulated from above, puppets don't.' She glanced at May. 'Hand puppets. Glove puppets.'

'Tell me about this one.'

'Marenka? She comes from a Czech marionette theatre. The Marenkas were used for the ingenue parts, including Sleeping Beauty.' Laure did not need to check up on her for she knew her contours and jointed crevices as well as the lines on her hand. Every painted, rattling inch of her.

'She's quite a girl,' observed May. 'She sort of... sort of dominates.'

It was true. Dressed in a calico gown with an intricately patterned lace veil thrown over her head from which a brown plait hung down behind, Marenka dominated the back of the display cabinet and demanded attention. *Look at me. Properly. I connect with your deepest, darkest fears. I feed your hungry imagination.*

May took a step back. 'Creepy?'

'You get used to her.' Laure pointed to a space between the

windows. 'When she first came, we hung her on the wall over there, which is the traditional way. But if a draught caught her, she clacked. Chantal and others found it a bit disconcerting. I did, too, I suppose.' She smiled. 'Banished to the display case, she has to behave.'

'Can I touch her? Please?'

Laure unlocked the cabinet and, reaching inside, May nudged Marenka who, obediently, shook out her limbs.

Laure closed her eyes in the face of the inevitable deep, dark dive into a memory. Shadows licking up and down pocked and peeling walls. Her friend, Milos, working calmly away on their strings and talking to one of his marionettes who he treated like family. Like his children.

'I deny absolutely that I come from a bourgeois background,' Spejbl had said to Milos.

'But Spejbl,' countered Milos severely, 'your father was a well-known shop owner.' He glanced at Laure. 'You mustn't tell lies in front of visitors.'

The click of wooden joints. The acrid sweat of puppeteers working furiously under the theatre's unreliable lights… these were filed away, as sharp and pungent as they ever were.

She opened her eyes. 'I used to work in a Prague marionette theatre. I think I mentioned. Before the revolution when things were difficult.'

'Oh?'

'I had a friend at the marionette theatre. He said—'

He said. Laure checked herself. She must always give Milos his name because the State would have tried to make him vanish and, God forbid, may have succeeded. Because he was her friend.

Milos had said: 'Please don't forget what we do here.'

May waited for Laure to finish the sentence. Laure shrugged. 'I can't remember what he, Milos, said.'

'Did Milos give her to you?'

'Actually, he didn't. As it turned out, someone else gave her to me. Many years later.'

May gave Laure space to elaborate but she didn't.

'She looks world-weary. As if she's seen too much,' said May.

'You may be right.'

May slotted a finger under the marionette's arm and raised it in a Nazi salute. 'Marenka, I must ask you on behalf of women everywhere who know about you. Did it work out well?'

Laure watched. 'She won't tell you. She's taken a vow of silence.'

'That fits. Nobody wants to admit to having been taken for a great, big ride. You could answer for her, Laure. *You* could tell me.'

Laure bit her lip and turned away. Resolved as she might be, the questioning got under her skin. 'Not really qualified,' she said, after a moment. 'Really.'

May was sceptical. 'Whoa. I've just dived up a *cul-de-sac*. Right? Can I look under her veil?'

'If you must.'

The lace was exquisite and too good for a marionette. Easing it back, May peered at Marenka's face. 'How odd. One eye is blue, one green. Did they run out of paint?'

'Getting hold of paint was always a problem. You had to take what you could get.'

'It would have been easy enough to mix?'

'True. But not everything was as straightforward as that.'

May was not in on the secrets but the mismatched eyes conveyed the message to anyone who understood: *not everyone thinks the same.*

May shrugged. 'Makes me feel a little odd, that's all.'

Laure knew those wooden features so well. Intimately. If age had crackled the painted complexion, the scarlet bow lips were still defiant.

May shot Laure a look from under her lids. 'How would you describe her?'

'Well,' began Laure. 'She's an innocent.'

'Ah,' said May.

'But not innocent. Marenka knows things. To look at her, she's wooden and stiff and, yet, she pulses with life.' She could hear her voice reflect the excitement she had once felt all those years ago. 'She's a marionette but possesses a soul.' She paused. 'You might think this rubbish. It isn't.'

'Go on,' said May. 'It doesn't matter what I think.'

'Marenka is a bundle of paradoxes. She can be seen for what she is. Or, you, the onlooker, can project an image of yourself onto her.'

Marenka was Milos's creation. He was the artist and painted into those odd eyes was the craziness and despair of how it had been.

'Does she have a prince?'

'He hasn't shown up yet,' said Laure. 'She's still waiting.'

'Same old story,' said May. 'In my experience, they rarely do.' She lowered the veil over Beauty's face and backed out of the cabinet. 'You said you never had two of anything. Shouldn't Marenka lose her veil now you've put the other one in? If you follow your own rules, I mean.'

'No,' replied Laure, more sharply than she intended.

'The eyes are weird,' May said. 'Haunting in their way. So, the marionette theatre. What happened to it?'

'Politics,' answered Laure. 'The company always hoped to perform in Paris but never made it because they weren't allowed to leave Czechoslovakia. Anyway, they got into trouble with the communist authorities. As I mentioned, it was years later that I was given Marenka.'

May peered at the now drooping marionette at the back of the cabinet. '"Politics made it impossible to keep our promise,"' she read out from the label. She shoved her hands into her pockets. 'Are you ever surprised by what you learn here?'

'All the time. These objects invite you to the edge of an abyss and urge you to look over.'

CHAPTER 9

Prague, 1986

*O*WAS IT NORMAL, WHAT SHE HAD SEEN IN THE KOBES'
bedroom?

She pondered over it. Perhaps it had been about power – as she
now realized her disastrous coupling with Rob Dance had partially
been about.

Forget Rob.

Had it been a sex game? Was Petr abusing his wife? In the
daytime, Eva frequently called him 'darling'. In the light of what
she had seen, what did it mean? Back home, she read about
terrible things that happened to some women in the papers but,
having examined her scanty knowledge of what was what in the
sexual department, she failed to reach enlightenment.

Whatever the explanation, Petr Kobes could not have been
more pleasant or more anxious to help Laure to find her feet.
But, it was unsettling not knowing whether to giggle or recoil
over the contrast between the man who ensured that the strap
on her rucksack was mended and the man who indulged in
disturbing and messy acts in his bedroom.

Neither Jan nor Maria slept well in the heat, with the result that they were often fretful by the afternoons and keeping them on an even keel tested Laure's basic childcare skills. She considered encouraging them to make a model village (something she had loved doing) but there was no cardboard or paints to be had. Card games were more successful but they had their limits.

During the day, they went for walks, sometimes to seek shade down by the river, sometimes up into the orchards and woodlands of Petřín Hill. The days were spent aimlessly and lacked routine. Jan frequently asked when they were going home to Paris and Laure promised to find out from his mother.

It was laundry day. Maria was having her post-lunch rest and Jan had been dispatched to his room with orders to read a book. Outside, the sun pulsed brazen yellow.

An ironing board had been set up in the utility room where clean washing was stacked. Eva sat at the window with her sewing box, mending a tear in Maria's yellow cotton dress (purchased in Paris) and Laure tackled the ironing. An aroma of hot, clean clothes and starch filled the room.

Laure had considered anxiously what she was going to say. She put down the iron. 'Jan is worried that you won't be returning to Paris.'

Eva's expression revealed nothing. Her stitching was painful to watch. In with the needle, a prolonged tug, out the other side, an inept pull of thread. 'Is he now?' she replied.

As she spread one of Jan's shirts over the ironing board, Laure said, 'The children see themselves as French.'

'Don't *ever* say that.' Eva's head snapped up. 'They are good Czechs. Good socialists. You don't know anything about it.' She savaged the thread with her teeth and thrust the mended dress at Eva. 'When you've ironed this, put it away. Maria mustn't wear it here.'

Laure happened to know that it was Maria's favourite dress but didn't say anything. The rebuff stung. For the first time, she wondered if she had been too hasty in agreeing to come to Prague. 'I'm sorry if I've offended you. It's just they talk about Paris a lot. They miss the park and their friends.'

Eva lowered her voice as if the walls might be listening in. 'Jan and Maria are Czech. Not Slovak, mind you, Czech. Their home is here. They must understand that and so must you.'

Laure was not sure that she did. Folding up the offending dress, she fell silent.

At the end of Laure's second week in Prague, the Kobes family were slated to attend a lunch to honour a delegation of railwaymen from the north of England. As an English speaker, Laure was also to attend.

Having got ready in an aquamarine sleeveless dress, Eva appeared troubled by the idea of the outing. Her lipstick was dark orange but there was a pale line around her lips. 'I warn you, it will be boring,' she said.

Petr hushed his wife. He focused on Laure with that trick that he had of making her feel that she was only person in the world. 'I will make every effort to ensure that you enjoy yourself.'

The hall hired for the event was so large that the fifty or so guests were dwarfed by its brick bleakness. The top table, the only one with the luxury of a tablecloth, was arranged at right angles to several trestle tables and had a microphone clipped to the edge. Whenever the microphone hiccupped, the electrician slapped down his beer glass and headed at speed over to it.

Trussed up in suits, the railway delegation looked dazed. Some had brought their over-heated wives, most of whom wore frocks more suitable for a Scottish winter than a Prague summer. They were being introduced to the Party wives who, as a group, had a tendency to bottle-yellow hair and very thin eyebrows.

Laure was seated between Jan and Maria at one of the trestles which had been magnificently laid with paper napkins and metal plates. Placed on each setting was a badge embossed with images of Lenin, Stalin and the Czech flag. To reinforce the solemnity of the occasion, pennants in eye-watering yellow and green flew from the water glasses into which they had been stuck and proclaimed in Czech and English: 'Welcome to our Brothers'.

Seated opposite Laure were a couple of the railwaymen whose accents triggered a moment of homesickness. Between bouts of coping with the children, she tried to engage them in conversation. They weren't inclined to be friendly until she informed them in her broadest accent that she was born-and-bred Yorkshire. Relations thawed. 'Not saying, mind, I approve of your neck of the woods,' said the older one who had a thin indentation at the back of his head where his cap usually sat.

Laure did her best to wriggle past their defensiveness. In desperation, she pointed out Eva and Petr on the top table. The younger man whistled. 'Your employers must be in with the chiefs.' He cocked a knowing eye. 'You won't get nowt unless you have some folk on the inside.'

Laure was tempted to reply that she had thought the communist doctrine rested on the absolute principle that no one should enjoy privilege over anyone else. Her scepticism must have registered with Bob who added: 'How do you think we got on this jolly?'

The food was totally out of whack for such a hot day. Thick meaty soup, a goulash, a plum dessert. There were lashings of it and between the main course and the dessert, there were speeches that proceeded with aching slowness because each sentence had to be translated from Czech to English, or vice versa.

At the high table, Eva fanned herself with a copy of the chairman's speech and slumped back in her chair.

A translator bobbed between Petr and the leader of the railways delegation and looked exhausted. By now, the beer drinking was advanced and it was obvious that most attempts at translation were doomed. Czechs and Brits were letting down what remained of their hair and toasting each other witless.

Eva's head fell forward onto her chest, and Laure, who had kept an eye on her, leapt to her feet. Petr got there first and slid his arm around his wife. Eva's breath rattled in her chest and she slurred her words. Petr shook her gently. 'Eva, I'm here. We'll sort you out.' He beckoned to one of the party men and issued a command in Czech. The man picked his way through the sozzled guests and left the hall.

'He's getting the car,' said Petr. 'Listen, can you take her home for me? I have to stay on here for a while.' He must have sensed Laure's alarm. 'She will be fine. She just needs to sleep.'

Laure was conscious of being the centre of attention. 'And the children?'

'Leave them with me.'

It flashed across Laure's mind that this wasn't her job. Nor did she know how to deal with the collapsed Eva. What did one do? Then, she caught sight of Petr's expression which was one of extreme distress. Pity won – plus, she knew she could cope. Taking a deep breath, she said, 'OK. Shall I put her to bed?'

'Thank you.' Petr dabbed at Eva's sweaty top lip with his handkerchief. 'If you knew how grateful...' At her table, Maria waved a pennant in their direction. Petr looked over to his daughter.

'She's so much happier since you came.' He then murmured, 'I think you are the good fairy to this family.'

Laure helped to restrain Eva against the chair. 'Has Mrs Kobes been drinking?'

'She's had a little. It never agrees with her.'

'Oh.' Things were more complicated than Laure imagined.

In a low tone, Petr said, 'She'll be upset by this, so we won't mention it again?'

Laure stared at his expensive French tie. She longed to ask, adult to adult: Are you cruel to your wife? You can be honest, I come from Yorkshire and we take these things on the chin.

Their gazes collided. She detected in Petr's dark gaze the gratitude of which he spoke and also something warmer and experienced a tiny thrill. Of what, she wasn't sure.

Petr cleared his throat. His customary composure had deserted him. 'I... we... really need your help, Laure. You are clever and discreet, and I know you understand.'

'Of course,' she replied. 'That's what I am here for.'

In her next letter to her mother, Laure wrote: 'Although things seem to be straightforward in this country, and the Party is in control, it is also complicated and there are some people who are favoured more than others...'

She stared at the garish pennant beside her on the table which Maria had brought home from the lunch and presented to her. 'Because you are like a princess,' she said.

Halfway through writing it, it occurred to Laure that the letter might be read by censors and tore it up.

Laure's contract stipulated that she had two nights off each week.

In Paris, that had been no problem and she had spent her evenings with a bunch of friends ensconced in cafes and *boîtes*. In Prague, she was unsure what to do with her free time. Yet use it she would, and asked to be relieved on the specified night.

As promised, Petr returned in good time from his office to help Eva. Laure heard him call out to her and the thump of his briefcase hitting the floor.

The children had staggered bath times with Jan coming after Maria had finished hers. Laure had already run water into the old-fashioned enamel tub and stuck Maria into it and was sponging her clean when Petr appeared in the doorway. He stayed there until Laure had wrapped Maria in a towel.

'A nice scene,' he said. 'The best.' He spoke in French and Marie shrieked with pleasure. Petr gestured to the chair. 'May I?' He sat down with a towel and Laure deposited the damp package that was Maria into his lap.

Petr blew into her neck before gently patting her dry with the ends of the towel. Laure looked up from the bath. Careful, full of pride for his daughter, he was absorbed in his task. 'Nice Daddy,' said Maria.

Laure was thoroughly confused, as she so often was in the Kobes household. Petr's behaviour as a tender father did not fit in with that of the wife beater.

'Do you know where you are going this evening?' he asked. 'Perhaps you're meeting someone?'

She felt a tiny pulse start up somewhere deep inside. 'I thought I would go to the marionette theatre.'

'Ah.' Petr helped Maria wriggle into the pyjamas which Laure had painstakingly ironed. 'You must tell me everything about it when you return.' His expression was benign but, for some reason, it bothered Laure. 'Be careful, won't you. People will look and listen to someone like you.'

Laure frowned. 'What do you mean?'

He cupped his daughter's damp head in his head. 'In Czechoslovakia there's a contract between the authorities and the people which trusts the latter to behave well and peacefully.'

'That's the same at home,' she interjected impatiently.

'Is it? Here, if you, or anyone in your family, is considered "unreliable", you might find your telephone line goes dead, or your driving licence is revoked. It can become difficult. The State is prepared to take measures.'

She was aghast. 'Do you approve?'

He smiled at her puzzled expression. 'It doesn't matter what I think.' He set a dried Maria down on the floor

Walking over the Charles Bridge towards the Staré Město, she told herself, yes, it didn't matter what Petr Kobes thought. All the same, she was intrigued to know if he approved of the 'State taking measures'.

Dusk was gathering. Once over the bridge, she followed the street eastwards and was plunged into the warm air trapped between the close-knit buildings.

She forced her way closer to the square, only to find herself subsumed into a crowd also heading in that direction. In danger of losing her bearings, she went with the flow, which came to a choking halt at the entrance to the square. This gave her time to take in the faces of the Astronomical Clock and the peeling ox-blood façade of the house opposite, which would provide her with a useful navigation point.

In a moment of magic and drama, and dramatically outlined against a pink and opal sky, the church's fantasy towers came into full view. Laure caught her breath. It was as if she had been pushed across a boundary between what she knew and a new world, as yet insubstantial and unknown but there.

Such was the press, she came to a complete halt as she tried to make her way across to the Jan Hus monument. A stage had been constructed directly in front of it and electrical equipment stashed on the steps. Technicians swarmed over it and a sound system was being tested. A banner strung across the monument read 'Anatomie'.

Had she remembered the geography correctly? The marionette theatre was in the end of the terrace behind the Hus monument – in the house with a tiny turret. Having finally struggled there, it was to find the entrance blocked by a stack of musical instruments. A girl with fair hair, pulled savagely back by an elastic band, was checking each piece off a list.

Laure made to enter but the girl pointed to the notice taped to the door which Laure took to mean it was closed. 'When open?' she asked in English.

The girl looked up. 'Tomorrow,' she replied in English. 'Please go.'

Back by the stage, the heat from the paving stones seeped through the soles of her flimsy shoes and her hair soon clumped into a sweaty mass at the nape of her neck. One of the technicians jumped down from the stage and landed beside her. Two of the spotlights flared on as three figures with long hair and black jeans hauled themselves up onto the stage and loped towards the instruments propped up against the microphones. Laure was close enough, and the spotlight so merciless, that she could see the open pores, the sweat and a tidemark on the drummer's neck.

There was a moment's hush on the part of the crowd before a raw, raucous sound punched into the air.

The wind was knocked out of Laure. Her eardrums screamed blue murder. Shockwaves shuddered through her from head to foot and, in an uprush of exhilaration and release, she swept up into a wild delight.

A third spotlight shorted with a bang and a shower of sparks. Nobody paid it any attention and it remained a sullen and blackened contrast to its companions. One of the electricians crept towards it but gave up.

It was hopeless to think she would understand the lyrics but it didn't matter. She knew, she just knew, they would be great. To her surprise, however, she did catch one or two English words.

What a performance. What a sound.

This was life, she thought. At last.

Narrowing her eyes, she craned her head back to get a better view. The trio absolutely owned the stage. They knew every inch of it: strutting, wheeling panthers out to conquer their territory. The bass player had a mane of thinning black hair, the drummer was thickset with big hands but the lithest and sexiest of the group, the one who sang and played with heart-breaking intensity despite being the slightest of the trio, was familiar. He wore the group's uniform of black jeans but had added a striped linen waistcoat with bone buttons.

Obviously an experienced performer – they all were – he coped easily with the sightlines for the craning audience. Whipping around, he raised his guitar and the ripped section of shirt under the arm revealed a spear of flesh. Along with most of the other women in the audience, Laure caught her breath.

He was riveting. He knew what he was doing. The audience was his and he played them. He had rhythm. He was sex incarnate. He was telling them that he understood their unvoiced desires, whatever their age or gender. Shrieks and gasps greeted his stage moves, his gyrations, the play of thin fingers over the strings. During a pause between numbers, he pushed back heavy brown hair from his forehead to highlight a bony profile.

Halfway through a song, and at the end of a prolonged guitar riff, he looked down at the faces clustered below him, intercepted Laure's wide-eyed stare and sang the next line directly at her.

Blood pulsing through her veins, she grinned at him and raised her fist in a salute. A man standing beside her jerked her arm back down. He frowned, shook his head and edged away from Laure.

The grin was wiped from her lips. Her elation vanished. Perplexed as to what she had done, she rubbed her wrist. Even more bewildering, a space opened up around her. Mortified, she tried to concentrate on the stage. It was being conveyed to her that she had transgressed. But how?

Out of the corner of her eye, she caught a glint of glass and squinted at it. A man stood at the window in a house behind the Jan Hus monument, training a pair of binoculars onto the stage. Below him, a second man in a leather jacket was positioned in a doorway, a sight she quickly realized was repeated around the square.

Her instinct was… well, what was it? To ridicule? To ignore?

Ignore was best. All the same, a finger seemed to run its way down the vertebrae in her spine.

As decisively as it had begun, the concert ended. Taking their cue from each other, the trio hurled a mega chord at the fans. The drummer leapt to his feet and the guitarists held their instruments aloft. The spotlights cut out.

The audience went wild.

Uneasy and unsure, Laure shrank back against the stage. The technicians had returned and were dismantling the equipment in double-quick time. The musicians jumped down to be enveloped by the crowd. A couple of women screamed.

She was left empty but longing for more. Limp almost.

It was certainly time to return to the Kobes' apartment and, still unsure of the geography, she sketched out in her head the route back. *Find the ox-blood house, leave the square by the same street, head for the Charles Bridge, walk straight ahead the other side, keeping St Nicholas in sight.*

At that moment, Tomas Josip looked over his shoulder, spotted Laure and smiled. Raising his hand, he beckoned. 'Come,' he said in English.

Intriguingly, Tomas did not choose the main streets but piloted Laure along small, sometimes claustrophobic, alleys which ran parallel to, and occasionally crossed, the thoroughfares.

He knew the way, ushering her through them as if he was sovereign of this clandestine cityscape of dim passageways and cut-throughs. 'This way, Laure.' He shuffled her this way and that, plunging her into a couple of alleys so narrow that they barely justified the term.

There had been a micro-second of doubt about taking up his offer.

'You're quite safe.'

'I have to get back to my employers.'

'And you will.'

'Is it safe?'

'No need to worry. Someone will take you back.' His smile

was lopsided and slightly mocking. 'If I'm lucky it might be me.'

The smile touched the sore place in Laure's heart. She had been so busy acclimatizing to the job and celebrating her liberation from Brympton and her grief-stricken home, that she had not realized that she had missed friendship, talk, joshing.

He came to a dead stop, turned around and she went smack into his ribcage. He grunted and she cried out, 'I'm so sorry.'

'It's all right,' he said. 'Only one rib is broken. It'll be fine in a month or two.'

'*What?* You don't mean it?'

He grinned at Laure's distress – and took pity. Placing his hands on her shoulders, he said, 'At most, a faint bruise.'

'Thank God,' she breathed.

The heat seemed to wrap them in tight, private world.

Slight as he was, his physical presence was almost overwhelming. Skin gleaming with heat, his grip on her shoulder, the suggestion of sweat and tobacco and drink all combined to make her feel light-headed.

He looked down at Laure and they found themselves smiling broadly at each other. He had, she noted, absurdly long, dark lashes. She looked down at his bare forearm, fretted with light gold hair. To her astonishment, she longed to run her hands over his chest and the curve of his shoulders.

'I'm a stranger,' she said. 'Why are you being so nice? People aren't nice to strangers.'

Something else crept into his expression. It was if he recognized a Laure that no one knew or suspected.

'I don't know why,' he replied, his face still bent over hers. 'Do you?'

His mouth was good humoured, with some stubbornness in its definition. She loved that. 'No.' As soon as she uttered it, she checked herself. She wasn't going to lie. Not with him. 'Yes, I do.'

He nodded as if he expected that answer. As if he was pleased with it. 'Could it be that you're not a stranger? Not really.'

'Yes,' she said. 'I think that might be it.'

'Good.'

CHAPTER 10

$\mathcal{OS}$HE WAS EXPECTING TO BE TAKEN TO A CAFE. INSTEAD, she found herself mounting an unlit sweeping stone staircase in what had once been – clearly – a grand house.

Tomas took her by the hand to help her up. On the first floor, he pushed Laure into a room that ran the width of the building and which would have been beautiful but for its shocking state of disrepair. The paint on the walls was all but obliterated and an elaborate plaster frieze was just hanging on. Cow-dung-coloured lino covered the floor into which had been ground cigarette butts and food. At one end, a trestle table had been set up with bottles and glasses. Despite the heat, the windows had been blacked out with sheets and rugs.

At Tomas's entrance, there was a muted cheer. A man thrust a filled glass into his hands and a woman kissed him on both cheeks.

Laure hovered uncertainly but Tomas put an arm around her shoulders and drew her forwards. 'Meet my friend,' he said in English.

A girl whom Laure recognized from the marionette theatre elbowed her way through the crush. The over-blonde hair had been released and allowed to hang down over her shoulders and she had changed into a red, wrap-around dress that looked homemade but revealed a ripe and desirable figure.

A torrent of Czech issued from her. Tomas listened patiently and put his hand on her arm. 'Will you be kind to my new friend?' Again, he spoke in English.

The appeal did not find favour. Lucia brushed off Tomas's hand and let loose a second tirade. Tomas turned to Laure. 'Lucia is suspicious. She thinks you may have been planted here by the police. It's not unknown. They like to know what people think and say in private.' He raised an eyebrow. 'They're particularly keen on getting to know the jokes people make.'

'Jokes?'

'Apparently, they reveal what you're really thinking.'

'I understand. Please could you tell Lucia that I'm an unlikely stooge as I don't speak Czech.'

To her surprise, Lucia appeared to understand. 'She speaks English,' Tomas explained. He lowered his voice. 'But we keep quiet about it. English speakers are not popular with the authorities. It's considered subversive.'

Lucia nodded, and Laure realized her hostility stemmed in part from apprehension. Should she turn tail and get the hell out? Laure watched the black-maned bass player from Anatomie mount the table from where he made obscene gestures to the back of the room.

Tomas's gaze rested on a gyrating figure close to them and the drinker hugging a bottle in the corner. 'Welcome to the world of never knowing,' he said into Laure's ear. He pointed to the figure on the table. 'That's Manicki. The fans love his long hair, which means he can never cut it and he longs to do so because he's a bourgeois at heart. And...' he pointed to the drummer from Anatomie leaping up to join Manicki, 'that's Leo. He likes to be inscrutable.'

There were no speakers in this place. Manicki was now singing a countrified song far removed from the rock concert. Several of the listeners had closed their eyes and swayed to the melody. Tomas thrust a glass into her hand. 'Well, Laure who dislikes yellow curtains, if you go and stand by the window, I have some living dangerously to do but I'll join you later.'

That suited her fine. She squeezed over to the window and leant back against it. Masked by the blackout, the clasp on the shutter dug into her back but it helped her keep a grip on who and where she was. She took a mouthful from the glass and nearly spat it out. It was neat vodka but, after a few more mouthfuls, she had no objection to it at all.

Tomas vaulted up onto the table. His guitar was handed to him and he cradled it. Up there on the table, he looked bigger and older, less frail, his profile sharp, clean and Roman. It was a lesson to her how one's physical appearance could convey quite different impressions just by being up on a stage.

Tomas nodded to the other two, struck up and all three launched into a wild and pulsing song. Fuddled by the vodka, she listened enraptured. The music thudded through her veins and was matched by an even more primary throb between her legs.

Lust. Pure lust. She had never experienced it in that way.

Closing her eyes, she gave herself to up to novel sensations... of being intensely alive... stripped of fear and shyness. Of being an adventurer in a new world.

Just as quickly, they changed tack. Tomas and Manicki faced other and played a sequence of melodic chords and launched into a folk song. Its melancholy, aching repetitions went down well with the party goers, some of whom looked close to weeping.

God knew how long she remained by the window – by now what she was seeing was filtering through to her in a haze. Much fondling was on display. Bodies were draped over each other, with one man efficiently unbuttoning a girl's blouse. The music ended and Anatomie slid down from their impromptu stage. Laure's sodden powers of analysis suggested to her that sex was what people did if they were restricted in their speech, when sensation *became* expression?

She was pleased with that *aperçu*. It was good. Profound, even.

Actually…her gaze drifted to the ceiling… actually, she could stay here all night. She was perfectly happy and not at all lonely. It was past eleven o'clock and the noise level had halved and everyone appeared to be whispering.

Tomas materialized. 'Are you surviving?'

She indicated her glass. 'That helped.' To demonstrate the truth of this assertion, she took a gulp. 'What am I doing here?'

He stuck his hands in his pockets. 'Have you hated it?'

'It's wonderful.' She hoped she didn't sound too childishly excited.

'Good.'

The crowd in the room was thinning. She turned and found herself almost pressed up against him. 'Where did you learn to speak English?'

'My father was half-English. He made sure we spoke it together. I might need it, he said.' Tomas looked at her. 'I think he was right.'

The vodka was swishing through her. 'My mother was French. *She* insisted that we spoke it together. Lucky us. We have two worlds in our lives.'

He frowned. 'Depends which one you're in.' He was silent for a moment. 'Many hoped that the better world was here. You will want to know why speaking English here can be dangerous? The goons consider it to be the language in which we plot against them.' He kidnapped Laure's glass and drained it. 'What are your impressions? How do we look?'

She sensed it was an important question but was in no state to answer it coherently. She ran her fingers through her hair that – to her dismay – felt sticky with vodka (how did that happen?) 'What I think is… what I think is that people are not talking about politics but they're thinking and feeling it with their bodies.' She frowned. 'Am I making sense?'

He grinned. 'Did you know that you look like a baby lioness? Wide-eyed but fierce, with hair that has a life of its own. My English is not *that* good. Please can you say what you said another way?'

She searched through the tatters of her reasoning powers. 'You say you're not allowed to voice certain political thoughts.' He nodded. 'So, if people are feeling rebellious about it, they let their bodies do the talking.' She pointed to a couple writhing in a corner. 'That's rebellion.'

'Lower your voice. Just in case.'

She did so. 'Don't you see?'

'That's why we need witnesses to how we live here.' He brushed back a strand of the so-called lioness's mane and her stomach turned inside out. 'You'll go home one of these days and you'll be able to say what you wish. You can be a witness.' He leant towards her. 'In fact, I have chosen you to be a witness.'

What had happened? One minute she had been sitting next to a stranger in a marionette theatre, the next she was being recruited into a resistance.

He looked so serious, with an intense, haunted expression that she knew could destabilize every molecule of her common sense.

She said faintly, 'Don't come any closer.'

'Why not?'

'Because I'll kiss you.'

Oh, vodka.

'Stop me, then.'

He placed his lips on her willing, yielding mouth and she felt her body liquify into want and desire.

Oh, goddess vodka.

'You move fast,' she said.

'In this country we have to.'

'But we don't know each other,' she said at last.

'I know.' Again, he kissed her. 'But I argue that I do know you, you know.'

'You don't know me.'

'I know you in the way that matters.'

She gave up. 'That's too many "knows".'

'That's terrible.' He traced the line of her jaw and she stood still, hardly daring to breathe. 'I could tell you many things... that you're beautiful, and almost certainly clever, and have appeared like a star on a gloomy night.' He checked himself. 'You look as though you don't believe what I say. Quite right. It might all be true. It probably is.' Again, a pause that Laure found more eloquent than words. 'But I'm talking about another connection and you will have to work it out. That's the best I can do.'

She swallowed. 'That'll do.'

His hands rested on her shoulders. 'I must take you back.'

They had to fight their way out of the room. Everyone wanted a piece of Anatomie, and Tomas in particular. Watching and hovering, Laure concluded that the group offered a rescue remedy to which everyone felt entitled to help themselves.

'Tomas.' Lucia materialized out of the crowd. She held a bottle of beer and another stuck out of the pocket of the red dress. 'Where're you going?'

'Taking our new friend home.'

Lucia looked from Laure to Tomas. 'I see,' she said in English. 'This is stupid. Stupid.' She turned away and slid back through the crowd.

Outside in the night street, the trapped heat from the day claimed them. Tomas took Laure's hand. 'I'm sorry there's no car. But feet are good. Where do we go?'

She told him.

'Ah.'

She was instantly aware of a change in his body language. A drawing back. 'You know that anyone who lives there probably works for the State?'

'My employer works for a pharmaceutical company. He's based in Paris most of the time.'

Tomas stuck his hand in his pocket and her heart sank. Somehow, she had transgressed and she had no idea why. Eventually, he appeared to make up his mind. 'Come along, then. Isn't that what you say in the UK?'

Her heart lightened. 'Something like that.'

'I must warn you, we will be followed.'

She sent a hasty look over her shoulder. 'Does one get used to it?'

'Consider it an alternative universe.' He put an arm around her shoulder. 'That's what we sang about tonight. Or rather, we sang about the universes we would like to be in.'

He was close enough to smell his sweat, the tobacco, the drink. None of it repellent. Rather the opposite: tantalizing. 'I caught some English words.'

He said, 'I told you English was subversive.'

'Ah. I'll whisper then.'

As Tomas led her down the street from the square and over the Charles Bridge into the Malá Strana, there was the counterpoint of someone else's footsteps behind them. The heat in the narrower streets was close to stifling and sweat dampened her sandals and pooled in the small of her back. In contrast, Tomas paced alongside her seemingly without effort and, at the sight, Laure's mood swung between the recklessness of the semi-drunk and apprehension.

A shadow threw itself over her and she slid to a halt. 'What's that?'

He took her arm and pointed upwards. 'A shop sign.' His fingers tightened. 'You will have to learn like all of us here not to box with shadows. We need our energy for the real thing.' His voice softened. 'Trust me.'

In the courtyard below the Kobes' apartment, Tomas faced Laure. 'Do you?'

She knew what he meant. 'Trust you? Yes.'

He was a star and knew it, but it didn't seem to have spoiled him. He also seemed to be someone who got things done. She liked that.

He was saying, 'Trust should not be lightly given.'

She nodded to acknowledge the point. 'I've taken you out of your way.'

'So? Will I see you again? I'm usually at the marionette theatre. Or someone there will know where I am. Will you come?'

He seemed on edge, impatient for an answer.

She asked haltingly, 'Lucia?'

A trace of irritation crossed his features. 'She's a fighter. Nothing is more important to her than our work.'

She felt herself flush. 'Oh.'

138

'Don't worry about it. However, for the benefit of the goon over there by the archway, I do have to kiss you.'

She flicked a glance in the direction of a burly man in a leather jacket at the entrance to the street who was making a play of lighting up. 'Kissing is political?' She understood the position, but she was also hoping Tomas would say that it was other things too.

'It is.' He drew her to him, his face suspended over hers. The sweat that had seeped into the corners of her eyes misted her vision. She was trembling on the edge of hallucination.

Tomas placed his lips on hers.

His body was hot, alien, but also almost feline in its lines and fineness.

The goon watched, absorbed, probably a little excited.

Tomas pulled away in order to look into her face. 'I don't understand,' he said.

'What?'

'How this…' he touched her cheek. 'How this has happened.'

She didn't need to ask what. She knew. She knew.

He moved slightly and his hip jutted against hers. 'You'll come to the theatre?' he murmured into her ear.

Laure pressed herself against him. 'Yes.'

She was helpless… drink, lust?

Tomas whispered, 'I'm going to kiss you again.'

'Yes. Yes, you are.'

It had begun.

At an early Sunday supper in the dining room, Laure and the Kobes struggled through one of Eva's unappetizing pasta creations.

Polite as ever, Petr wanted to know what she and the children had done that day. Laure described their trip up to the castle. 'I had to give Maria a piggyback up the last few steps,' she said. 'Nearly killed me.'

'That was kind.'

'She held my hand coming down as I don't like heights.' She grimaced. 'We've got a good thing going, Maria and me. We danced at the bottom. People thought we were mad.'

Eva ate slowly and, not for the first time, Laure observed a qualitative difference in her since coming home. And certainly after the disastrous delegates' lunch.

On some days, she seemed anxious and given to rapid monologues. On others, subdued and listless. When Laure first met Eva, she had not been skinny. But not plump either. In the past few weeks, she had put on weight around her midriff and looked sallow and tired.

They ate mostly in silence.

A preoccupied Laure had no objection. Jan and Maria had been noisy all day and she was grateful for peace, any kind of peace. The pasta sauce had been made with smoked fish and was salty and pungent and she had to concentrate to get it down. After a struggle, she put down her fork.

'Lost your appetite?' Petr looked up from his food which he had not finished either.

'I hope you will excuse me, but the heat...'

'I'm sure that's so.'

There was a flicker of humour as he said it but, as was often the case with Petr, she wasn't absolutely sure. 'I'm not used to it.'

It was only half a lie. Laure and heat were good friends, but she was in the grip of something more perplexing. After Rob, and the agony she had endured over his indifference, she had told her friend Jane that she was sworn off becoming even mildly diverted by anyone. 'I'm not bothering ever again.'

Jane had called her a drama queen but Jane's mother took her aside. 'He's a wazzock that one,' she said. 'Just you tell everyone that his organ is the size of a pin and you couldn't find it.'

Yet, here she was, kidnapped by a sensation that wasn't going to release her any time soon. There was a name for it: bloody, hurtful, useless sexual attraction.

Petr pushed his plate aside. 'Forgive me, but you have a boyfriend, I think.'

Laure felt a thump of anxiety. 'I wouldn't say that.'

Avoiding Laure's gaze, Eva got to her feet. 'I need to check on the children.'

Laure stacked the plates – the same fine porcelain ones she had noticed on first arriving – and took them into the kitchen where she put them into the washing-up bowl to soak. She steadied herself on the rim of the sink before returning to the dining room.

Petr looked up. 'A boyfriend?'

'No,' she replied.

Petr took a mouthful from a tankard on which was embossed a coat of arms. 'I think you do.'

'Perhaps you are muddling the terms,' she countered. 'A friend is different from a boyfriend.'

'I'm aware of the difference.' He drank more of the beer and set the tankard down with a snap. 'I've been speaking French as long as you.'

But not as well. She shut herself up before the words could pass her lips, observing instead, 'That's a beautiful tankard'.

Petr ran a finger over the armorial cartouche. 'It belonged to the family who used to live here. They... left it behind.' He tapped the rampant lion quartered with stars. 'Why don't you sit down?'

Laure obeyed and they faced each other across the table. Despite the questions, he seemed relaxed. He leant across, took her glass and poured some beer into it. 'You really should try this. It's part of our national life.'

Laure obeyed. From time to time, she drank with the best but this was an alien brew. 'I don't know much about beer but this seems… good.'

He regarded her with some amusement. 'You're a bad liar.'

Laure ducked her head. 'Yup.'

He reflected. 'I hope you're not homesick.' A questioning eyebrow went up and she shook her head. 'But, if you are, you must promise to tell me.'

'You're very nice to me.'

He was looking down at his glass. 'You're an interesting person. And kind. Kindness is an expression of a healthy moral life and anyone who is good to my children, has our gratitude.'

She was embarrassed and, to counter it, she picked up the glass and regarded the contents. 'I should warn you, Yorkshire people don't give up easily.'

'What else don't you give up?'

He sounded very intense and she choked on her mouthful. 'Lots of things.'

Petr seemed to relax. 'I hope you don't want to give up working here. You fit in well.' He reached for the packet of cigarettes on the table behind him. 'Could you pass me the ashtray?'

Laure pushed it over the polished surface of the table towards him. It was ridiculous but, in that moment, it flashed across her mind that she was inhabiting a parallel world and it was *she* who was married to Petr and *she* who occupied Eva's place at the table.

'So, his name?' Petr asked.

'Whose?'

'The man who walked you home the other night.'

She recalled how Tomas had recoiled when she told him where she lived. 'Am I being watched?'

Petr shrugged. 'Many people are followed. It's normal. We like to make sure they're safe.'

'Normal?' Was she talking in a foreign language? 'I haven't broken any laws.'

'Here, it's not so such much the rule of law but the rule of men.'

Laure swallowed. 'What are the rules?'

'Difficult to say.'

'That's absurd.'

'You'll learn that many things in this country appear absurd.'

On this point, she was going to be stubborn. 'But how do you know what I did?'

'I told you. We like to make sure you're safe.' He sounded almost apologetic. 'There's one thing of which you can be certain. Beautiful young foreigners falling for rock-star dissidents end up the worse off. Rock stars, and people like them, have their own agenda.' The subject was a little raw, not least because she had been brooding over it. But, at least, he was being tactful. 'Those trembling new feelings, Laure, could be one-sided.'

He seemed sincere enough and she was reassured.

'I'm anxious everything goes smoothly,' he said.

Nothing wrong with that, she thought.

Petr traced the cartouche on the tankard with his forefinger. 'So? His name?'

'If you know I've been followed, then you will know.' Before the words were out, she realized that, since Petr almost certainly had been informed of it, this was the wrong battle to fight. 'Tomas Josip.'

'That wasn't so hard, was it? Tell me a bit more about him.'

'I don't know any more than you. Eva probably knows.'

There was real concern in his tone. 'I'm responsible for you and you must look on me *in loco parentis*. You are under my care and I should honour that obligation. I *must* do so.'

Laure didn't know what to think.

'Did you enjoy the marionette show?'

The change of tack was a relief. 'Loved it. The prince was… er, very charming. Before he got to the princess, he had to be rescued by a bear.' Having just tumbled to the obvious, she paused. If the bear wore trousers embroidered with hammers and sickles, which it had… If this was Czechoslovakia, which it was… the bear represented a helpful, friendly Russia. Even if a sickle had been stuck squarely on his backside by someone at the marionette theatre with a sense of humour.

'A bear?'

She faltered. 'I believe so.'

'We like our stories to be filled with witches, woods and wild animals.' Petr gestured to the plaster figures on the wall and smiled. That simple movement of his mouth turned him from the serious employer into a teasing, charming person.

'It was wonderful,' she said with a rush of feeling. 'Magic.'

He got up and laid a hand very briefly and lightly on her shoulder. 'I can't tell you how refreshing your response is.'

'Petr, the children are fine,' Eva interrupted from the doorway. The electric light from the corridor cast an unflattering light on her, making her even more sallow and washed out.

144

Petr glanced at his wife. 'Laure, we have something to discuss with you.'

Eva cut him off and an exchange in Czech ensued. Petr answered, and then, switched back into French. 'My company wishes me to remain here for the next year before returning to Paris. Jan and Maria...' his voice gentled as it always did when referring to his children... 'like you very much. You told us that you were taking a year off from your studies and we would like it if you stayed here with us for that time.' He seemed aware that he had caught her off guard. 'Please, think it over. Give us your answer in a few days.'

Later, Laure looked out from her bedroom window over the roofscape of the Malá Strana. Brympton was becoming a memory: the red-brick house that was home, the bus queue (the place to harvest the best gossip), the wind that whipped down from the fells.

Wasn't it snakes who sloughed off skins? Laure had sloughed off that early part of her life and here she was: exposed, exhilarated, ready to grow a new one.

She spread her fingers over the window pane. Below, the hidden pulse of a grey, subdued city was beating, subterranean and unknown.

CHAPTER 11

Paris, today

*B*ACK HOME IN TIME TO GET READY FOR A LONG-ARRANGED dinner with Simon in the Marais, Laure tossed her keys into the bowl by the door. They landed with the habitual clatter that threatened to crack the china one day.

It was unusually cool and fresh inside the flat and, for once, silence issued from the courtyard. Tugging at her dress zip, she headed for the bathroom, only to come to a halt. A stillness had been caught in the rooms. An element had changed. Or else something was missing.

Where was Kočka?

Her bag dropped to the floor. Laure launched herself into the sitting area and spotted at once that the window, which she had left on the half-latch, was now wide open. Kočka's towel was spread over the sofa, ruffled and indented, indicating that, at some point, she had been there.

Turning in a quarter circle, she ran her eye in a systematic fashion up and down each quadrant before checking the next until she completed the circle.

Laure called 'Kočka', which was absurd as the cat had no idea of her name. Dropping to her knees, she peered under the sofa and chairs hoping to see the curved torso and a pair of world-weary, unblinking eyes. Next, she searched under the bed and through the kitchen. Finally, she hung out of the open window before running down to the courtyard.

Kočka had vanished.

She returned upstairs and stood in the centre of the room.

Her nails dug into her palms. She had made a mistake in imagining that she wouldn't get involved on a deep-down level instead of a manageable one. It was the difference between a helpless, visceral response to a frail little cat whose claws had dug into her pulpy heart and the sensible, practical course where Laure did her best to ensure a stray was comfortable and fed – and nothing more than that.

'Where are you?' Again, she searched the apartment. Kitchen, bedroom, sitting area. '*Where* are you?'

At the back of her mind was the absurd demand: *you can't leave me.*

Please.

But the realization hardened that Kočka had probably abandoned Laure and was back battling her way through the Parisian streets. The familiar, bitter grief crept over her.

Reluctantly, drearily, she went over to shut the window.

Then thought better of it and left it half open.

An hour later, in the Marais restaurant, Simon put down the implement with which he had been extracting snails from the shell. 'Something's wrong.'

Normally, the scents of garlic and melted butter would have been ambrosial but, at this moment, they sickened her.

She explained.

Simon said, 'But you weren't going to keep her.'

'No, I wasn't, was I.' She was hoping she wouldn't let herself down but her eyes filled up. 'But I can't bear to think of her back on the streets, suffering and hungry. At the mercy of God knows what.'

He leant over and smudged an escaped tear with his thumb. 'I haven't seen this side of you very often.'

She dashed her hand across her eyes. 'That's because it isn't a side. Just a blip.'

Simon finished the snails. 'I know you work very hard at being contained and I have two things to say about it. One, it doesn't fool everyone. Or, rather, it doesn't fool me. Two, it's a waste of energy. We all have feelings, some of them run very deep indeed. It's a negation to hide them.'

She managed a half laugh. 'Have you been on a mindfulness course or something?'

'Actually, yes. And you should have been with me.'

This was unexpected. 'Do you and Valerie talk about those sorts of things?'

'We do now.' He leant over and refilled her glass.

'Lucky Valerie.' She thought for a moment. 'Since we are talking this way, you do love Valerie? More than anything. And have done so for a long time?' She swallowed. 'It can last?'

Simon looked at her with a great deal of compassion. 'Yes. Why do you ask?'

The salient memories about Tomas were still reliable but, as time passed, she struggled to remember the smaller details, or the precise texture, of their time together. Could she recall, truthfully, the fervour and fever of emotion, the aching lust, her delight in the rightness of it? No, but also yes. *Yes.* Could she pinpoint the moment when she understood that her feelings for him and, by extension, the cause were so intense that she felt liberated from herself, the Laure Carlyle from Brympton?

If she was truthful, and truthful she should be, the memories of the political resistance hidden in Anatomie's lyrics tended to be sharper. So, too, were the performances at the marionette theatre.

But, never forgotten were the subversion, the secrecy. The hilarity. Tomas warned her to be careful and never to repeat what she knew to anyone. Yeah right, she remembered thinking at the time. How discreet was discreet? Most of Tomas's circle made their political affiliations known and were careless with their talk. Anatomie had only to strike up a chord and everyone knew what they were on about.

She wondered if they ever understood how innocent she had been. Certainly, she had failed to understand the layers of complicity existing between the watchers and the population on which they spied which ensured tiny sprouts of rebellion were ignored. Until they weren't.

Simon was waiting for her answer. She lifted her glass and said lightly, 'Because in this wicked world it's good to know.'

She made the taxi driver drop her at the canal and walked back home through the violet night, the kind that normally made her feel glad to be alive. Tonight, it was different as she was dragged down by a feeling that she could only describe as misery.

For God's sake, what was one small, feral cat?

Answer: it could have been *her* one small, feral cat.

The dispirited shrub in a corner of the courtyard had somehow managed to produce a few white blossoms. Oddly, she found it a comforting sight and Laure stopped to admire their glimmer in the dusk. This was a mistake. Madame Poirier rose from her chair outside her flat where she kept vigil.

'Madame, you should be aware that you left your window open today.'

Laure stared at her. For a hopeful second, she thought Madame Poirier was about to tell her that a cat was on the loose. 'It's very warm for this time of year, madame.' She barely managed her customary politesse and, turning around, fled for the refuge of her front door.

Upstairs, she stood for a long time at the window of the sitting area, straining to see if a cat shape was padding across the roofs. After a while, she turned back to the room and her gaze rested on the black-and-white photograph of a beach with the spumy sea running up it.

She poured herself a glass of wine and sat down to catch up on potential donations.

Working was like wading through mud. Again, she checked outside the window.

'I will not be broken,' Tomas told her. 'Never.'

All these years Laure had been schooling herself to accept that, almost certainly, one way or another, Tomas had been broken. He had wanted to keep his ideals, his purpose, his music, and it devastated Laure to think that he might have bludgeoned into other ways of thinking.

If he was alive.

In the bedroom, Laure got undressed and cleansed and moisturized her face with the most expensive creams she could afford. (Why not?) Having stepped out of her underclothes, she reached for the oversized T-shirt she favoured for sleeping in. Air played over her back and breasts. It was almost a caress and longing caught her cruelly.

Could he be alive? She had failed to find him when she tried but it was possible. Just.

If so, did he ever turn his face to the west and think of her? That girl?

Perhaps he did.

Not knowing was a hydra-headed, tormenting adversary. It never admitted defeat, it almost never retreated. It bided its time in the rock pools and under the stones of the mind and spirit, waiting on the turn of the tide to race back in.

If he was alive, Tomas might well have loved others. Women? Men?

Every seven to fifteen years, the cells in the body were replaced. Bone, skin, stomach, liver. The lot. Having read about it in a scientific journal, Laure was cheered because it suggested renaissance and renewal were possible. But it also meant she was walking around with every cell in her body replenished and he would be too. They would have learnt new ways of thinking – or she had – developed unfamiliar physical responses, new knowledge and desires. They would move differently, eat differently, their views on sex, love and politics almost certainly would diverge.

'I wish I could touch you,' she said aloud. She almost added, *just once*, but that was to be stupid. Just once would not be enough.

Later, she lay in bed and sobbed for one fragile little cat.

For the question that had never been answered.

And all the other things, too.

The daily post arrived with a larger than usual haul and the subsequent discussion of its contents took up much of the working day. The cigarette packet on the inside of which were columns of numbers written down with the word 'divorce settlement' was shocking and amusing. The shoebox filled with sea shells with no return address was an enigma. Laure gave in to temptation and plunged a hand down into them, enjoying the feel of their whorls and curves and the faintest of salty tangs. The note that came with them read: 'Sadly, the tide went out and never turned.'

After closing time, Laure made her rounds, satisfying herself that the lights were out and the alarms set.

She was on the bottom rung of the stairs and overheard Nic and May talking in the lobby.

'Can I ask you out to dinner?' May asked. She was teasing and laughing.

'Yes, you can but whether you *may* is another matter,' said Nic.

Laure found herself frozen to the stair. That exchange was an echo – eerie and dislocating – one from long ago.

'OK. *May* I take you out to dinner? In fact, I insist.'

'I thought you'd never ask.' Nic's footsteps sounded on the wooden floor. 'Are you always so bossy? You know what they say about domineering women?'

May laughed, a sound filled with excitement and anticipation. 'The same as they say about domineering men.'

'Let's go and discuss it.'

The door opened.

Laure waited until she heard the door shut behind them. The madness and ache of that time, *her* time, were old companions and they were with her now.

Outside the museum, Laure gave herself a pause. A street-cleaning vehicle was grinding up the street. Two cyclists with sit-up-and-beg vehicles lumbered past. Madame Becque waved from the grocery.

Irritatingly, her sixth sense swung into play. *Was she being followed?*

Occasionally, this happened. It was a conditioned reflex from the past, a fallout, usually re-triggered by sleeplessness and emotion.

Every sense on high alert, she picked her way down the street towards the triangle of earth where she had first seen Kočka and rattled a packet of cat biscuits. She did not hold out much hope and there was no rustle of undergrowth, no answering sound and no glimpse of an emaciated brindled body.

She thought of the weary golden eyes, the tiny puft of the feline heartbeat under her fingers, the bony, fragile skull. If life had been kind and equable, Kočka would be slinking through the violet night, in a garden where poppies burned in the sun, roses rustled and ripening fruit scented the evening air. She would be lying on warmed stone, replete and dreaming.

The phone in her bag rang. Reluctantly, she fished it out. 'Hallo.'

'Laure, it's May. I wanted to ask you a couple more things.'

'Can't they wait? Anyway, thought you were with Nic.'

May was the dog with the bone. 'I am, but I'll be working on the article before I go to bed. It would help me a lot if we had a discussion. I know … I know the copybook is still blotted but I hope we are past it?' She was warm. She was cajoling. She was contrite. 'Can we get over it?'

The words clustered in Laure's ear. Animals could shake water off their coats and she longed to shake off May in similar fashion.

'You're right to bear a grudge,' persisted May.

Grudges consumed the spirit. Laure knew that only too well and swallowed her irritation. 'I'm on my way home. You can talk to me as I go.'

'First off, have you found the cat?'

Laure softened. 'I haven't but I'll keep looking.' She avoided stepping into a pile of dog faeces. 'What did you want to know?'

154

'You lived in Prague before the communist regime fell and in Berlin just after the Wall came down. I wondered if you wanted to talk about your experiences there and how they affected your decision to set up the museum?'

The questions were like gnats. To be swatted? She pulled herself into line. 'I'll think about the answer.'

After a moment, May said: 'You haven't forgiven me. But I don't expect it.' She added, 'It's odd, isn't it? For the time it takes, interviewer and interviewee are spliced together. While it's going, it's a marriage.' Laure heard her intake of breath. 'After it's over we can divorce.'

This was almost childlike in its analysis, but correct, as Laure well knew. Keeping a sharp lookout for more dog messes, she silently acknowledged May's cheek and candour. Possibly, she had no morals but they now understood each other better. 'Ask away,' she said, feeling the release of not fighting it any more.

'Your sponsor? Did you ever get to the bottom of why they suddenly gave you so much money?'

'I'll answer that too tomorrow.'

'You know,' said May, 'I think I understand why you chose the Canal Saint-Martin for the museum.'

'Why did I?'

'Because... because it's a place where people go who have nowhere. Who think, perhaps, they don't belong. It's a place to put out a hand and feel that there is something to be gained from nothing.' There was a short pause. 'Of all people, you must understand how that feels.'

Laure looked towards the canal where the autumnal trees dipped towards the water and couples were making their way across the ironwork bridge. To where the tents of the homeless clustered on the banks.

Put out a hand.

May was right.

The phone call ended.

In a change of plan, she walked down to the canal and, instead of turning for home, crossed the nearest bridge to Chez Prune. Having managed to nab an outside table which had a view of the water, she ordered red wine, then a second glass. It was to dice with getting drunk but she was going to enjoy it in a Paris that tonight was in languorous mood.

'Learn after me.'

Tomas's voice was in her ear.

'*From* me. It's learn *from* me,' she pointed out.

He never liked being corrected on his English. 'Are you listening?'

She nodded. 'Of course.'

'This is who we are. In 1948, there was a *coup d'état* and the communists took over. By 1968, we were supposed to be used to the idea that "socialist consumerism" was the way to the good life. It wasn't the good life. It wasn't free. Dubček tried to make the country better and to barter with Moscow. It was called the Prague Spring. He failed and the Russians sent in the tanks. We got Husák and what they called "normalization". What that meant was persistent surveillance. It was the mud which covered everyone. I wrote a song about it. "The Discovery of Fear".'

Disguised as a love song because of the risk, it hadn't been Tomas's best. It didn't matter because it went down a storm.

It was quite a story, her time in Prague. Full of love and fear and grief. But those three things were proof that she had been alive. Electrically so. Even the consequence, the on-going inner debate with conscience and recrimination, was a kind of proof.

She rang May back. 'If we are to continue, I think I should know more about you.'

'Really?' responded a startled-sounding May. 'If I told you that my bedroom was decorated with pink rosebuds, the bed was hung with white net and had satin bows and the wooden floor was waxed weekly by the maid on her hands and knees would that help? Oh, and my full name is May Eugenie Marcia Williams and my mother is known as Miss Melia.'

Laure laughed. 'And?'

'I think I mentioned I was expected to marry a trust fund.'

'I want to ask you a question,' said Laure.

There was a perceptible hesitation. 'Ask away.'

'OK. May Eugenie Marcia Williams, what would you bring to the museum?'

It was May's turn to laugh. A little uneasily. 'I'll think about it.'

'If you want my cooperation, I need to know.'

'That's not the way it works,' said May, sounding off balance.

'It is with me,' said Laure.

'I'll get back to you.'

'That's my tactic.'

The second glass of red was finished. Time to go.

Later in the week, Laure made her customary notes as she walked through the museum. The windows needed cleaning and a hinge on a cabinet was on the cusp of breaking.

Making practical decisions was a soothing activity. She liked the order that was necessary to take them. She liked the neatness of the schedules and objectives.

In Room 2, a couple of girls were staring at the 'Ron Maiden' T-shirt and exchanging views in low voices. At Laure's entrance, they scurried out. A tall, bulky man was standing in front of the recently displayed bridal veil. A short-sleeved shirt strained across his stomach and the belt holding up his jeans was doing sterling service. His head was bowed and he had laid the palm of his hand against the glass, something that visitors were asked not to do.

Laure made to step forward and checked herself. The man's shoulders were heaving and she suspected it was the spurned bridegroom. Or someone in the same boat. In which case, he should be allowed licence. There was a temptation to tap him on the arm and to tell him: *this, too, will pass.*

Except, in her experience, that was not the case and to lie about it was almost worse than the offence.

She backed out of the room and left in peace a weeping, grieving man to gather himself together.

In Room 1, a gaggle of schoolchildren with rucksacks that they should have left in the cloakroom were pressed up against the cabinets. Children were a mixed blessing in the museum. Very often they were bored but some asked remarkably pertinent questions. There were squeals from this contingent and it was a fair bet that they were absorbing zero. An exasperated teacher with fair hair scraped back into a bun was trying to engage their attention. Giving up the attempt, she chivvied them to the door. Laure buttonholed her and asked her politely to deposit the rucksacks into the cloakroom.

Nic was in the office, absorbed by a document on his screen. He did not look up at her entrance. 'There's something that might interest you.'

She was anxious to transfer her notes to the screen. 'Can it wait?'

'Yup.'

The phone went. Nic answered and handed it over to Laure. 'Jacques Bertrand.'

Laure made a face. Jacques Bertrand was their lawyer and he usually only made contact when there was a problem – as indeed there was. Jamie's father was objecting to the milk tooth in the matchbox and the implication conveyed by its labelling that he was a negligent parent.

The conversation having wound to its close, Laure dropped her chin into her hands. Jamie's father was furious and insulted. 'So insulted,' said Laure, 'that he must be guilty.'

'In what era did you become a cynic?'

She made a face at him.

It was late and Nic began to pack up. He took his time to switch off his computer and to stow his laptop. 'I never knew you were interested in rock.'

It was a left-of-field question and she had to search for an answer. 'I'm not.' She added, 'Particularly.'

'Never a wild child?' Nic was smiling in an infuriating manner. 'The bare-breasted rock chick?'

Laure leant back in the chair. 'What *is* all this?'

Nic zipped shut his laptop bag. '"Tunnelling".'

'For God's sake, what are you talking about?'

But Laure knew precisely what he was talking about and a frisson went through her.

'"The nation is on its knees but we're not. We're upright".' He lowered his voice. '"The raw emotional power of music is superior to the word".'

She pressed her hands down onto her desk. 'Where did you dredge those up?'

'Have you heard of the internet?'

'Stop it, Nic.'

His answer was to toss an envelope down in front of her. It was addressed to her personally. 'Look inside, Laure.'

The envelope was bulky and had an elusive scent but not a feminine one. A herb? An aftershave? For some reason, her pulse was raised as she extracted from it a black-and-white photograph sandwiched between two leaves of cardboard.

It was taken in evening sunshine in a large park or garden in front of a building probably built in the late eighteenth century. The space was crammed with people – young and middle-aged, with one or two elderly leavening the mix. Most were dressed conservatively: the men in ill-cut jeans or shorts, the women in knee-length skirts and blouses. But there was a good percentage who had got the bit between their teeth and were wearing T-shirts with plunging necklines, flowing skirts and leather fringes.

In the distance on a raised platform were three figures. They had unkempt hair, T-shirts and embroidered waistcoats. Two were on guitars and the third on the drums. One of them, a slight, handsome, rakish figure, had taken up position at the central microphone. The camera caught an absorption, a passion. A tension.

The press was thickest around the stage but several nearest to the camera had linked arms and swayed in a tightly constructed human chain across the foreground.

There was no litter and no vendors, at least in the camera's sights. It looked hot, magical and raucous.

Nic was smiling in an irritating way. 'Recognize?'

A painful lump forced its way into her throat. 'Can't say I do. A pop concert somewhere?'

Nic's smile widened. 'My mother always taught me to tell the truth.' He bent over and tapped one of the figures closest to the camera. She had long hair, a flowing patterned scarf and huge shining eyes. 'If I'm not mistaken that's you.'

CHAPTER 12

Prague, 1986

$\mathcal{L}$AURE'S ROUTE ACROSS THE CHARLES BRIDGE TO THE Old Town Square was becoming well worn. Straight on from the bridge, avoid the pothole by the crooked house and keep the Disney church towers in line of sight.

'I'm often at the marionette theatre in the evenings. Or, someone there will know where I am. Will you come?'

Laure wanted to. Very much. But Petr and Eva's warnings remained fresh in her mind. Where was this line running between the political and the personal? She had no idea. At home, the last thing she ever did was to question the status quo. In Prague, she was being set daily puzzles.

A fork was a fork was a fork? Apparently not.

Escaping the afternoon torpor, she had ferried the children to the marionette theatre twice and the outings had been a success. Hot and restless, they stepped into a place where the make-believe was what mattered. Eyes wide, Maria gasped and buried her head in Laure's lap. Jan shouted with laugher. Their reactions gave Laure enormous pleasure and she surrendered to the magic too.

This evening, however, she was going there on her own.

A minor source of frustration was her skimpy wardrobe, her one good thing being a black cotton dress patterned with pink roses. Eva frowned when Laure emerged from her room in it.

'The neckline's too low,' she said.

Laure had bought the dress in Paris and, for her, its cut, seams and drape exuded Left Bank and she was proud of it. Recollecting how she had nerved herself to enter the Parisian department store and how the assistant's superior manner filleted her confidence as she decanted her stockpile of savings onto the cask desk, she went to its defence. 'I think it's fine.'

Battle lines sprang up between Laure and Eva and, being younger, much prettier, firmer bodied, Laure emerged the victor. It was a shabby victory. Of course it was, and she made an effort to damp down its satisfactions.

'If you get us into trouble, I'll never forgive you. The city is not safe at night.' Eva was tight-lipped and her accented French wobbled.

She was seeping unhappiness like water from a sponge. Laure's conscience stirred and she made an overture. 'You must be pleased to be back home with your family and friends.' Not that Laure was aware of any family or friends visiting the apartment.

'Home,' echoed Eva, as if the concept was an unfamiliar one. 'Yes, of course.'

Laure fiddled with her neckline. 'Eva, are you content if I stay on? Would you prefer someone who lives in Prague to look after the children?'

'No... no.' Eva's response was genuine. 'The children know you. They like you. Nothing's more important. We've been given special permission to bring you with us.' In a gesture that was becoming habitual, she clutched at her midriff. 'I need help. You do understand?'

The doubts arrived. Should she escape the puzzling family set-up and the apartment filled with plastic chairs and what, she now suspected, was looted china and glass? Should she take the chance to escape a city where, it seemed, facts only became facts if they were approved of by the authorities?

At the marionette theatre a notice scheduled an 8 p.m. performance. There was over half an hour to go but Laure singled out a bench in the auditorium and settled on it. Backstage, there were lively discussions going on, and the lights were being tested.

Dressed head to foot in puppeteer's black, Lucia emerged. Black suited her and she looked magnificent. Like the warrior she was supposed to be. Sighting Laure, she frowned and came over. 'Too early.' Her English was comprehensible but heavily accented.

'I don't mind waiting.'

Lucia ran her eye over the dress and lifted an eyebrow. 'It's no use waiting for Tomas. He isn't here.'

'Right,' said Laure, keeping her friendly smile fixed.

Lucia stuck her hands onto her hips. 'You know something?' Her accent deepened. 'You are a nuisance and perhaps a problem.'

Even allowing for disparities in Lucia's grasp of English, this was rude and Laure braced to fight back. 'Don't you like foreigners?'

'They can make life difficult. They take revenge.'

Both were having trouble with the language which was slipping and sliding. 'They? Who takes revenge?'

She shrugged. 'Listen, you are not... us. We do not know how you think or what you believe. The foreigners he brings here are trouble. It happened before. Tomas should have nothing to do with you.'

'Why don't you find out what I think?'

'No point.'

165

The hissed words were a challenge. Lucia turned on her heel and vanished, leaving Laure marooned on her bench.

'Don't worry,' said a voice in English from backstage. 'Tomas is coming later. He and Leo are trying to sober up Manicki.' A stocky figure with receding sandy hair emerged into view. Like Lucia's, his English was heavily accented but his was of a different order and more fluent. 'I'm Milos. I look after the puppets and do set designs and lighting. I am so important they cannot do without me. And, to keep me in bread and vodka, I paint portraits of fat Party officials.' He sent Laure a gap-toothed smile of singular sweetness. 'You must not pay attention to Queen Lucia. She wants war and is hard on anyone who's not in her army.' He peered at Laure. 'Don't be upset. Why don't I introduce you to some of my children?'

'Children?'

'Forgive me. I mean, the marionettes.'

He led Laure backstage to a small room where rows of marionettes of all shapes and sizes hung from the wall and shelves, stacked with boxes, reached from floor to ceiling. The windows had been thrown wide open to counter the heat and the sound of people passing filtered in.

'Meet the Kaspars,' said Milos, laying out a pair of marionettes on the table. 'I think you will know them as Punch and Judy. They are the oldest ones in Europe. Not these, of course. But who they are.'

Splayed out, the Kaspars resembled small corpses.

'And these...' he pointed to a pair of marionettes with pig-like features and black suits hanging by the window, 'these are father and son.' With a gentleness usually reserved for babies, he touched the older-looking one with a finger. 'This is Joseph Spejbl. He's very stupid and says stupid things. This is his son, Hurvinek, who's clever.'

166

Laure wiped the sweat off her cheek.

'The Nazis hated the Spejbls. They arrested the man who made them and put him in prison. *Then* they came back and arrested the marionettes.'

'Arrested *marionettes!*'

Milos looked at Laure. *You have no idea.*

That was true.

It was cripplingly hot inside and her armpits were damp. Milos was obviously busy and she thanked him and, as an emergency measure, dived into the garden. Here she lit a cigarette, a recently acquired habit. The cigarette was Czech and its smoke was rough on the back of her throat but she persevered. The smoke drifted upwards and its aroma mingled with that of the tobacco plant in the corner.

'So, you came,' said a voice.

Her heart thumped as she swivelled around. 'As you see.'

Despite the heat, Tomas was wearing the linen waistcoat, which he took off and folded over the back of the garden bench. The light fell full over him. Slight of frame, eyes narrowed against the evening, thick eyelashes, hair slicked back, he exuded energy, boldness and... an irresistible unkempt quality.

'Nice dress.' He sounded approving. 'Not bought in Czechoslovakia, I think.'

'Paris.'

'The goons will suspect it.'

She tugged at the neckline and felt a blush hi-jacking what cool she possessed.

He pulled her down onto the bench. He was smiling, as he so often was. 'You like the marionettes? Marionettes and puppets, and the *Laterna Magika* are very strong in our traditions. Not so much in yours, I think.'

'Punch and Judy.' She wrinkled her forehead. 'Not much else.' Did she know anything about her own traditions? 'But here is different. You have spells and enchantment.' She struggled for coherence. 'This is a place where, if you want to watch properly, you must forget yourself. It's part of the experience.'

'Then, you know.'

Emboldened, she continued. 'You think you are watching one thing, but it's really about something else.'

She had blundered. Tomas's smile switched off and he pressed down on Laure's arm. It was a warning to shut up. He removed his hand and said in a low voice. 'I knew you were clever and that's a smart observation but not one to discuss here.'

She opened her mouth to reply but he waggled his finger. *Don't.*

A silence drifted and folded between them. Curiously, it wasn't in the least awkward, which it could have been, but… exciting.

Tomas was the first to break it. 'Would you like to help out here? For the summer?'

Her cigarette had burned dangerously close to her fingers. She dropped the butt and she placed a foot on it. As she extinguished its spark, another glowed. 'What do you mean?'

He gestured to the auditorium. 'We need messengers and furniture moving. Lots of mending. We need people to step in to help if there's an emergency. There always is. You know, lighting or broken strings.' He bent over, picked up her cigarette butt, wrapped it in a piece of paper and placed it in his pocket. Laure watched with some surprise. 'I'm a mad old tramp? Yes. Tobacco is expensive here and we save things.'

'Even the smallest traces?'

He searched her face. For what? To ascertain if she was a safe person? 'The smallest traces build up into big things.'

She licked lips which had gone dry. 'My employer has asked me to stay on the for the year. I'm thinking about it.'

'I wonder why.' Tomas's eyes narrowed. 'And will you? Stay?'

She considered lighting up a second cigarette and reckoned it would make her appear nervous. 'I would like to know more about this country.'

'And would you like to know more about me?'

She seemed barely able to breathe. 'Yes.' *Oh yes.*

He shifted closer. 'And I about you.'

Her response to the exchange must have appeared maladroit – that was because she didn't know how to handle its intensity. 'I *should* know more. About the country, I mean.'

He gave an unamused laugh. 'There's too much to know. But you will have noticed that our geography puts us at a disadvantage.'

The audience was beginning to file into the auditorium. Tomas glanced over to the door, got to his feet and raised his voice a touch. 'What you must remember is that the State is a good and efficient one. It looks after its people. Have you got that?'

She was bewildered. 'I think so.'

His smile was a thousand suns shining down on her. 'I predict you will be a good pupil. Promise me, you will learn well.'

Even more muddled, Laure nodded. 'I promise.'

'If you stay in Prague, everything you hear will contradict the last thing you heard, and your employer will probably be using you.'

'That's—' she cut herself off.

Tomas finished the sentence. 'You were going to say that's what he said about us.' He didn't wait for a reply. 'Old tricks. Remember he'll be checking on you.' His eyes were now flinty. 'For God's sake, let's not worry about it. If you stay and help here, I warn you that Lucia won't like it. You mustn't mind. She's had bad experiences which makes her suspicious of people, particularly strangers.' He touched Laure's chin with a finger. 'It's natural and I think you'll understand.'

Louche but not horrible with it, focused but seemingly not, Tomas's charm was wrapping her ever more tightly. 'Why do you take an interest in me?'

'When I first saw you, you seemed lost. I mean out of place.'

'Is that surprising?'

'The look on your face suggested that it went deeper than being a tourist without the guidebook.'

'*Prague on a Shoestring* is very helpful.'

He made her stand up and moved very close. 'Would you rather I said it's because you're beautiful?'

She would have done. Much rather. 'You forgot to add... and irresistible.'

Tomas laughed. 'I knew I wasn't wrong.'

She drew in a breath and decided. 'I could help out now if you wanted.'

He looked at her. 'I do want.'

There was a marked inflection on the 'want'.

Time to go inside: and Laure made herself as comfortable as possible on the bench for the performance of *Don Giovanni*.

The curtains were tugged back. A single marionette in a black cap and Pierrot costume lay crumpled on the dim, almost dark, stage. Only his outstretched hands had any light on them. Unusually, his puppet master stood directly behind him.

It was black-clad Lucia, her strong features blurred into the shadows.

From backstage sifted the high, sweet notes of a violin playing a lament. Very slowly, Pierrot reached up a hand, then a second. He unbent his knee, then the other and stood upright. Laure recognized the Prince marionette without the kerchief and red-checked shirt. Under this light, the mouth was accentuated and had become tragic and the features had shed their merriment.

He experimented with walking. Up and down. Up and down – a universe of bewilderment, anxiety and grief enshrined in the trembling figure. Then he turned, faced the audience, and placed his hand over his heart and left it there.

He was alive, she thought.

His hand fell to his side, and he appeared to stare straight at Laure. *Come with me.*

Laure sighed – and the Pierrot flowed through her.

He was leading the watchers over a boundary… between the real and the make-believe, between the inert and what lived, to the point where logic was abandoned and the illusion held sway.

The marionette looked up at its master. The master – Lucia – looked down at the marionette. Marionette and master gazed deep into each other's eyes.

Who controls whom?

The music yearned and made her ache.

What can I live for?

Very deliberately, the puppet lifted his wooden hand, took hold of the string attached to his leg and, as he fixed his gaze on the puppet master, pulled the string up and down. His leg obeyed him.

He shook his head. Disbelief? Rejection?

Laure was gripping her hands so tightly that her nails dug into her flesh.

The high, violin note was held. The marionette reached up and jerked the string that controlled his leg out of its mooring, disabling it. In front of the audience, he crumpled slowly, a figure of pain. A wooden hand trembled as, again, he reached up and detached his second leg. Then one of his arms. Mutilated, shaking, he looked around at the audience.

No. She bit her lip to bite down on the involuntary cry.

With his remaining arm, the marionette pulled the string that held him to life, dismantled his own head and fell forward.

He was now a heap of marionette bones on the stage.

The entire thing only took a couple of minutes and the curtains were whisked shut. The suicide of a marionette? The defeat of a puppet master?

She felt sick. She felt terrified. She felt she had seen nothing so exquisite, so clever. So brutal. Or, so haunting.

Laure looked around. No one applauded. Some in the audience rearranged themselves on the bench, others talked to their companions. She wanted to shout out: *but you have just seen genius.*

Then she understood that the condition of watching what they had just seen was silence and those around were versed in subversion.

'Are you OK?'

Tomas slid towards her on the bench. In answer, she held out both hands which were trembling with aftershock. He took them, held them and stilled their movement. After a few moments, he bent over and kissed them.

The curtains were parted and the overture to *Don Giovanni* struck up.

The following day, Laure knocked on the door of the dining room where Eva and Petr were eating supper and told them she accepted their offer to stay on in Prague.

'Are you sure?' Eva gave one of her disturbing laughs.

'Yes, I have arranged for my mother to send over books from the reading list which will help me prepare for next year.'

Petr presided over this exchange. She couldn't be sure but she thought she detected a hint of satisfaction in the dark eyes when she told them of her plans to work at the marionette theatre two nights a week. 'If that's OK with you,' she added hastily.

Petr's reply left a margin of doubt. 'I strongly recommend that you do no such thing.'

He didn't wish her to but, equally, he wasn't going to stop her – which he could do. Why? Perhaps he really wanted her to work at the theatre so he could question her about what went on?

She reckoned she was becoming a good pupil, a fast learner in the 'language' of this country.

A drained-looking Eva pushed aside her plate. 'You must know that you can't count on us if there's trouble.' She got to her feet. 'I'll say goodnight.'

Laure made to clear the dishes but Petr indicated that she should take Eva's vacated chair. Petr propped his elbows onto the table and began to talk about the children, the weather, sights he had seen in Paris. Anything but Laure's involvement with the marionette theatre.

The sky darkened and a group of pigeons patrolled the roof top outside the window. Petr lit a cigarette. A welcome coolness slid into the room.

Laure relaxed. Here she was again – inadvertently – trying on for size what it was to be a woman of a house. It was rather fun to contemplate and utter nonsense. Petr smoked quietly, every so often glancing at her from under his lids. 'Did you know my favourite English book is *Winnie-the-Pooh*? It appeals to us Czechs because it so absurd. And funny. We understand the combination. And, it's easier to get hold of than most publications.'

'It must be so awful,' she said without thinking. 'To not be able to read what you wish.'

Petr shot a look at the ceiling as if he expected the cornicing to be bugged. 'What's yours?' He got to his feet, took a slice of bread from the bread basket on the table and went over to the window.

Laure considered the flippant answer: *anything with sex, drugs and rock 'n' roll.* 'Not sure.'

He beckoned to Laure. 'Do you want to feed the pigeons? Eva doesn't like me doing it as she thinks they're pests. Which they are. But nice pests.' He tore a piece off the slice, balanced it on his palm and held it out. She pitched it towards the bird and it missed, rolling down the roof to the gutter.

'You're no good,' said Petr teasingly. He threw a second fragment. This time the pigeon pounced while his smaller companion fluttered his wings in protest. 'Mine, I think,' said Laure and lobbed a bread pellet towards it. A yellow beak jabbed down.

'One all,' she said.

He smiled. 'Right. You're on.'

They stood companionably at the window throwing bread pellets at the pigeons who couldn't believe their luck. Two to Petr. Three to Laure championing the smaller pigeon which had a slight pink tinge to its wings. 'His missus,' she said. 'Her name is Tina Turner.'

'Mine's Karl Marx,' said Petr.

'My culture versus yours.'

'If you like.' He turned a smiling countenance on Laure.

'Did you notice something?' He shook his head. 'They're both as greedy as each other,' she said.

Petr laughed. After a moment, Laure joined in.

With a flap of wings, the satiated pigeons took to the wing. Laure and Petr remained at the window, looking down at the darkening city with the cooler air flowing over their faces.

'See the buildings?' He gestured to the roofs, domes and spires that punctuated the cityscape. 'Some were palaces, some were the town houses of the aristos. Some belonged to rich merchants.'

'But no longer?'

'Yes, all that has gone.' After a moment, he added, 'I know that you reckon I'm living the privileged life no longer possible for those out there.'

Did she have the nerve to ask: how come you live in this beautiful, requisitioned place? She didn't and remained quiet. It didn't matter because she was pretty sure he knew what she was thinking. She squinted up at him. She was pretty sure, too, that he would have asked himself the same questions.

'It's very nice of you to keep me company,' he said at last. 'You remind me of...' He stopped himself.

Laure felt it was only polite to ask, 'Of?'

'Of myself,' said Petr. 'A long time ago.'

CHAPTER 13

*S*HE MADE IT HER BUSINESS TO GET TO KNOW THE BUILDING that housed the marionette theatre. Although it was well proportioned with many windows, it also had dark corners and shadows. Dirt filmed most surfaces and edged window frames and cornicing. Most of the rooms were empty of furniture. In some of them there were mattresses and sleeping bags that smelt of unaired clothes, sex and spilt booze. Backstage, there was a warren of rooms, including the one that did double duty as a kitchen and green room. The passage that led to it from the auditorium was lined with cracked mirroring, which had the effect of fragmenting the reflections in it.

If you come, said Tomas, you will never say anything of what goes on in here. That's the promise you make to us.

The second floor was used by Anatomie to store their instruments – two guitars, drum kit, keyboard and a precious amplifier. 'It's treated like a new-born baby,' said Milos, 'because it's impossible to replace.'

Which one was Tomas's guitar? She longed to touch it but continued up to the attics, placing her feet in the depressions worn into the staircase. At one point, she put out her hand to steady herself on the wall. It was warm and slightly moist and she had an odd notion that she was being sucked back into time.

With few hitches – or, so it appeared – Laure was absorbed into the life of the company. Wearing the uniform of black jeans and a black T-shirt, she made her evening pilgrimage twice a week to the Old Town Square and brewed tea, cleaned and ushered.

As Tomas predicted, Lucia made it her business to address as few words as possible to Laure, but Milos had appointed himself her tutor, a role that pleased him. 'I'm not allowed to travel,' he said, 'so you must tell me about things and places.' Missing a couple of upper front teeth, he had a habit of clamping his top lip over his bottom lip to hide the gaps, which made Laure ashamed of possessing such good ones.

On one occasion, she arrived early to discover a meeting was being held in the auditorium. A man guarding the entrance prevented her from entering. He flapped his hand in the direction of backstage. The double doors were open a crack and she glimpsed a black-clad group of twenty or so, smoking furiously and clustered around a figure typing out a document.

Obediently, she went backstage and did not refer to what she had seen. By the time of the performance, the meeting had dispersed.

Tomas kept his distance.

Would he or would he not seek her out? She had a dreadful presentiment that he had been playing with her or, worse, he had forgotten about her and she felt, insanely, irrationally, jealous of the people around him. Yet, when he turned up one evening and told her to fetch her bag because he was taking her out to dinner, she was irritated by his high-handedness.

He sensed it. 'Forgive me, Laure?'

She answered a little stiffly. 'Nothing to forgive.'

He put his hand on her shoulder – and her flesh burned. 'I've been with Leo. He's had a bit of crisis. A woman.'

They headed for a place he knew in the Malá Strana and, as they crossed the Charles Bridge, he said, 'You've not really explored the city, I think.' She shook her head. He pointed to a statue. 'St John of Nepomuk. He was a... what's the word? A martyr. He was thrown into the river because he refused to give up his beliefs. People touch him for luck.'

The restaurant was so modest that it scarcely merited the term, being a small room at the back of a shop that sold leather goods. But it opened onto a small back garden where tables had been set out covered in brown paper peppered with stains from previous diners.

Tomas regarded the glass of beer placed in front of him. 'I don't know how to say this but I'm afraid you'll have to pay your half.' He raised rueful eyes to hers. 'I wish it was not the case but a musician like me is not allowed to earn much money.'

The confession, and the humiliation of it, sent an arrow into her heart. 'It doesn't matter.'

'It does. We are considered decadent and the State makes sure we don't earn much. But, if I was a miner, it would be different, even though as a miner you might not be that productive. But don't worry or pity us. We know how to handle it.'

He was watching her carefully.

She leant forward and asked in a low voice, 'Is it safe to talk like that here?'

He did his trick of raising an eyebrow. 'Why do you think we're eating outside?'

She ducked her head. 'I'm ashamed of my ignorance.'

'Don't be.'

His voice contained a caress. She was finding it difficult to breath normally and, to keep herself on the straight and narrow, she dug a fingernail into the soft part of her thumb.

'After turbulent times, Czechoslovakia is now living through *normalizáce*, which…' Tomas heaved a sigh, 'is not as nice as it sounds.'

She thought of how little she knew and should hurry up and get to know.

'See the waiter,' Tomas said.

Obediently, she glanced across the warm, shadowed garden to a stooped and elderly man doling out food onto plates.

'Once upon a time, he was a respected and successful head of a secondary school. Then he made a mistake.' Laure widened her eyes. 'He was accused of giving the eulogy at the funeral of a known dissident. Immediately, his contract was terminated, and…' Tomas snapped his fingers. 'He was unemployable and that's his condition for life. Result, he ekes out a living here. If any of the authorities come, he hides in the kitchen.'

Laure wondered if Tomas should be telling her so much, so soon in their acquaintanceship.

Their soup was placed in front of them and Tomas picked up his spoon. 'The debate has to be: is he lucky?' He used the edge of his paper tablecloth to flick away the fly making tracks for his bowl.

She tried to think through the implications but she knew she was losing the capacity for clear thought. 'I don't know,' she replied. 'Is he?'

'In the old days, he would have been thrown into the Bartolomějská, and beaten up, possibly killed. These days, the approach is subtler and there is nothing to be done. He will never have a better life. It's impossible.'

'But he must appeal,' she whispered. 'Surely.'

'Here what is written by the authorities is the truth, even if it everyone knows it is erroneous, including the authorities.'

180

Laure couldn't eat much of the soup. Putting down her spoon, she stole a look around the tiny garden, which had filled up with diners. After he had finished his, Tomas reached for her half-emptied bowl. 'Can I?'

'You can,' she said naughtily, 'but also you may.' She wasn't sure he appreciated the linguistic semantics. No matter.

Without looking up, Tomas said, 'We're being watched. If he comes over, let me do the talking.'

'How do you know?'

'It happens.' Tomas was matter-of-fact. 'Often.'

The stew that appeared was much better and Laure enjoyed it. 'Am I tasting juniper berries?'

Before Tomas could answer, a man approached and stood over them. He was elderly but fresh-faced enough, and quiet-looking. He was dressed almost entirely in grey. It occurred to Laure that grey was particularly useful, not only for camouflage but, in a country where basics were apparently difficult, it was easier to disguise when not spanking clean.

He said something in Czech and Laure recognized the words 'Tomas' and 'Anatomie'. Tomas looked up from his plate. 'Can we talk in English for the sake of my companion here?'

Without missing a beat, the man switched into accented English. 'You are Tomas from Anatomie.' Tomas nodded his head and the man turned to Laure. 'And you must be?'

Tomas introduced Laure and mentioned she was employed by the Kobes. The stranger did no more than glance at Laure but she got the impression that he had absorbed every detail.

'You're very good,' he was saying. 'In fact, I've tried to buy your recordings but they are impossible to get hold of.'

Laure found the accented English extremely sinister.

Tomas sent him what Laure recognized as his professional charming smile, designed to render its target immobile. 'You would be very clever if you did as shops are banned from selling then.'

'That's a shame.' Without fuss, the man sat down. 'I'm Major Hasík.'

The elderly waiter had disappeared, and a space had formed around their table.

'Are you working on some new songs? Apparently, one or two have been performed in France. Am I correct? I'm told and, I may be wrong, that a couple of the lyrics poked fun at this country.'

'Really?' said Tomas.

'Really,' said Major Hasík. 'And perhaps not such a good idea?' He shifted in his seat. 'I gather you like to get out to the countryside. A healthy thing to do. Do you go mushroom hunting? Where I go the woods have been picked clean. I am always anxious to know where there's a good supply.' He searched in his pocket, produced a card and laid it on the table. 'Do please phone me if you ever come across any. It would be so good to know.'

Tomas barely glanced at it. 'Where I live, the phone has been cut off.'

'Shouldn't you get it mended?'

'I'm told it can't be mended.'

Major Hasík stood upright. 'How odd. Why don't you get in touch and I'll see what can be done?' His smile was pleasant and helpful. 'I'm afraid people in this country don't want to work, so they tell you that things can't be fixed. I know someone in communications who can help.'

'Don't bother,' said Tomas. 'I find it more peaceful not using a phone.'

Laure watched his exit. 'How did you know he would speak English?'

'They often do. A tool of the trade.'

They didn't stay long after Major Hasík had gone. Laure handed over what money she had on her, and Tomas made up the difference. 'Sweet, lovely, generous Laure,' he said. 'One day, I'll do the same for you.'

After he had paid, he tucked his hand under her elbow and took her down to the river where they walked along the embankment.

One or two cafes were shutting up shop. The smell of summer water filtered up from the river as Tomas kissed her, resting his hand on her breast. Astonished by the power of her response, she pressed herself against his narrow torso.

She felt... she felt... what? Very gently, Tomas smoothed one of her eyelids with his thumb and murmured something in Czech. Her flesh was on fire and she knew that she had got herself into something which was political and sexual and very complicated – and her heart sang at the idea.

On the way back to the Kobes' apartment, Tomas asked if she had a bank account in England and did it work. It did, she replied and described Brympton's high-street bank flanked by potted geraniums and its women tellers behind the counter who wore white blouses and eye-poppingly bright lipstick.

'Nobody watches you when you go in?'

'Of course not.'

'You could put in money, or take it out, and no one would ask questions?'

'In general, no, it's absolutely private. Why do you want to know?'

'Am I asking too many questions?'

'No.'

He reached for her hand. 'Be wary, sweet Laure. I could be an informer.'

She gave an uneasy laugh. 'I didn't imagine for one second that you were.'

Tomas laughed too. 'You have just demonstrated that you're not a Czech.'

'Or Slovak?

'Slovaks are Slovaks.' He came to a halt. 'Look at me, Laure. What do you see?'

'Someone who ate half my dinner.'

All those months ago, desiring Rob Dance was to be permanently ravenous, but the sensations she experienced then were as nothing to the ones that consumed her now.

Tomas's hands hovered over her shoulders as if *he* couldn't keep his hands off her. 'Do you believe what you see?'

'Must I?' Did she trust her own responses? 'Yes.' She swallowed. 'How old are you, Tomas?'

'Twenty-seven.'

He looked and seemed older.

'You?

'Twenty.'

He smiled and moved closer. She inhaled tobacco and fresh male sweat and her heart leapt and her senses flamed.

It was at the close of an early evening performance when Tomas next turned up at the theatre.

In the interim, Laure had thought about him ceaselessly – which made her impatient with herself as she didn't want to be at the mercy of her feelings. She didn't want to be watching out for Tomas like a lovesick teenager. Or to have every nerve ending stand up whenever he was around. She didn't wish to spend her free time cataloguing every physical characteristic in excruciating detail. Hair, hands, turn of the foot.

Or his mouth which was so expressive and frequently smiling. At her.

Standing in the shadows over by the exit, Laure observed the children's reactions after the yellow curtains had jerked shut. Admittedly, some were taciturn, but most had been set alight by the performance and their excited treble chatter dominated the bustle and noise of the audience's exit.

A hand slipped into hers and she jumped.

'Missed me?'

'Maybe.'

'Only maybe?' His fingers closed tighter over hers. 'That's not so good.'

She wanted to ask where he had been but stopped herself. She was not going to be the needy, begging thing that she had been with Rob Dance.

'I've been out of town,' he said. 'I couldn't leave a message.'

He *had* been thinking of her after all. She swallowed. 'I've been busy too.'

'I want you to meet someone,' he said. 'Can you come?'

'Give me fifteen minutes.'

The marionettes stowed, and the costumes packed up, she joined Tomas at the entrance where he was talking to Lucia. At Laure's approach, Lucia waved a hand at Tomas and moved off.

Laure turned to Tomas. 'Where are we going?'

'To see someone I'm fond of.'

The heat claimed them as Tomas piloted her through the streets towards the old Jewish quarter and stopped at the entrance to a large apartment block on its perimeter. His hand in the small of her back, he guided her inside. 'Don't say anything,' he said. 'I'll explain later.'

Inside the lobby an elderly, black-clad woman sat at a makeshift desk. At Tomas's entrance, her head bobbed up and Laure was aware of a hard gaze directed at them both.

The hand on Laure's back tensed.

'Tomas Josip,' said the woman. The tone was hostile.

Tomas steered Laure towards the staircase. 'Up,' he commanded, overtaking her.

Laure cast a swift look over her shoulder. The woman was now writing in a large ledger.

'Comrade Concierge,' Tomas said in a low voice over his shoulder as he ran up the stairs. 'She rules the street like all the concierges. They are the backbone of the State, feeding in information. They get drunk on information. They spy on their children. But pity the person who drops cigarette ash on one of their staircases. I'm a decadent.' He panted slightly as they hoofed up a third and narrower flight of stairs, up to the top of the building. 'She hates me. The great delight of her life is to report on me. The bugger is, she's incorruptible. Most of them like to be slipped a gift. This one doesn't.'

Laure was fitter than Tomas and caught up with him. 'Don't you wish for better,' she cried, 'than being spied on by old women?'

'Shush,' he turned around and placed a hand over her mouth. 'Shush.'

Obediently, she lowered her voice. '*I* want better for you.'

He balanced precariously on the stair above her. 'I believe you do.'

'I know it's none of my business. But I can still wish you didn't have to bribe everything and everyone.' She looked up at him. 'And you were free to write your songs.'

186

'That's *your* freedom.'

She frowned. 'But not yours.'

'I like the idea. I love the idea. But I live here.'

She said stubbornly, 'It doesn't stop me wanting it for you.'

His face softened. 'Come here.' She hopped up to his step and he pulled her close. And on that narrow wooden staircase, Tomas bent over and kissed her to within an inch of her life.

Would she ever forget? The feel of his mouth on hers? The fight to keep balanced? The staircase spiralling beneath them?

She repeated. 'I won't stop wanting it for you.'

'Don't stop trying,' he said in Laure's ear. 'It's wonderful to be cared for. To have someone care, I mean. I love your stubbornness.' His mouth found the soft place under her ear. 'I love your freshness. Your sweetness. Everything about you, in fact.'

She put up a hand and cradled the back of his head. If it was possible to die of happiness, or emotion, she was dying.

'Come.' He took her hand and led her up the final few stairs to a door that looked a recent addition.

Tomas rapped on it and it opened to reveal a pale vitamin-starved-looking man of forty or so. He beckoned them inside to an attic where there was a tiny passage with a couple of doors leading off it.

The place smelt of illness – a hint of germicide and urine – and was dark and claustrophobic.

'This is my cousin, Pavel,' said Tomas. 'He looks after my great-aunt who we've come to see.'

A rapid conversation in Czech took place and Tomas grew serious. He asked some questions in Czech and drew Laure aside. 'My great-aunt has been taken ill. I didn't know.' He ran a hand through his hair. 'I'm sorry but I'm afraid it would be best if you left. Will you be able to get back on your own?'

She nodded. With obvious relief, Tomas turned back to Pavel.

As she made her way downstairs and past the snooping concierge, Laure reflected on the ironies. She belonged to Tomas in a fundamental way, of that she was sure. Even after such a short acquaintance she was sure. Quite sure.

But she did not belong to his world.

CHAPTER 14

Berlin 1996

*O*N HIS HOTEL ROOM OFF THE ALEXANDERPLATZ, PETR Kobes dressed with his usual care for the evening reception. Suit, pale-blue shirt, silk tie. The tie was from Paris and one of his favourites.

His room was on the fourth floor of one of the newly built hotels which had sprung up since the reunification of East and West Germany. The view from it was of a city landscape pitted with old bombsites and unlovely former communist blocks of flats. One good thing was the number of flourishing trees, now in their winter livery. These, Berliners informed him, were the replacement for those chopped down during the war and its aftermath when it was feared no tree would ever flourish in the city again.

The telephone by his bed rang and he picked it up.

'Just checking up on my old dad,' said a voice.

His daughter, Maria, was calling from Paris.

Petr sat down on the bed. 'Could we have less of the old? Forty-six is still a teenager.'

They spoke in French, rather than Czech, which had become the habit between them. He pictured her, almost certainly fiddling with the ends of her hair, which she had grown long, and almost certainly smoking a French cigarette to which she had taken with gusto.

'Are you all right?' he asked tenderly. 'Enough money?'

Nineteen-year-old Maria was at the Sorbonne to study politics and economics and Petr was conscious that even now, years later, his daughter's grief for her mother ran deep and inconsolable. During the good periods, Eva's spirit embraced them as a containable, even benign, memory. In the bad times, it was as impenetrable and unforgiving as the Golem haunting the streets of old Prague.

'Are you serious, Dad? No one ever has enough money in Paris.' She changed her tone. 'Of course, I'm fine. It's me checking up on you, remember.' There was a pause. 'You know we will be doing communism this term. I'll be ringing you for the inside info.'

At his end of the phone, Petr raised an eyebrow.

'Dad, you do still believe, don't you? Or has it all gone? The ideals, the methods, the benefits?'

The notion that he had spent his life and energy in the service of an ideology which was generally considered to have feet of clay saddened and depressed him. But perhaps that was what courage was all about? Knowing that something might not come good but still being prepared to put your future on the line?

How did his children feel about his life and work? Unsure of their hidden political sympathies, he was careful not to question them in case sides had to be taken. But he did remember, word for word, the letter that his former au pair, Laure, had sent him on her return to England.

'If you give up on the freedom to think, then your being will dissolve drop by drop. But, at least, that won't happen to Tomas, whatever you may have done to him.'

The letter was bitter and unforgiving and always caused him pain whenever he thought about it. Yet, and this always touched him to the quick, the parcel in which she had sent it included a hot-water bottle for Eva. Hot-water bottles were hard to obtain in Czechoslovakia and Eva had been fond of them. He could not quite understand why he acted as he did but, having got the letter out of the clutches of the censors, he destroyed it. But not the hot-water bottle.

'I still believe in its aims,' he replied, with a stab at the fervour which had once propelled his actions. 'These are good and true. I'm a Party man, through and through. But that doesn't mean that the Party should ignore the need for change.'

'Spoken like a diplomat.'

The bargain had been forced on him on his sixteenth birthday, made as he faced the unknown man in a beige mackintosh and a pork-pie hat. Five minutes previously, this stranger had knocked on the door of his parents' rooms in the Malá Strana and asked to speak to Petr Kobes.

'I am he. Your name?'

'It's of no importance.'

Without asking permission, the man placed his briefcase on the table. The briefcase was made of good leather and looked new and Petr eyed it curiously. Not many of those around. The nameless visitor opened it and passed papers over to Petr. 'You need to read and sign these.'

'Why? What's in them?'

The focused gaze from under the pork-pie hat told Petr that it was unwise to ask questions.

'You will be working for us,' was the reply. 'We have been observing you and you are considered the right material. Signing will give your formal permission. We like to have matters documented.'

'But—'

'If I were you, no "but"s.' The stranger's gaze moved around the room that doubled up as kitchen and living space, taking in the empty shelving, the patched lino flooring, the two-ring gas hob, the tin kettle and, eventually, came to rest on the door behind which his ailing mother was sleeping. 'You will be needing to get hold of your mother's medicine in the future.'

Petr still didn't reply.

'I don't expect you would enjoy military service much either,' the stranger added.

Everyone in Czechoslovakia knew that those sorts of statements contained a threat that could last for a lifetime and it was mad to ignore them.

After he had signed, the man produced a package from the briefcase. 'Chocolates for your mother.'

Petr could not remember when he had last seen a box of chocolates, if ever, and they riveted him. This, of course, was their point.

The man nudged the chocolates into the centre of the table where they rested, incongruous in gaudy tinsel ribbon. 'We will continue to observe you,' he said.

He replaced the papers in the briefcase and left as unobtrusively as he had arrived, bearing with him the blueprint for Petr's future.

On cue, the door to his mother's bedroom opened. 'I knew they would come sooner or later.'

A suspicion ignited.

Petr whipped out a chair and eased her down into it. She had been – still was – a beautiful woman but one whose experiences during the Second World War in a Nazi war camp had left her pretty much a physical wreck and her gait was unsteady. He knelt beside her. 'Did you do this?'

She cradled his face in her hands. Since she lost several of her teeth in the camp, she rarely smiled but she permitted herself one at that moment. 'My son.' She allowed the words, pregnant with love and tenderness, to fold him in an embrace. 'This is the best thing for you.'

Somehow – God knew how – she had got hold of some scent and he smelt its faint, violet fragrance on her wrists which he would for ever associate with her. 'How do you know what's best for me?'

He knew his mother. She was, and ever had been since the defeat of Fascism, convinced, that in choosing communist values to guide her life, she was right. 'Communism is the morally acceptable way, the only way. It is the only position capable of achieving goodness.' She released his head but kept a hand on his shoulder. 'I know you so well, Petr. You must keep a watch on your thoughts and desires. If you ever find there's a gap between the Party's commandments and your own wishes, you will be ready to clamp down on them. Consider them as bourgeois weaknesses.'

He thought of the implied threat to her medication. 'They're bullies.'

She skewered him with a ferocious intensity. 'They will look after you.'

Petr knew of old that this was how it would be. A pang went through him – for the relinquishing of something irreplaceable. His freedom to choose. 'It will be at a price, I think.'

She shook her head. 'Not so.'

'You've packed me up into a convenient parcel.'

He anticipated what was coming next. The crippled, twisted legs under her patched skirt (which must have been at least fifteen years old) trembled. 'You must always remember that communism is the absolute opposite of Nazism and you must never doubt it. Only yourself.'

He knew, his father knew and she knew, that the psychological and physical damage she had suffered had not only destroyed her health but left her struggling to think well of human beings.

'Sometimes,' she said of those memories and the consequences, 'I can't fight them. But they won't kill me.' Yet, in a sense, they had.

She registered Petr's disquiet. 'Don't worry.'

So, in that moment, ensnared by his love and an even more powerful pity, he permitted his mother to take away the freedom to make his own choices.

In the cupboard that did duty as his bedroom and smelt of damp rot and the results of his furtive wanking, he spent a sleepless night. At one point, his hand crept towards his crotch but he stopped himself. He needed to exert control, to stifle the flare of rebellion, and to plan. Towards dawn, it occurred to him that his future would never have been any different and it was best to make a virtue of necessity. Knowing his fate, he would be the more powerful, the more effective and, perhaps, the freer for it.

It was his business to believe – and believe he would.

The decision made, he fell asleep.

The State looked after Petr and, in return, he became word perfect in what was required.

The *Státní Bezpecnost*, the StB, trained him in the covert and labyrinthine. These methods were to be put into practice wherever operatives were deployed which could be in industry, in medicine, in politics. Or, even as the lowly shopkeeper.

Keep your mouth shut and never raise you head above the parapet.

Understand the enemy target and learn the details. His vice, her favoured newspaper, his shoe size, her brand of toothpaste.

The chosen were taught how to submerge into the thought process of their targets, to identify their weaknesses and to understand their psycho-dramas. The trick was never to plunge in so deep that sympathy was evoked. *Never think of a weeping housewife ordered to spy on her son as anything but a useful cypher.* Trainees were warned of the dangers of transference.

'Get to know their smell,' said one instructor, a nasty piece of work if ever there was one. 'Where they drink, when they make love, where their children go to school.'

He played them a film, a grainy, flickering set of images, of a young mother being reduced to a wreck because her bicycle tyres were constantly flat. She never knew if it was bad luck or, as was the case, that she was being harassed for having subscribed to a banned newspaper.

'Very simple,' said the bully. '*Very* simple.'

Petr never shared any of this work with his parents. Once or twice, he thought his father might be on the verge of asking questions but his mother, who had a sixth sense, managed to head him off. In that way, his parents remained innocent of the techniques employed for infiltration, monitoring and manipulation of those the authorities targeted. Or the methods required to exfiltrate political dissidents who had escaped to the West, only to be returned home and squeezed dry.

At twenty, he became a junior sales representative for Potio Pharma's Western Europe division, then a senior manager based in Paris, a position which meant he could exploit Czechoslovakia's need for hard foreign currency and, as important, for industrial intelligence at which he became expert at harvesting. Assured of his status, as much as it was possible to be in the current regime, he married Eva and had the children.

He thought of his mother's toothless smile and her unremitting fervour. 'The trouble with your mother,' Eva had once said (it had been a good day) 'is that she feels guilty for surviving the camps. Turning fanatic is her way of dealing with it.' Being older than him, Eva considered herself wiser. She was, too, in some respects. 'If we sacrifice everything we care about for a political system and expect others to do so too,' she warned him, 'then we will become like the Nazis.'

The Velvet Revolution happened in 1989 and the communist regime was disbanded and discredited. His parents were long dead, obstinate in their beliefs to the last. Very soon after that Petr was made CEO of Potio Pharma, in which capacity he was currently in Berlin.

He checked his tie in the mirror and brushed his hair back.

He was always mildly surprised that he didn't look any different.

Mother? Eva? What would you think now of your son and husband, the good Party man, now full-throated capitalist?

Outside the hotel, the cold was intense, and the wind was a devil which fought its way down Petr's collar and percolated through the layers he was wearing.

He ordered the doorman to hail a taxi. Sitting back thankfully in its warmth, he reflected on the fault lines of this newly united city.

The Wall had been hacked to pieces and bits of it were being kept as a souvenir in biscuit tins all over the globe and a divided Germany married itself. *Ossiland* and *Wessiland* were declared man and wife.

A romantic union… but not without problems. Technically, the East German Communist regime was finished but, as Petr well knew from his own country, it wasn't. Like a murdered corpse, it left traces of its DNA all over the place and, as in Prague, there were lingering anger, tension and resentments to deal with.

'There has been no proper analysis,' Petr wrote in his report to the board of Potio Pharma, 'of how the intensity, the anxiety, and the unreality of a dream-come-true could destabilize even the most practical of people and the Germans are very practical.'

He was in Berlin on a reconnaissance designed to test the links between the new Czech Republic and potential trading partners. The reception, to which he had been bidden, was the brainchild of a group of East German industrial barons keen to lure Western businesses to set up factories in the East. Whereupon, with their abundant supply of workers, rock-bottom wages and cheap real estate, they would proceed to happily undercut their Western competitors.

Not everyone approved. 'The East will be the workbench of the West', one bitter ex-party leader had been reported as saying. In return, the *Wessi* would try to milk, or to steal (whichever was the easiest) any intelligence they could lay their hands on about the Russians.

But it was all hands to the deck for the business of re-orchestrating Europe. The cultural attachés, including the British, had cooked up a programme of activities, which were to include a trip to a bakery, a motorcycle factory and tonight's reception. As ever, he reflected with amusement, it was a stew of competing interests and ideologies but he was not complaining.

The taxi slowed in the bunched traffic around Alexanderplatz. From what he could see, the square was rammed with the younger generation of Berliners. Restaurants and buildings blazed with light and naphtha flares ringed the ugly *Fernsehturm*, or TV tower.

Not for the first time, he acknowledged that the all-encompassing grey of the Prague of his upbringing was hefted into his psyche. Even though he knew Western Europe reasonably well, and liked to think he understood how it worked, the prodigality of its lighting bothered him.

A hefty percentage of the punters in the square were drunk or drugged. Mostly in a good-natured way but, as he well knew, some of these people would be poor, and if they were *Ossis,* possibly resentful and, perhaps, disapproving of the *Wessis'* affluence, which made them dangerous.

Beer and sausage booths were doing a roaring trade. A group of singers with electric guitars belted out torch songs. They were having trouble with the power supply and the accompaniment was intermittent. No one seemed bothered. The new order had arrived and they were going at it with music and booze.

When the history was written, it would be revealed how each side had spent a percentage of the national budget on people and machines with the aim of outwitting the other – and, in the GDR, the Stasi developed into the most efficient surveillance organization ever known.

During the last days of the GDR, the Stasi tried to destroy their mountains of files and paperwork recording the decades of surveillance. The joke ran that for the most efficient surveillance system in the world, they hadn't been very efficient. Left behind was a paper mountain, from which rose (as Petr well knew) a miasma of spite, vengeance and repression.

In the new democratic dawn, these had to be investigated and teams of 'Puzzle Women' patrolled long tables on which were arranged thousands and thousands of paper fragments from which they were bidden to construct a new story of Germany from the old ones.

My wife thinks bourgeois thoughts.

I suspect my neighbour of listening to forbidden broadcasts on enemy radio.

Citizen B met a known dissident in Jüdenstrasse.

State snooping, and its findings, was pretty much the same in any country.

The reception was being held on the first floor of a concrete office building in a street close to the site of the former American Chancery in the Mitte district. The heating had been turned up to tropical levels, which resulted in thirsty guests doggedly getting drunk. The room was too large for the number of guests and devoid of comfort. Except for a couple of framed photos of combine harvesters in fields of suspiciously gold corn, the walls were bare. Marooned on the swirly patterned carpet were small groups who did not give an impression that they were enjoying themselves.

Petr was given a guest list but, before he could acquaint himself with its contents, he was waylaid.

'Hallo.' A tall, rangy woman in a navy-blue dress with white trimming who he took to be an embassy wife accosted Petr with the confidence of the English landed classes. 'I'm Sonia.'

'Petr Kobes.'

'Not German, I think.'

'Czech.'

Her expression radiated good humour and drunkenness. 'English. And I was just wondering if I had transgressed very much in a previous life to find myself in this building which is beyond depressing.' She lowered her tone. 'Do you think there are ex-Stasi here?'

'Without a doubt,' he replied, attempting to calculate if the disingenuousness was genuine or not.

'Someone told my husband that when the Stasi headquarters were taken over, they found an international supermarket stuffed with goodies. And those terrible files on everyone, of course. Plus, a whole floor furnished with the most expensive furniture.'

'Yes, I heard that too.' Petr managed to glance down at the list in his hand and nearly dropped it. A name had leapt up at him.

An unusual combination of French Christian name and English surname. *Laure Carlyle.*

He prided himself that he was a man who knew how to control his emotions but, at this moment, he could barely speak. 'Would you excuse me?'

Sonia shrugged. 'I've frightened you. Well, good luck with Berlin. It's… it's not Paris.' She peered closer at him. 'Oh dear, you look shell-shocked.'

He did not reply because he was literally not capable.

CHAPTER 15

*T*HERE SHE WAS, ONLY A FEW FEET AWAY.

Even though a decade had passed, it was hard to put into words what had happened to him then. Or describe what had taken place in his heart and mind.

By his reckoning, she would now be thirty or so and that seemed from his vantage point at the other end of the room to be about right. Her hair was the same chestnut flecked with auburn but cut differently and she was thinner. It was her skin, luminous and almost transparent, which give him the final clue. That had not changed.

Engrossed in conversation with an old ex-Stasi bully, she had not noticed him and, light-headed and alarmingly? stupidly? elated, he allowed himself a few extra seconds to gaze on her.

The hand holding his glass felt unsteady and, to give himself a breathing space, he turned away.

Mistake: one of the British diplomats pounced. By now, Petr's English was fluent and, tiresome though it was, he engaged in the social fray.

'It must be fascinating to be here to witness the new Germany taking shape.'

Either the diplomat was an unhappy man or he did not

understand his profession. There was a marked hesitation before he replied: 'yes and no'.

Wrong man and wrong job, thought Petr, a predicament for which he had little sympathy.

He could not prevent himself looking past the diplomat's shoulder to where Laure was. 'Adjustment is always the challenge,' he offered.

'A shambles if you want my opinion,' was the reply.

'Isn't "shambles" a little strong?' Petr said. 'The East Germans are being practical. Trade and manufacture stand a better chance of making things work than governments.'

The diplomat stared down at his glass. 'Barking, half of them. The party die-hards suffer from *Mauer im Kopf*. You know... the Wall in the Head.'

Detaching himself from the disaffected diplomat, he began a slow, but inevitable, progress towards Laure, the magnetic pole to which he was drawn.

A stocky man in a dark, formal suit with swept-back fair hair touched her on the elbow and drew her aside. Public school? Oxbridge? Almost certainly doctrinaire about the freedoms enjoyed by the West? They conferred in low voices. Glancing up, she caught sight of Petr and, for a fraction of a second, her eyes widened.

What would she see? Obviously, not the thirty-six-year-old husband and father of two young children of a decade ago. He was aware that middle age was slackening his features, bulking his waistline and greying his hair at the temples. Anxiety and the tricky business of keeping on top of political changes must also have taken a toll.

The slight stiffening of Laure's shoulders at his approach told him that she had been waiting. She broke off her conversation. 'Petr. A long time.' She swung into action. 'David, this Petr Kobes who used to be my boss in Prague. Petr, this David Brotton who is currently my boss at the British Embassy.' Her lips twitched. 'Bosses, meet each other.'

Close to, Petr saw that she had become truly beautiful. The younger Laure had been fresh, tousled and bohemian and wore ill-advised low-cut tops and tight jeans. Now, thinner and with shadows in her eyes, she had been completed and was something else. More mysterious, less open. He glanced down at her left hand. No ring.

David Brotton, the boss, was clearly experienced at this sort of encounter. He proffered a clean, square hand. 'How do you do?' He glanced at Laure. 'What sort of boss?'

'I was an au pair for Petr and his family. We lived in Paris and in Prague,' replied Laure.

More likely than not, this was information with which David Brotton was already familiar. All three of them in this conversation knew that Laure's history would have been turned inside out and hung out to dry before she obtained work in anything like a British Embassy.

'And very welcome she was, too. She was a life-saver when my wife became ill and ended up staying to help us much longer than we had originally agreed.'

He kept his gaze steady. The odds were that Laure and Brotton were both spooks, or on the edge of that world. The British MI6, and most other countries, embedded spies in the embassies.

'She's a life-saver here too,' said David Brotton gallantly. 'The best cultural attaché I've ever had.'

A couple of girls were circulating with trays of drinks. They were dressed in tight black dresses and frilly aprons and were being masterminded by a man in a shiny suit. Laure accepted a drink from one of them. 'Those dresses look uncomfortable,' she said.

'I think our hosts wanted their Western guests to feel at home.'

David Brotton laughed. 'And we do.' He glanced at them both. 'If you'll excuse me.'

Left alone, Petr and Laure took their time to begin. Eventually, she drank a mouthful of the passable gin and tonic and said, '*Bonjour*, Petr.'

'"The best cultural attaché I've ever had"?'

'You wouldn't believe,' she said, composed and professional, only her eyes betraying any emotion.

As ever, they spoke in French.

'What are you doing in Berlin?'

'I'm here at the invitation of my friend Herman Ludz. He is working for a big pharma firm in which I have an interest.'

Laure glanced in the direction of a chunky balding man, wearing a purple tie, surrounded by acolytes. 'Ex-Stasi,' she said. 'But you'll know that.' She allowed a second to elapse. 'I wouldn't expect anything other.'

'We all have histories,' he replied.

She acknowledged the point with a nod. 'Isn't it odd how history is not concerned with justice? Many of the ex-Stasi have got themselves very good jobs. Marketing. Insurance.'

'Is that so very odd? Those jobs need organized people. And administrators. Who else? They're lucky to have a trained cadre to step in.'

'You always were a practical person.' She sounded very dry.

'Should I take that as a compliment?'

'Take it how you wish but I expect it's how you manage to live with yourself.'

He had not expected a direct challenge, or the underlying aggression, quite so soon. 'I expect it is.'

Laure appeared to recollect her manners. 'And Eva? And the children?'

'Eva's dead.'

He could never say it easily. Contained in the words were guilt and rage for the marriage which had promised so much. Suddenly, he felt he could not bear to be in this room, at this reception. Or, at this point in his life.

'Dead...?' Shock made her stutter.

'Soon after you went back home.'

The cool manner cracked. 'My God, the poor children. I'm so sorry. So sorry.'

He had schooled himself to be matter-of-fact. 'The children suffered. Of course. But they're grown now. Jan is training to be a lawyer in Prague and Maria is at university in Paris.'

'Do you have a photo?'

Petr took his wallet out of his pocket and flipped it open to show a photo of his son and daughter.

'Curious isn't it? At one time, I was familiar with their every breath. Now, I wouldn't recognize them. But they are good-looking.' She touched their faces with a fingertip. 'Are you living in Berlin?'

There it was: the innocent, polite question which was almost certainly being asked all over the room. The technique was to release just so much information and nothing more. 'I'm here on business. Then back to Prague.'

Ploughing grimly on with her job, the waitress with the reddest lipstick and lowest neckline nudged Petr's elbow with a tray of drinks. Laure declined but Petr helped himself to a fresh one.

'It's a coincidence that we've met.' He was wrong. There had been an inevitability about meeting Laure. There had to be. 'Perhaps we could have a drink?'

She was now in possession of herself. 'What on earth would make you think that I wish to see you?'

'The past.'

'No.'

Flat. Non-negotiable. 'I was… fond of you, Laure. It was, as you must admit, an impossible situation.'

'Whatever you may think, there's nothing to connect us any longer.'

'But there is,' he said.

He had caught her off guard and, for a second, there was a glimpse of the young Laure who had enchanted him. 'There isn't, Petr. But I will grieve for Eva. She did not have it easy and I'm glad to know the children are thriving.'

He searched the beautiful but, as he now saw, haunted face, and regretted the loss of its openness. 'It *is* the past.'

'It will *never* be the past,' she replied with a ferocity that took him aback.

'So, no forgiveness for either of us?'

Laure pulled herself back into her embassy persona. 'Does forgiveness matter? It would make it easier for you perhaps. As for me, a psychotherapist or a priest would advise me that to forgive is the best thing for mental health. Let alone the spirit.' She looked away. 'For all sorts of reasons, I had a go at it. But I can't.'

'You could try again,' he suggested gently.

There were shadows at the back of her eyes. 'No.'

'Does that mean you cannot forgive yourself?'

'That's a false assumption.'

He spread out his hands in a gesture intended to convey: *I don't agree.*

She gestured to the now thinning numbers of guests. 'David is signalling that my lot should go. Meanwhile, by the look of it your side are partying hard. They look hungry for deals and new business.'

'They are hungry. The West does not hold a monopoly on ideas or energy.'

'No.' She smoothed the sleeve of her blouse and a flash of emotion escaped. 'I always think... I can't help thinking that, if I had met Tomas three years later, it would have been all right.' She blinked. 'It would have been all right.'

'Do you know what happened to him?'

Her gaze slid past his shoulder. 'You know I don't.'

He took his card from his wallet and held it out. 'We could try to find out.'

It was a deliberate, and cruel, challenge and she gasped audibly. '*What* did you say?'

He repeated it, watching the expression in her eyes – the colour of which she had once, dancing around the apartment with Maria, referred to jokingly as 'gooseberry'.

'Why would you help?'

'Because—'

She cut him off. 'There's nothing you could tell me, Petr, that I don't know. I was employed by you, I loved Tomas, there was trouble, and I left to come home. That's all. I now have my work here and I'm concentrating on that.'

It was a good story and he was almost fooled. Neither too provocative, nor too boring but neutral.

As he knew she would, she accepted the card. 'Chief Executive,

Potio Pharmaceuticals.' An eyebrow flew up. 'You've turned capitalist.'

She meant: Aren't you still working for the Státní Bezpecnost?

'If you phone that number, the message will get to me.'

The late evening was murderously cold. He buried his gloved hands in his overcoat pockets and headed eastwards towards his hotel.

Always, he liked to walk. A city's topography provided clues to its inner life but the first thing he had noticed about the former eastern sector was the sickening smell, a mix of Trabant fuel and the cheap brown coal, which the *Ossis* had to put up with. Compared to here, Prague was positively fragrant. Where his grandparents had lived near the Letná Plain, for instance, it was still possible to smell moist earth on the spring winds and to sniff the forsythias flowering on the Strahov. There were other things too which he loved: the noisy gulls on the Jirasek Bridge, the rush of water under the bridges…

He smiled at the thought of them.

North of him, in the distance, was the Tränenpalast, nicknamed the Hall of Tears, a checkpoint where Germans on the opposite side of the divide had been forced to say goodbye to each other.

Tears. Desperation. Recklessness. People in disguise, forged papers…

Perhaps Berlin would never eradicate the Wall from its consciousness? Perhaps it would always be dominated by the psychosis induced by the division? Interestingly, some of the buildings that he was walking past were pock-marked with bullet holes from the Second World War and the murk cloaked the bombsites still awaiting renovation. In his heightened emotional state, he imagined that they exuded a spectral legacy of persecution and warfare which offered an additional perspective. Berlin and its history were a lot older than the Wall.

He halted to take his bearings. West Berlin had lighting but, in the part of the eastern sector where he was now walking, public lighting was intermittent and he was not absolutely sure of his route.

Unwise as it was to be walking in the dark unaccompanied, he relished the freedom. Life without surveillance was a luxury. (Had he ever imagined that he would feel like that?) If the Germans and British *were* keeping an eye on him, it was more likely to be for business reasons, not political ones and hardly at this hour.

Three-quarters of the way down the Unter den Linden he walked into a cafe. It was warm and clean, with touches of chrome and a tiled bar and a pretty waitress. Installed at a window seat, he ordered coffee and a ham and cheese sandwich and helped himself to a newspaper from the rack.

In the bright, new shiny world his reading habits were no longer scrutinized, nor were his jokes or his choice of clothing for he had been under no illusion that, in the contradictory, tortured, absurd universe of the Czech Communist regime, even a Party man did not escape surveillance.

He ordered a second coffee and drank it, reflecting on the surprise that the evening had yielded and reprising what happened in the past.

Anyway, now he was calmer, he could assess himself better.

Outside, an elderly woman with bunioned feet and cracked leather shoes shuffled past. *Ossi* or *Wessi?* She looked old enough to have lived through not only the communist era but Hitler's as well.

How might the conversation be going between Laure and her boss back in the British Embassy building in the Unter den Linden?

There would be the report on him, and others like him. These would be analysed. From what he heard, several British MPs had been approached by the StB not so long ago. The British being wary, the approach had yielded nothing of any note, apart from a remarkably detailed intelligence report, put together by the British, on the Czech industrial sector. This had been smuggled back to Prague and people at Petr's level got to read it. Unsurprisingly, it featured him.

'Potio Pharma. CEO Petr Kobes...' Here someone had noted in the margin, 'A survivor as a surprising number of those old commies have proved to be'.

Potio Pharma. Established post the so-called Prague Spring in 1968. Pharmaceutical in origin. Since the Velvet Revolution in December 1989, has been diversifying into bio-technology. Headquarters in Prague. Emerged viable after the communist regime although there were several problems with levels of pollution that threatened the purity of their products. They have always displayed a hard export drive and maintained a team of salesmen who were probably engaged in industrial espionage as well.

Since the regime change, they have bought up smaller companies and, currently, are one of the top five Czech pharma companies. They have taken to the capitalist mode with vim and vigour but try to disguise it...

Evidently, the writer of the report had a sense of humour.
Objectives:

- *Regulation of the distribution of pharmaceuticals with limited margins*
- *Regulation on distribution*
- *Return on R&D investment*
- *Proliferation of licensing and co-marketing agreements'*

The marginalia displayed less restraint. 'i.e. Keep socialist in flavour and rake in profits by other means. Cake and eating thereof.'

It was odd reading about his company from another point of view. Odd, but educational and he appreciated the Oxbridge turn of phrase.

The report continued. *No link has been established between Potio Pharma and the Russian poison factory (established by Joseph Stalin) or the manufacture of chemical weapons, including nerve agents and other substances listed in the recent Chemical Weapons Convention (CWC), although this cannot be definitively proved.*

Past history suggests Kobes was engaged in industrial espionage for StB searching for information on research and techniques which the then current regime lacked and was desperate to obtain. It is possible that he was involved in the exfiltration of a dissident who was living in Marseilles in 1984. It is thought that Kobes was the instigator and money man. This has not been proved.

Bloody fuckers, he thought, on reading the above. But what surprised him was the level of personal detail. *Inside* detail. Someone had fed it in.

A widower, he is deemed to be a family man with a notable affection for his children. He is known to enjoy the benefits of Western Europe and takes care to dress well.

Now, he had met Laure again, and the more he thought about it the more convinced he was that she was working for the British in an intelligence capacity, however minor. He wondered if she had been tapped for the information.

If Laure had contributed, he knew she would have viewed it as a revenge.

A long shot, but it suggested that a link between her and him still existed.

The idea hurt and excited him in equal measure.

CHAPTER 16

*T*HE FIRST OF THE MAJOR MEETINGS FOR WHICH HE WAS IN Berlin was scheduled for the Wednesday morning.

All parties anticipated it being a taxing one. However, Petr's presence as Potio Pharma's CEO, rather than a junior board member, helped to smooth negotiations. By late afternoon, the blueprint for a joint research and development had been hammered out, to be handled equally by Berlin and Prague.

Thursday's meeting with a rival pharmacological company was less successful. Something in the air – a mood music – muddled intentions. In the good old days in Czechoslovakia what the bosses ordered happened. Not any longer, and he was aware he had not eradicated the expectation from his manner. Midway through the negotiations, it occurred to him that his own past, such of it as was known, almost certainly accounted for the faint hostile undercurrent.

He took a gamble and suggested that the meeting was terminated. 'I hope, gentlemen, that we can all look to the future and not to the past which was a different place.'

The slight relief on the faces of his West German counterparts told him that his assumptions were probably correct. Descending to the lobby with Eduard, his assistant who had joined him from

Prague, he reflected ruefully that, in the new thrusting Berlin, an old commie still had the stink of a corpse about him.

'Is there something worrying you?' asked Eduard.

'Should there be?'

'Only you hate unfinished business and it's not like you not to fight harder.'

It hadn't taken long for Laure to crack. A message was waiting for him in reception. It was from her. 'I'm taking a group to see a recently discovered tunnel. Will you join us?'

There it was. The rope from the past coiled around them both.

He looked up at Eduard. 'An invitation from the British Embassy. Part of a cultural programme to make us love each other. Here's your chance to see a tunnel dug by escapees.'

Eduard was puzzled. 'Why would we be interested in a tunnel? Hardly tactful, is it?'

Petr explained, 'Did you ever hear of Anatomie? A dissident rock group. Their hit song was "Tunnelling" and my contact in the embassy is probably having a joke.'

Too young to remember much before 1986 when Anatomie was barnstorming around Czechoslovakia, and still at the stage when he was unsure of how to assess the immediate past, Eduard looked baffled. 'If you don't mind, I'll head for the nearest bar.'

A little later the taxi dropped Petr in Oderberger Strasse, close to the entrance of Mauerpark which had marked the former boundary between East and West. It was a rundown, seedy area with graffiti scrawled over the buildings and dismal street lighting.

Laure was waiting for them flanked by several women, plus a tall, square-faced man in a Loden coat and a baseball hat. The women were Embassy wives and the man was their German guide.

It was bitter weather made worse by the wind, and the group had dressed for the cold in heavy overcoats and hats. Petr judged that Laure's serviceable grey coat had been chosen to suggest a lowly embassy status which may, or may not have been, near the mark. He had not made up his mind on that point. With it she wore a black beret (which looked French) pulled down over her ears. Apart from a polite greeting, she paid no special attention to Petr. As they moved around, he observed her masterminding the group with a calm, assured competence, a definitive marker between the older Laure and the younger one.

The group was led into an anti-tank defence building which, explained their guide, had been abandoned after the end of the war. 'This made it a perfect place to dig.' He shepherded them over to an opening in the concrete floor. Here a shaft had been driven into the earth and reinforced with crude wooden posts. 'It was discovered some weeks ago when engineers working on new underground water storage systems cut across it. It's known as Tunnel 15 as, it has been established, fifteen people managed to get out through it before it was shut down.'

The shaft was approximately five metres deep. Dutifully, the group peered down into it. Petr glanced around at the rapt faces. Did he sense a superiority in the attitude of the British clustered around the shaft? An inner monologue that ran along the lines: we would never allow a society where people felt they had to dig to escape?

But what, he reflected grimly, did the class-ridden British know?

He went to stand beside Laure. She shot him a look that told him nothing.

Their guide continued, 'Tunnel 15 runs for about eighty metres and comes up in a disused outside lavatory behind a block of flats. There are several stories about the escapers, some of them fanciful.

It's estimated that many more people planned to go through, but they were betrayed. The shaft in the East was sealed off by the authorities.'

The British women murmured among themselves.

'As you know, the authorities built the Wall between East and West Berlin in 1961, which ended up approximately a hundred miles long. This tunnel was begun in 1964 when the attempts to tunnel were at their peak. It is unusual in that it was dug from West to East, not the other way around.'

Foetid air with no life in it seeped up from underground.

'Cold War tunnels have a special place in Berlin's history,' said the guide who did not look especially poetic or empathetic. 'They're symbols of survival and a willingness not to give up.'

Petr dug his hands into his coat pockets. For a communist, ex or otherwise, the subject was uncomfortable. For the nth time, he reflected on history's contortions. 'Not so long ago it was the Third Reich who was the oppressor,' he said into Laure's ear.

'Communist, fascist… same difference,' she whispered back.

The guide asked them to gather around. 'There are several things to remember if you are planning on digging a clandestine tunnel under a wall…' Something approximating humour was discernible on the broad features. 'First, once you have hit the water table stop digging downwards and go forwards instead. Two, operate with a password system otherwise you won't know if the group has been penetrated. Three, a screwdriver will melt if it touches the electric grid. Four, to stop guards becoming suspicious it is necessary to live on the site. Five, if you are going to dig, it's best to choose a nice, light sandy soil like we have in Berlin.'

Petr glanced around. At 3.6 metres, the height of the Wall may have obscured some comings and goings, but Stasi guards would have been mounted in the buildings and the watchtowers. Digging and constructing a tunnel would have taken nerves of the first order – and probably an engineer.

Normally, he refused to put himself into others' shoes as it weakened resolve. But now he could not help thinking what a fearful, dangerous business it must have been. An undertaking that would rip nerves to shreds. He glanced at Laure. She looked appalled, as if she couldn't begin to imagine what it took to drive someone to escape through a crumbling shaft.

He shifted up to stand beside her. 'It's always worse thinking about it than doing it,' he said.

'It's a thought to cling onto,' she replied, with barely disguised bitterness.

The guide continued: 'We gather that the group who dug this tunnel lived on site for over five months, sleeping here in week-long shifts, using buckets of water to keep themselves clean. It was a heroic achievement. Although they had no idea where they were going to emerge, they kept on digging.' He paused for effect. 'Luck was on their side and they found themselves in a disused lavatory behind an apartment building.'

Petr could imagine. Stench worse than dead bodies. Filth.

He pointed to the shaft. 'When the escapees came over, an electric winch was used to haul them up. We've put down a ladder. It's been secured but, if you wish to go down, it's at your own risk.'

The group took turns with the embassy wives going first. One or two found the ladder tricky. They returned to the surface looking both shell-shocked and in the grip of an excitement that they tried to tamp down. Laure and Petr went last.

'The rule was absolute silence whilst either digging or escaping,' said their guide, warming to his subject. 'Voices carry from underground. And, of course, there was no question of using explosives to make the work progress quicker.'

The descent was tricky and, with each step down, the air grew more rank. Petr went first and held out his hand to help Laure down the final rungs but she refused it. To access the tunnel proper, it would be necessary to drop down flat and to edge forward on the stomach, which was not advised as water had pooled on the beaten earth floor.

'Anatomie's hit "Tunnelling", said Petr. 'I think it was banned.'

She did not blink. 'You know it was.'

'Whose song was it?'

She took a while to reply. 'Tomas's.'

A couple of electric lights had been rigged up, which had been switched on. Petr crouched down and peered along the long and dark stretch. It did not look big enough even for a slim person to force themselves through but, in flight, people achieved the impossible.

'They build their tunnels in underground cities to outwit the winter,' went the lyric of the song.

If he remembered correctly.

Hot air flowed over his face, smelling of decay from hidden miasmic rot. It was all he could do not to retch.

Laure hunkered down beside him. She took one breath and clapped her hand to her nose. 'Oh God, to think of them nose to tail...' her voice was muffled. 'Probably terrified. Pushed on by adrenaline. The guide says that a baby was brought through.'

He swallowed the saliva swilling around his mouth. 'Not sure I could have done it.'

'You didn't have to.'

She wasn't being malicious, merely matter-of-fact, but the

218

remark caught him on the raw. 'Is that why you got me here? To make the point? Or to punish me?'

They were almost pressed together. He could feel her warmth and smell her floral scent. History and politics made for hard taskmasters – something which he had always known – but it had never been brought home so cruelly that their divisions deformed love and compassion. And, almost certainly, understanding.

They also made yearning for someone on the other side a sharp and thankless experience.

They stood up. Laure pushed back her beret. 'You say you couldn't have done what these people did here. No, nor could I. But he did. In his way. And thousands like him. I want you to think of him. I want you to understand something of what he went through. Before…' She didn't finish the sentence.

He didn't have to ask who she meant.

She tapped the side of the earth shaft. 'At least those who came here got away. They beat the system.'

Her lipstick was a beigey-mink colour which made her mouth look achingly young and tender. Even in the murky light. The way her top lip moved when she spoke and the strand of hair reminiscent of a silk skein escaping from under the beret was shamefully mesmerizing.

He brushed soil from his sleeve. 'When it worked the system was good.'

She gave a short laugh.

'I believed society would be better for what we did.'

That was true. For many years, it was true.

'I accept that,' she replied. 'I also see it's impossible to apologize when it goes wrong.'

The guide's voice echoed down to them from the lip of the shaft.

'The tunnel is two feet high and three feet wide. It had one luxury. The tunnellers had managed to string up electric lights so you weren't forced to crawl in darkness. One escapee did get stuck and had to be pulled free.'

Beside him, Laure gave an intake of breath. 'Even the air seems desperate,' she murmured. 'At least, some made it.'

'You think of him a lot.' It wasn't a question.

'Not all the time, but yes.' She paused. 'Less, as time goes on. Of course. But he's never not there.'

Their guide continued. 'You could bring nothing. Only your papers and the clothes you stood up in.'

'He's part of my life, Petr, whether I like it or not.'

Her eyes seemed to bore into him.

Back on the surface, the wind hit them. 'Why did you invite me?' he asked.

'Because I wanted you to see what you never saw.'

Astonished, he stared at her. 'You think I don't know?'

'No,' she replied. 'I don't think you do.'

It was all he could do not to grab her by the arm. 'During the war my mother was thrown into a Nazi camp where her mother, my grandmother, was beaten to death. She told me about it. All the details. She made me promise to spend my life contributing to the general good. I agreed because I agreed with the aim and I've tried to do that.'

She was incredulous. 'Communism! After everything that happened.'

He shrugged. 'No one knows how things will turn out. Not even you, Laure.'

Her voice softened. 'Are you admitting that it went wrong and communism and fascism have things in common?'

220

He didn't answer.

'I'm sorry about your mother. And your grandmother.' She turned her face out of the wind. 'Let me see. Is it the profound feeling of brotherhood that says that you must spy on everyone from morning to night? Or the upholding of equality that says only Party officials have telephones that work and get to shop in the Tuzex stores where Joe Public is banned? Or is it the fervour with which the workers perform even the most menial tasks because they believe in the general good. Or is it that they're frightened witless?'

She was speaking so softly that only Petr could hear.

The guide was in full flow. 'The story goes that, of the fifteen people who got through, five were from the same family, the Webers. The Stasi were clever in working out who were engaged in anti-Party behaviour.' He paused for effect. 'For instance, listening to, or watching, the BBC was forbidden. Of course, they couldn't patrol the airwaves so officials would visit kindergartens and ask the children to draw their favourite television character. Little Joel Weber was anxious to obey and drew a beautiful picture of the BBC's Bill and Ben, the Flowerpot Men. That was that. The family had only had a few hours to get out. The story goes that when Grandmother Weber arrived there was concern she was too stout to get through until she revealed that she had wrapped her cat up in a bag and tied it around her middle. But get through she did, dragging the cat behind her.'

Laure asked Petr, 'Does it ever worry you that you've survived, and very well, and others did not?'

He bent down and picked up a stone. Rounded and very dark in colour, its hunched shape was reminiscent of a beetle. Flipping it from one hand to another, he said. 'You have to be careful, Laure, about these things. Don't go blundering in.'

The guide rounded off the session. He waved his arm in the

direction of the building. 'After the discovery of this tunnel and others, it became increasingly dangerous to build tunnels and dissidents trying to get out resorted to alternative methods. Some made it to Prague and got out that way. Others to Budapest.'

He felt, rather than heard, the name on Laure's lips. *Tomas.*

Tomas could be added to the phantoms who lived with them: the eternal dissident, the eternal escapee. If he had been an East Berliner, Petr had no doubts that Tomas would have crawled along a rank and narrow tunnel, with earth clogging his nostrils. As a Czech, he had had to choose other methods.

The group were thanking the guide and Petr took the opportunity to tell Laure, 'I'm leaving at the weekend.'

'Which day?'

'Sunday afternoon.'

She was adjusting her beret, pulling it down over her ears against the wind, and he wondered if she had heard him. 'I'll drop you at your hotel in the car.'

He pressed the stone that he had picked up into her hand. 'Have this as a souvenir.'

The car was one of the embassy fleet, a bonus which he noted with satisfaction as they were more comfortable than most. Their driver seemed a solid, dependable type – but you never knew – with a short back and sides and expensive-looking driving gloves.

He drove them back close to the former East–West crossing point at Friedrichstrasse station and down towards Unter den Linden. There were cranes, delivery lorries, stacked piles of building materials, the glitter of large department store windows and, every now and again, the vista of a derelict building awaiting its restoration.

She watched him absorb this cityscape renaissance. '*Did* you ever lose the faith, Petr?'

The question rubbed him up the wrong way. 'Are you gloating? But yes, I've had to change my mind because everything else has changed.' He sent her a wintry smile.

'At least you now have a choice as to what you believe.'

He recollected his mother who, in effect, had had no choices at all.

He wondered how much French the driver understood. 'Capitalism is no feather bed. It's inefficient and muddled and just as corrupt. Our system, my system, thought about people first. Yours thinks about money first.'

The car cruised alongside a major building site over which could be seen a forest of scaffolding.

'Capitalism doesn't rely on state repression,' she said. 'It puts its faith in a free press and an unbiased judiciary.'

Petr was determined to keep things on an even keel. He said lightly: 'If you say so.'

The traffic had thickened and the car ground to a halt more than once. He craved a cigarette but refrained.

Laure asked if he had found the visits useful, adding, 'Western companies are still probably suspicious of you.'

He leant back against the comfortable upholstery. 'They should be. We will undercut them in drug production and those sourcing drugs for the West will be quick to take advantage.'

'You're a capitalist at heart.' The minky-coloured lipsticked mouth issued the tease.

To his shame, he felt almost boneless with desire at the sight and looked away. 'You like your joke.'

There was a long pause.

She made a noise in the back of her throat which he interpreted as disgust. 'You were a spy for the StB under the cover of working for Potio Pharma. I didn't know that at the time.' She looked at him. 'I do now.'

He touched her arm. 'Laure, be careful with your accusations. They could get you into bad trouble.' At his touch, she froze. 'The StB was a plain-clothes secret police force. Not a spying outfit. Check your facts.'

She shook him off and her French grew more rapid and he wondered if it was to prevent the driver understanding. 'You know – *we* all know now – it was also an intelligence and counter-intelligence agency dealing with any activity which was considered anti-state or thought to be influenced by the West. You may have been working for Potio Pharma but you also worked for StB.'

She opened her handbag and produced a paper. Unfolding it, she laid it on his knee, making sure that the initial logo for StB's masquerade company at the top of the page, which only he and his colleagues would know, was visible.

He felt himself go pale. Glancing at the driver, he said, 'Put that away.'

'If you answer this question. Is that your signature at the bottom?'

The driver dropped his speed and turned east into Unter den Linden.

Petr stared ahead. 'Where did you get hold of that?' He didn't expect the answer and ran over the possibilities of who might be responsible – the careless or the traitorous. There were plenty of both operating in the relevant departments. 'Was it Brotton?'

'You don't expect me to answer, do you?' Laure replaced the document in her bag. 'There is further documentation that alleges you had direct links to a unit in the StB known to have used drugs and torture to obtain confessions.'

'I know why you're doing this, Laure.'

'Then we agree on one thing.'

'Be careful what you wish for? Isn't that another saying in your country?'

A single snowflake floated across the car window, followed by a second.

'What happened to Tomas?'

Now, Petr understood. She wanted to obtain the information out of him on her terms.

When he did not reply, she added, 'You owe me, Petr.' She shaded her eyes. 'Does it make it better if I say that it's torture not knowing… does my weakness appeal to your better nature? It should.'

'If that's blackmail it doesn't work, Laure.'

She didn't deny it. Her lips tightened. 'You can find out, I know you can. You have so many contacts. Old scores. Old paybacks that you can call in.'

His hand rested on the armrest, testing its padded luxury under his fingertips. 'Tomas never goes away.'

'No, he doesn't,' said Laure. 'And won't. And certainly not while we know each other.'

What had happened to them in the past was too difficult to admit friendship. All the same, Petr had an idea that, on a certain level, Laure was pleased to see him.

He sighed. 'He was arrested, but you know that. It wasn't the first time, so it would be bad for him. That's the sum of my knowledge. It was as it was. People vanished. All the time, Laure. You saw it.'

'But you had a vested interest and would have made it your business to find out.'

He swore under his breath in Czech. 'Suit yourself.'

'You owe me,' she repeated stubbornly.

225

'Perhaps I do. But maybe you owe me, Laure. Did you ever consider that?'

Astonished, she turned back from her contemplation of the famous boulevard which the now falling snow was dusting with a cold beauty. 'I hope you know what it's like to feel almost mad with anguish knowing that someone you love is incarcerated.' She said simply.

'I do know,' he replied. 'Incarceration comes in many forms.'

'Oh, please,' she said.

They sat in silence for the rest of the journey.

The driver nosed the car into the drop-off point of the hotel. Petr leant forward and placed his hand on the door handle. 'I leave you with this thought. *You* put me in an untenable position. No regime looks kindly on defectors, let alone a regime that had Russia's hands around its neck. I was known to be employing someone consorting with dissidents. I was at risk of bringing down my family. They would have killed us. Some of us. One of us.'

'Yet, you would allow them to take Tomas.'

'Dog eat dog. Isn't that a saying in your country?'

With a quick movement, she turned away and he saw that there were tears rolling down her cheeks. '*If* Tomas is dead, I want him to have a grave. I want everyone to know that he loved freedom and was imprisoned and murdered for saying so.'

CHAPTER 17

Prague, 1986

*T*HE HEAT CONTINUED AND IN THE LAUNDRY ROOM AT THE Kobes' apartment, the stack of clean clothes mounted. There was so much of it that Laure was forced to allocate an hour or so a day on the ironing.

She didn't give a toss. Ironing was mindless. It gave her time and space to think and to brood over her meetings with Tomas: what he said, what he *did*.

She felt for him in her pounding heart. In her sleeplessness. She felt for him in her shaky legs and aching arms. The fever in her groin.

What was he thinking? And: was he thinking of her?

She tried to memorize the lyrics which he was setting to the melody he had played to her at the marionette theatre. They had been taken from a satirical pamphlet circulating underground entitled 'The Seven Wonders of Czechoslovakia'.

'Although everybody has a job, nobody works,' she whispered, spraying water over the shirt with which she was wrestling. The cuff needed adjusting and a button had worked loose.

'Although nobody works, the Plan is fulfilled up to 105 per cent.'

The water left a waterfall of moisture on the skirt of Eva's cotton dress.

'Although the Plan is fulfilled up to 105 per cent, there's nothing in the shops.'

Petr put his head around the door. 'I thought I would find you here.'

He would know perfectly well where she was. Eva and the children had gone to visit their grandmother and she and Petr were alone in the apartment. Nevertheless, she was glad to take a break. Wiping her top lip, she asked, 'Is there something wrong?'

'I always regret how many people ask me that.' He sent her one of his attractive smiles and added wryly, 'I wish people would ask me what was right.'

She nodded politely.

He leant against the windowsill. Despite the temperature, he was formally dressed in well-cut trousers and a light-blue linen shirt. 'Have you been in touch with your mother? Does she agree to you staying on?'

'Actually, Petr, it was my decision.'

She appreciated the boldness of that last statement, which suggested she had – finally – taken a grasp on her life. In truth, since she was only permitted a three-minute telephone call to England, it was difficult to ascertain what her mother thought but she had seemed encouraging. 'She's fine about it. She's thinking of returning to France to live some time in the future.'

'Would you mind if she did?'

'No. I'm half French and a big part of me feels at home there.'

He seemed to approve. 'Feelings for one's country are a good thing.'

The iron was a heavy, old-fashioned one and, increasingly, given to spasms of rebellion. She adjusted the dial and picked up one of Maria's frocks.

'I appreciate that you are in a very different country here and it must be hard for you.'

Where was Petr going with this? She thought rapidly and decided to blind him with knowledge. 'I understand that this is a country where a social contract between the State and the people works very well. The State promises to deliver economic growth, a high standard of living and free health care and education. In return, the population agrees to conform to the rules and regulations.'

Highly amused, he laughed. 'Dear Laure,' he said, 'you really don't have to cite such things to me.' He considered for a moment. 'You have left out one thing, which is the passion felt by the people who believe in this doctrine but have to work hard to deliver it.'

She glanced sharply at him. This man appeared to be so easy with himself, so kind, so undoctrinaire and, yet, he was favoured by the authorities. Also, she reminded herself, avoiding the good-humoured gaze, this was also a man who had held down his struggling, bloodied wife by her wrists.

'Is Eva quite well?' she asked, thinking perhaps she might get some clarity on the situation. 'I mean, does she have bad dreams?'

'She does.' He looked thoughtful. 'About that time when you saw... I think perhaps you imagined you saw something sinister.'

Laure felt herself colouring up. 'I didn't *imagine.*'

'Eva was having a bad dream. I had cut myself in the bathroom and hadn't staunched it when she called out.'

He was watching her reaction. For any hint of scepticism, she supposed, but she wasn't going to give in that easily. She *had* seen something disturbing.

'It's curious, isn't it, how one of two people can see the same event very differently.'

'That's true and one person usually sees it incorrectly.'

The iron gave a shriek and hissed. Petr crossed the room and snatched it from Laure. 'Step back,' he ordered and switched it off at the plug. 'Are you all right?' Laure nodded. He examined the iron's cooling base. 'I told Eva we should get a replacement.' He replaced the iron on its rack. 'No more ironing today.' He glanced at his watch. 'Let me take you out for a cold drink before my meeting.'

'OK,' she agreed.

He waited until they were outside before taking up their previous conversation.

'You know…' he said, 'for most people here the standard of living has never been so satisfactory.'

They were seated at a wooden table outside a cafe in a square close to the church with suspiciously vivid-coloured glasses of orange juice in front of them. There were a couple of cast-iron lampposts dating from an earlier age and the red roofs of the houses flanking the square took on a brighter colour in the sun. The tree at its centre, however, appeared to be struggling to survive.

Petr followed Laure's line of sight. 'I'm afraid the air is not so good here,' he said. 'For the tree, I mean. But for *people*, the absence of war and division has been nothing but positive. People understand that. They want a good life with a strong family. They concentrate on domestic matters.'

She stared at the tree. Its leaves were shrivelled around the edges and the bark was spilt in several places. One of its main branches had spilt almost in two, revealing a scaly epidermis. The pollution must be terrible, she thought.

'But…' Petr focused on Laure. 'We do have to be careful about those who disagree. They can endanger stability. They are not reliable workers.'

'"We"?'

'Those people can lose their jobs and be detained for a period. But that can be beneficial all round because not only does it teach them a lesson but also everyone else learns as well. Or, if they are performers, they might be forbidden to perform.'

She was watching an elderly man walk past pushing his shopping in a rusty pram.

'Like your friend perhaps?' he continued. 'You will appreciate that he's not considered a good worker. He neither grows food nor works in a mine. His work is superficial, and the State takes note.' He leant back in the chair. 'Have you ever talked politics with your new friends? If you are tempted, please don't.'

She noted genuine concern on his face. 'May I ask you something, Petr?' He nodded. 'Do you really work for a pharmaceutical company?'

Risky.

'Did your new friends put you up to that question?'

'I've never discussed you with them. Do you?'

His reply was pleasant but held an edge. 'What makes you think I don't?'

'You don't go to the office very much and you ask me a lot of questions.'

'One should always ask questions, Laure. I will answer yours. I work for Potio Pharma and have done so for many years. Pharmaceuticals is an important industry. Lives depend on it.'

She looked again at the dying tree. 'Will you excuse me while I go to the Ladies?'

Inside the stuffy cubicle, she sat on the lavatory seat and took a deep breath. In a basket on the floor were copies of the official Party newspaper, *Rudé Právo*, torn into squares. At the marionette theatre, Milos had told her that it was the favoured newspaper for lavatory paper because it had the largest pages, was printed on high-quality paper and, because rival newspapers were blocked, it was obtainable most places.

She should never have asked that question. Foolish Laure.

When she returned, Petr had paid the bill. 'You're beginning to see that Prague is not Paris. And I think you think that I'm interfering. Or worse. But I'm not.' He stood up.

The strap of her rucksack had caught around the chair and he leaned over to disengage it. He held out the bag. 'You've been very helpful to the family and I'm grateful. I don't want anything to go wrong.'

Because the sentiment was genuine her wariness melted a fraction. 'Giving me the job helped me too.'

'That's good to know.'

Eva had been in bed for nearly a week. Some sort of bug, she said.

Laure struggled to keep the normal routines and was fully occupied looking after the children. Fetching and carrying, she learnt (with some dismay) she harboured a dark strand in her spirit. Helping Eva get to the bathroom and witnessing her gag over her food provoked a guilty contrast that she, Laure, was young, strong and fresh-skinned.

On several occasions, Petr made a point of asking her to share the evening meal with him. It had almost become a routine. It seemed to please him to have Laure sitting across the table and to demand from her descriptions of life in England. Laure was happy to play along but, as the week progressed, she found herself wild with impatience to take herself off.

At the first possible opportunity, Laure headed for the Staré Mĕsto. An unexpected, but brief, shower fell as she crossed the Charles Bridge and, in the few minutes before the moisture evaporated, the city glistened like a painting.

Approaching the square, she spotted Lucia and Tomas up ahead. Tomas had a newspaper tucked under his arm and Lucia carried a canvas bag which had seen better days. They were talking intently. At the sight, a nasty feeling settled in her stomach.

Walking several metres behind them was a man in a grey suit who, she cottoned on, was tailing them. Of medium height and so stocky that his jacket was threatening to give at the seams, he was having a job keeping up with his prey.

Laure found the idea rather thrilling – as if she had been caught up in a novel. Then she felt ashamed. This was no game. Quickening her pace, she overtook him and, on drawing level with Tomas and Lucia, she said in an undertone, 'You're being followed.'

'Without a doubt,' said Tomas, smiling at her. So saying, he stuck two fingers in the air. Lucia grabbed at his arm and hissed at him. Pointing at Laure, she switched to English: 'Go away. You make Tomas do stupid things and draw attention to us.'

'No, I don't.' Laure defended herself. 'He does that himself.'

Lucia flushed. Without saying anything further, she pushed through the crowd ahead of her and disappeared. Laure watched her and turned to Tomas. 'Am I causing you trouble? Perhaps I should go.'

A shade of impatience crossed his face. 'That doesn't mean you should go.' He drew her into the shelter of a doorway. The goon walked past. There were sweat stains under the armpits of the grey suit and his face was bright red.

In a wonderfully tender gesture, Tomas swept his fingers over Laure's cheek. 'Things are changing, here, Laure. *Will* you be a witness to what's going on?' Unsure of what he intended, she nodded all the same. 'Lucia is frightened, and she has reason to be. Her family have suffered. Her parents were once top civil servants. Now, they wash dishes.'

'Like the waiter?'

'Like the waiter.'

'I understand.'

'You probably don't,' he said. 'But let's go.'

At the marionette theatre, preparations for the evening performance were going ahead. Laure went through the now familiar routines.

Check floors and benches for litter.

Check lights were operational.

Check water was available for those overcome by heat. (A man fainted during the previous performance.)

Check rudimentary first-aid kit which consisted of a packet of aspirin and a few sticking plasters (God help those who had a heart attack or cut an artery) was stowed in the correct place.

Backstage, Milos was repairing one of Spejbl's strings. He was looking battered. His nose required retouching and his trousers had seen better days.

Laure watched Milos at work, his balding head gleaming with the heat.

'Spejbl finds life difficult, doesn't he? He's slipped. It's rather sad.'

'Don't talk about me like that', said the puppet.

Laure glanced at Milos who was working away with a secret little smile on his lips.

'Spejbl, so sorry. I didn't mean to offend you,' said Laure.

'I deny absolutely that I come from a bourgeois background,' said Spejbl.

'But Spejbl,' said Milos severely, 'your father was a well-known shop owner.' He glanced at Laure. 'You mustn't tell lies in front of visitors.'

'Don't you mean, don't tell lies in front of people you know. Visitors won't know if you are lying and, therefore, won't care.'

'I'm not a visitor any more,' said Laure.

'No, you're not. You're part of the team.'

A small glow lit up in Laure.

'Earn your keep. Next time you come bring some coffee. This marionette is dying for a good cup.'

Working calmly and methodically, Milos kept his head down.

Laure recollected the kitchen in the Kobes' apartment where packets of coffee were stacked in a cupboard. 'I'll try. I didn't realize it was so difficult to get hold of.'

'Foreigner.'

It was said so affectionately that Laure grinned.

Milos slotted the final string into place. 'Is that better, old man?'

'*Jawohl.*'

Milos tapped the battered nose. 'Wrong era.'

'Don't you give me history lessons.'

Backstage, the atmosphere was building as it always did. Nerves and tension boiling together. The possibilities were many. A performance could soar. A performance could bomb.

A performance could be watched, noted and reported.

That uncertainty triggered a rush which Laure had grown to relish. Every day brought a new sensation, a new experience – exquisitely intense.

She left Milos tidying up and went into the room used as a kitchen by the troupe to fetch the water for the backstage.

The room did not merit the term, having only a sink, a tap and a rickety table in the centre. Someone had brought in a gas ring on which the kettle was boiled and a couple of cups, one of which was minus its handle.

Laure filled a jug with water, wiped a tray decorated with a peeling transfer of the Charles Bridge and located the glasses. As she lifted the tray, someone grabbed her shoulder and she almost dropped it. Rattled, she whirled round.

Laure was confronted by Lucia in her black subfusc and concealing black headscarf. 'My English is not so good today.' Anticipating a clash, Laure set down the tray. 'But you must be told. You think he likes you? Think again.'

'Tomas?'

'Who else? He's making use of you because of who you are. He does that.'

At that moment, Laure discovered that being forewarned did not make dealing with a painful situation easier. 'I know I'm not Czech, if that's what you mean.'

'No, you are not.' Lucia spun out the words. 'And you won't understand.'

'Perhaps I don't mind.'

A flash of real fear went across the other woman's face. 'You come here with your foreign clothes and money. Yes, you have a job, but it's…' she was searching for the words. 'Your job is stupid. Not real. You work for privileged people.' She stopped mid-flow, glancing over her shoulder to the door, as if to assure herself no one was eavesdropping. The doorway was empty, and she renewed the attack. 'You will never know what it's like to live here.' She tapped her chest. 'Deep down.'

236

The dramatic gesture irritated Laure. 'This is silly,' she said, and made to pick up the tray.

Lucia blocked her. 'Shall I tell you what happens when you have something nice in Czechoslovakia? Even the smallest thing.'

Unsure of where this was going, Laure threw out: 'You enjoy it.'

Lucia thrust her face into Laure's. 'Stupid girl, it gets stolen. That's what happens. You can hide it at the bottom of the river, but they find it.' Her English stumbled. 'That's how we live here. That's how we die here. That's why we fight. For you... whenever you get fed up, you can go. We have to stay.' She gestured to the room. 'You think of this show as something amusing but it's not. It's where we make the future. Make ideas. Make the debate.'

'Are you talking politics?'

'Everything is politics in this country. You are too stupid to see.'

Evidently, 'stupid' was a favourite word of Lucia's.

'Lucia, please get out of my way.'

'You won't steal him. You should go home.'

'I've no intention of stealing him.'

'You have.'

The two women glared at each other until Lucia stepped aside. Laure picked up the loaded tray and made her way backstage.

Watching Lucia manipulate the marionettes during the performance, Laure realized that she had missed something important: the power of memory.

The puppet master had to memorize each rattling movement, each step, each interchange. One false move, and the show went wrong. One false or omitted move and the message was spoilt.

If Lucia was correct and everything in this strange country

was to do with politics, then life must be spent watching others. How exhausted they all must be and how their minds must run along a single track, which would explain, in part, Lucia's attitude towards her.

'Did I finish telling you about all the Seven Wonders of Czechoslovakia?' asked Tomas when Laure mentioned that she and Lucia had fallen out. 'It might help you to understand.'

'How old is Lucia?'

'My age.'

Post-performance he had turned up. Hoarse from a gig near Wenceslas Square, eyes glistening with vodka and adrenalin, reeking of tobacco and fresh sweat. He seemed so frail, and yet his visceral impact on her made her knees buckle, her stomach lurch.

They were standing in the passage that led from the stage into the kitchen and he had pulled her close. His lips were close to her ear as he murmured, 'Although there's nothing in the shops, we've got enough of everything. Although we've got enough of everything, everyone steals.'

His mouth rested on the favoured tender place of her neck, a fraction under the jawline.

'Although everyone steals, nothing ever goes missing anywhere.'

Uncertain how to respond, she pressed her body against his, registering his slightness and thinness with a kind of terror. He pulled back an inch in order to look down into her face. 'It's Czech humour, Laure. We have a way of laughing at ourselves, at the system, at the idiocy of the universe. We don't expect outsiders to understand it.'

She laid a hand flat against his chest, seeking to feel his heartbeat, all too aware of his separateness and longing to bridge it. 'Everyone is very concerned to tell me that I'm an outsider.'

238

'We also cry at ourselves. Particularly at the big paradox.'

'Which is?'

'Which is understanding that the world is a terrible place because you have to choose between the homeland that promises suffering and the suffering that afflicts those who choose to renounce their homeland.' He grinned. 'What is one to do?'

She said uncertainly, 'So, the paradox is to choose between two sufferings.'

'Which one do you choose?'

It was a rhetorical question and he didn't expect Laure to answer it. Her exhilaration tripled. Somehow – how? – she had been thrust into a circle that treated subjects like this as important.

'Come to the *chata* this weekend and I'll tell you. The boys will be there. You'll like it. It's where we are at our best.'

She knew perfectly well what the invitation really was.

CHAPTER 18

*L*ATE-ISH ON A HOT SUMMER FRIDAY AFTERNOON WAS NOT
the best time to take the train out of Prague's main station.

There was a long queue at the ticket kiosk where she met Tomas
who was wearing his linen waistcoat and had his hair tied back with
a black shoelace. 'We'll be lucky if we get a seat,' he said.

The corridors in the train were packed. 'Which do you prefer?
Death by proximity in the corridor or in a compartment?' They
squeezed into a compartment, which was already fully occupied
and stifling. 'Sorry,' said Tomas cheerfully to the occupants. He lifted
Laure's rucksack and stowed it in the luggage rack and balanced his
guitar on top. 'Very sorry.'

The passenger by the window raised his head and Laure was
amused by his startled look as he recognized Tomas. Tomas favoured
him with one of his smiles that could charm a monkey from a tree
and shook his head when the man made to give up his seat to him.

Fortunately, the journey was a short one. The train ground
through Prague's suburbs which gave way to countryside dotted
with birch and ash, through which threaded streams and rivers.

Not that Laure could see much. She concentrated on keeping her
balance and tried not to mind the reek of the meat sandwiches that
the woman in front of her was handing out to her family.

Apparently, *chata* was the name given to huts and cottages in the country to which every man, woman and child decamped whenever possible. 'If you can get around the building-licence racket,' said Tomas, 'you can build. Depends on who you know. If you can't, you rent. As decadent musicians, we have to rent.' He went a little moody for a minute or two. 'But no goons,' he said. 'No restrictions. No propaganda.'

Laure watched the sandwiches being consumed, anxious that she had packed the right clothes. Jeans. A cotton skirt. The dress that had aroused so much comment? She was no longer as fond of it as she had thought. It seemed, somehow, *inappropriate*.

From the station, it was the matter of a twenty-minute walk to a hamlet outside where Tomas ushered her up the path to a one-storey, clapboard building with a red roof. 'We bribed the owners into letting Anatomie take it for the season.' He was extra wry. 'Which wasn't easy. We're marked men and nobody much wants to do business with us.'

Her rucksack strap was digging into her shoulders and she shifted it. Tomas reached over and took it from her. 'Have you been arrested?' she asked.

'Twice. Each time you lose a life.' He observed her appalled expression. 'It's how it is here.'

Rubbing her released shoulder, she asked, 'Do you ever think of escaping to the West?'

The words had not left her lips before there was a subtle alteration in his demeanour. A shuttered expression replaced the smiling ease. 'Why do you keep asking?'

She was bewildered. 'I— sorry. Have I offended you?'

'Don't ask those questions, Laure. Just don't.'

He turned his back and banged on the door.

Manicki opened the door and it was obvious he was drunk. 'Sorry.' His hot, alcohol-laden breath almost knocked her back. 'I had to keep up with the others.' He led them into a sitting area which had a stove and rooms opening off it.

It was chaos. A prone Leo snored on the sofa. Someone else was behind it, probably male judging by the heavy lace-up shoes. Dirty beer glasses were everywhere, the stub end of a sausage and breadcrumbs littered the table and the room stank of sweat, cigarettes and sour beer.

Tomas aimed a kick at the body behind the sofa. 'Sorry,' he said. 'It wasn't meant to be this bad.'

Still recovering from the way their conversation had gone wrong and, yes, revolted by the squalor, Laure said, 'Should I go?'

'No. But go for a walk while I get things straightened out here.' She tried to smile. 'You'll have to forgive them.'

Outside, she could breathe easy. The accumulated heat from the day washed over her bare arms and the sun was at its evening angle. Fringed by healthy-looking ash trees, the cross-roads that formed the centre of the hamlet had a number of *chata* fanning out from it towards the woods in the distance. There was nothing in the way of diversion, so she circled slowly around the hamlet. The summer undergrowth was dry and snappy and where they grew thickest the trees threw black shadows.

In several of the gardens, families were eating to the accompaniment of tinny-sounding transistor radios. Children ran around freely, making a lot of noise, and family dogs panted in the shadows. Laure watched two toddlers under a tree pouring water from one bucket into another with tin cups.

It looked so normal. It was normal.

She sat down on a bench at the crossroads. At least trees did not change, nor did sunlight and the sky and it was a relief to look at them. Otherwise, she was blundering around in a foreign setting.

After a while, Tomas came searching for her. He caught up with her on the path that led away from the buildings into the wood. He had washed, shaved and changed into a pair of mended but clean jeans and a T-shirt. 'Reporting for duty,' he said.

She was a little dismayed. 'Not too much of a duty, I hope.'

His eyes narrowed. 'I'd forgotten,' he said softly. 'How awkward it is to be your age.'

'I'm not that much younger than you.'

'But I feel much older.'

She indicated a family scene in the house closest to them. 'Do you remember telling me that, although there's enough of everything, everyone steals?'

'In theory, there's enough of everything.'

'You made it sound as if it was anarchy out there but what I see here reminds me of England.'

'No one steals in England? No wonder you want me to go there.' He touched her breast. 'May I do this?' One eyebrow went up. 'Or, should it be: can I?'

She laughed and felt a lot better. 'You're a good pupil.'

His fingers felt rough on her soft skin. 'Actually, there's an Eighth Czechoslovakian Wonder of the World which says that, under our great party leader Husák, may he live forever, these rules have worked for forty years. Provided we never utter the word "Russia".'

In a trance, Laure allowed Tomas to lead her along the path leading into the wood. Inside the leaf canopy, the evening shadows were creeping along the ground and the birds had quietened. There was a smell of dry vegetation and hot stone, and the ground warmth percolated into her feet through her thin-soled shoes.

She knew what she was being led towards. And was glad. Madly, deliriously so.

Tomas halted. 'Are you sure?' She nodded. 'We can return the minute you want.' He smiled wryly. 'Sex can be ridiculous. Funny and serious and cruel.'

She didn't wish to hear about his experiences, albeit in a coded manner, especially if they involved… Lucia? She took a deep breath. 'I don't know much.'

He scrutinized her face. 'I don't think you enjoyed it. Am I right?'

Talking about Rob still bothered her. 'He didn't care for me and I cared for him. An old story.' Talking about it was always a mistake because it stirred up the feelings.

He took her hand and traced a circle in its palm. 'We are in the forest, a place of magic and new discoveries. You've been sleeping and I have come to wake you up.'

'You make it sound as if we are stories.'

'We are. Lovely and exciting ones.'

At that she flushed self-consciously. Was it so obvious that she was longing to experience love? Proper love. Not like the wretched obsession with Rob but the elemental response to the vivid dreams, expectations and sensuous reveries… the unknown parts of her mind, the shadowy places in her psyche?

They ventured deeper into the wood where the air was very still but the colours vivid – deep greens, a clump of orange and yellow, the bloody dots of early berries. The crack of twigs under their feet, the rustle of a disturbed animal, the sly flash of fungi in the fissure of a root, shadows casting pools of darkness between the trees which they passed. The call of an ancient, mythic territory was luring them into its heart.

By the time Tomas came to a halt in a clearing with a spread of turf, her shirt was clinging to her back. Panting with the heat, she dropped down and peeled the drenched cotton away from her arms.

Tomas knelt beside her. 'You are the Sleeping Beauty, I think.'

She turned her head and stared deep into his eyes. 'But you haven't been through the hedge of thorns.'

'Oh yes, I have. You were asleep.'

'It took a long time.'

'Don't worry. He always gets there. Somehow.' He touched her drenched shirt. 'Why don't you take it off?'

It was then that she felt afraid – of what she was getting into, of the pain she feared might lie ahead, and its finale. How could there be a good ending?

Tomas eased the shirt off her. 'Do you mind that it's here?' he asked. 'Privacy is hard in this country.'

Instinctively, she wrapped her arms around her torso. 'But it should be here. Out in the wild.'

He stroked her bare shoulders. 'I'm not going to hurt you.'

No, he wasn't going to do that. That was the one thing of which she was sure, and she unwrapped her arms and put them around him.

Despite the turf, the ground was hard and hard objects pressed into her back. Her inexperience was very evident and, to begin with, she felt wooden and disadvantaged.

'Stop worrying,' he said. 'I will make sure you are OK.' He kissed a breast. 'You are very beautiful and sweet. You've got leaves in your hair and you look like one of the sprites that live in the wood.'

'You said I was a lioness.'

'That, too,' he said so tenderly that Laure thought she would faint from emotion. 'Now, are you still afraid? I will take great care of you.'

She looked into his eyes and saw that he was honest and open. 'No, I'm not afraid.'

After a while, she forgot about the stones pressing into her spine and concentrated on the sharp sensations and hungers. True to his word, Tomas made it easy for her and his consideration made her want to laugh and to cry.

When it was over, they lay in a sweaty tangle. It was growing dark and the rustles in the undergrowth increased and a night breeze stirred the leaves at the tops of the branches. But there was no threat, only a vast peacefulness.

Tomas's head rested on Laure's shoulder. He smelt warm, male and entirely seductive. The intimacy of their entwined bodies made her catch her breath. Falling in ever deeper love, which she knew she was doing, was to be set free from oneself. It was the freedom to blend into someone else and take on their world.

Yes.

She squinted up at the tree canopy and thought: please don't let me get old.

Tomas stirred. 'I can hear you thinking.'

'I imagined for a moment what it must be like to be old and without... this.' She placed her hand on his back.

'You're not old.' Tomas lifted his head. 'And you don't have to be without it. No?'

With a deep joy and thankfulness, Laure closed her eyes.

Manicki and Leo were too hung-over to be welcoming. When Tomas and Laure returned to the *chata*, they muttered something about the drink having taken a toll on their language skills and, slumped in chairs, they returned to the business of getting over the hangover.

Efforts had been made to tidy up. The dishes had been washed up and the empties stacked outside the door. But the air still reeked of cigarettes and unwashed male bodies.

Tomas flung open the windows and propped open the door. Manicki muttered about the insects and Tomas replied that they should have thought of that earlier.

She helped Tomas to clear the table and he set sausage and bread down on it. 'Not fine dining but you must be hungry.'

Her senses still singing with surprise and delight she did her best to eat the sausage. To say it was pungent was an understatement and it took some chewing. The bread wasn't much better but it did the job of quelling her hunger pangs.

Having observed the niceties, Tomas said 'sorry about this', folded his arms on the table top, rested his head on them and fell asleep.

She took herself to the bench outside and allowed her mind to drift. As she sat in the dappled shade, she heard her father's voice urging her to tidy up. *Untidy room, untidy mind.* It brought a lump into her throat and, at the same time, made her smile.

Towards late evening, the men stirred into life and held a jam session at the crossroads. Almost immediately, an audience assembled.

They smoked, they sang, they danced, they joined in. A girl from the next-door *chata* wearing the tightest of jeans slunk over and gazed at Manicki with ill-concealed lust. An elderly man parked himself on a felled tree trunk and gave a thumbs-up. Children were silenced.

Sounding raw and ragged – unsurprising given the excess of the previous evening – Anatomie sang in Czech. Provocative songs, she reckoned judging by the effect they were having and worried they were taking risks.

The three didn't look at each other much. It wasn't necessary. Musically, they knew each other inside out. Their moves coordinated, their chords were of split-second timing, their pulsing sexual invitation collective.

A strange man caught her hand and made her dance. Blood pounding and breath catching, she let herself go until she was breathless.

The world spun around. She was caught up by the dark whispering trees, the late-night warmth, the scents of a summer night. She had become unearthly. She was pagan. She pulsed with fire and desire.

She was no longer the girl who had arrived in the country only a few weeks ago.

It was almost dawn when Tomas linked his hand into Laure's and said, 'Come to bed with me.'

They fumbled their way into a room with a narrow bed and crashed down onto it. The sheets were rough to the touch and unaired and the mattress was terrible. Laure didn't care. Down the short passage, Leo and Manicki were blundering around in their rooms. From Manicki's issued the sound of a female shriek.

Tomas gathered Laure to him. 'I'm not capable at the moment.' He was hoarse and exhausted. 'Do you mind?'

The intimacy of the confession made her catch her breath. 'No.'

His laugh was a rasp. 'Shouldn't you be saying that you do mind? It would be more complimentary.'

'It wouldn't have been true. I'm tired and sore and would like to sleep.'

'An honest answer.' He pulled her even closer and closed his eyes. 'You smell of flowers.' Within seconds he was asleep.

Her sleep was harder. Unused to sharing a bed, she tried to keep still because of Tomas and stop herself rolling into the dent in the centre. Also, she was too exhausted to sleep and her mind was seething. She needed to make sense of what was happening – the sex, her feelings for Tomas, the discoveries that were crowding down thick and fast in this complicated country in which she found herself.

But she must have slept. When next conscious of turning her head, it was to see sunlight thrusting through the window and striking the wooden floor. At first, she focused on it, but it was too bright and she moved her gaze onto the wooden walls. These varied in colour from honey to dark brown and had pleasing knots and whorls on which to fix. Birdsong sifted through the open casement window along with a piney, grassy scent. Tomas was pressed up against her, which was uncomfortable but not unbearable. She thought: *this is what happiness is like.*

A hand touched her thigh and she sighed with pleasure. 'Is that a yes?' asked Tomas.

'It is.'

He rolled on top of her. 'I must warn you that I'm unwashed, unbrushed and stinking of alcohol.'

He wasn't joking. 'It doesn't matter.'

The sunlight fell across her face and she blinked.

'Do you know you're beautiful, Laure?'

They stayed in bed the entire morning, emerging at lunchtime. Leo and Manicki were outside sunning themselves on the bench. There was no sign of anyone else.

Leo waggled a finger in greeting and said in English, 'You are commanded to speak very softly.'

'Good morning, Leo,' she said.

He clapped his hands over his ears – long-fingered, lovely hands, she noticed. 'Too loud. Too LOUD.'

She giggled helplessly.

Laure tried to memorize every detail of that day. The sun on her skin, the birdsong, the soil between her bare feet. The taste of the excellent stew conjured into being by a wild-haired Manicki who turned out to have a domestic streak. The sight of Leo flat-out on the grass. ('He doesn't speak much.' Tomas prodded the prone body with a foot. 'But when he does, watch out.') A sense that she had been invited into an exclusive kingdom from which other comers would be repulsed.

She tried not to be obvious, but she could not prevent herself sneaking looks at Tomas who was wearing a faded blue shirt the colour of an English summer sky. The colour, she told herself, of love. He had, she noted with fascination, a habit of gesticulating with his left hand. His feet were long and thin but he was thin generally. Too thin, perhaps. In the light, his brown hair held a spectrum of chestnut and copper.

More than once, their gazes collided and the fusion of desire, tenderness and excitement that went through her body was to be hit by an electric bolt.

'Do you know precisely what your employer does?' Manicki asked at one point in the long, lazy afternoon.

They had been discussing the privileges meted out to the few. Or, at least this was what Laure gathered from quickfire translations. Big cars, private medical treatment, the larger apartments. Laure replied that, as far as she knew, he represented his pharmaceutical company in France.

'Don't be taken in,' said Manicki in more than passable English. He was lying flat on his back in the grass. 'He's probably doing some industrial spying. That's why he gets the big flat and you. It's worth it to them for the information he brings back.'

Manicki's theory made sense. The suspicions, vague and half-formed, which had been chasing around her mind came together. To her surprise, she felt sharp disappointment. His treatment of Eva apart, she was beginning to like Petr and felt that he treated her fairly. But, as she had to concede, she had a habit of taking everything at face value. That Petr might not be on a level was more than possible.

'Watch out for him,' Manicki added.

The sleepy drawl had changed into something more challenging and she wondered if he meant: *you should not be with us.*

Laure was due to catch the train back to Prague in the evening and, reluctantly, went indoors to pack. When she emerged, the conversation had become heated.

Tomas made room for her on the bench. 'Leo is arguing that the lines of conflict are no longer between the rulers versus the ruled but running through individuals. In other words, people don't know who they are. What they are.'

Back home, this would have not been the sort of conversation that would have gone on. *Where's the dope pick-up? Who's drinking where?*

She slotted her arms through the straps of her rucksack. 'I don't understand.'

Tomas came to her aid, settling it into the small of her back. 'What Leo is trying to say – and badly as always—' Leo aimed his sandal at Tomas who ducked. 'What Leo is saying *brilliantly* as usual is that deception and division is quite natural to us all.' He adjusted a strap. 'Take the ordinary man.'

'Or woman.'

'Or woman. Someone, say, who runs a fruit and vegetable stall in the city. Or a butcher's. Do you notice anything about them?'

'Slogans in their shops. Like "Workers of the Word Unite".'

'Now, does this man – or woman – believe in the international worker solidarity? Almost certainly not. No, what he or she is saying by displaying the slogan is: I am behaving as you, the State, wishes. Therefore, you must leave me in peace. So, it doesn't matter what he or she believes.' He spun around. 'Am I right, Leo?'

From his prone position in the long grass, Leo grunted.

Tomas slotted his hand into Laure's and their fingers entwined. 'Then, he has accepted,' she spoke carefully, 'to behave in a certain way in exchange for peace and he tolerates the State's proscribed message.' She looked across to the trees. 'That guarantees he can get on with his life.'

'Good girl. You see, opinions come in many shades.'

Manicki reached for his guitar and struck a chord. 'Does that happen in England?'

'Sometimes, I suppose.' She shook her head. 'No, the State doesn't operate in that way. Not even for the criminal.'

Leo sat up abruptly and said something in Czech, spitting out the last few words.

Tomas bent down to retie the lace of his plimsoll. 'My vegetable seller is reproduced millions of times all over the country and we are a nation of zombies as a result. There's no choice.'

Manicki struck another chord, a melancholy one, and Tomas sang, 'Darling my promise to you was a good life. Where did it go wrong?'

In this country politics seemed to get into everything and Laure didn't want to think about them. She wanted to think about love and when she would next see Tomas. 'Hadn't I better go?'

'See you.' Leo kissed her on the cheek goodbye, which surprised her, but Manicki avoided any physical contact.

'Is Manicki suspicious of me?' she asked as they walked to the station.

'Not of you so much, but of your situation. He thinks you could cause trouble.'

The blood surged into her cheeks. 'I would never betray you. Or, say anything about you.'

If she had hoped for reassurance, it was not forthcoming. 'None of us ever know,' said Tomas.

When the station came into sight, he stopped. 'Shall we make a promise?' he said.

She searched his face. 'If you like.'

'Let us promise to be what we are. No politics between us. Just ourselves, enjoying this time. Yes?'

Her voice trembled. 'Oh yes.'

He saw her onto the crowded train, kissed her lingeringly goodbye but said nothing about their next meeting.

She watched the countryside slide past and slowly change from the pastoral to the Prague suburbs where the twelve-storey *paneláks*, or housing units, some three hundred metres long, rose drearily above the plain.

Was anyone watching her? The woman in the headscarf, the teenager with a bruise on his cheek? The man sitting next to her smelt of garlic and could not have been less interested in Laure. Or, was that the impression he gave?

The habit of suspicion had taken root in Laure. It was, she reflected, irrelevant as to whether it was a good or a bad thing to have evolved. It had happened.

CHAPTER 19

*B*ACK IN THE KOBES' APARTMENT, LAURE UNPACKED HER rucksack and struggled to control her tears. She wanted to be at the *chata*, getting drunk, smelling the summer, listening to the birds. Most of all, she longed to be lying beside Tomas.

She stuffed the rucksack into the cupboard and sat down on the edge of the bed. In any life, she supposed, there were times when events did not seem quite real and could not be thoroughly explained. Perhaps the trick was not to try?

She got up and went over to the window. Propped on the sill where the light was best was the hand mirror she had picked up at the State-sponsored market stall in the Old Town. Handbag sized, with stupid shells stuck onto the handle, it was the only one available outside the family bathroom. Its smallness meant that she had to scrutinize one feature at a time. She examined her nose, her mouth, the hair falling over her right shoulder.

Her experience with Rob Dance taught her that falling in love put you at a disadvantage. It destabilized sense and splintered sensibility. It provided no answers and had a big signpost with 'Humiliation' written on it. But, perhaps, Tomas had seen something behind her gooseberry-coloured eyes of which she was not yet aware? An intelligence? For sure, it wasn't worldliness but, maybe, he had detected an instinct, growing stronger by the day, not to conform but to question.

Perhaps Tomas liked the fact that she was more-or-less a blank sheet, something that he would have spotted at once?

The questions went back and forth.

To be with Tomas was a risk that she would end up again under that signpost. She was not of his world. Other women were interested in him; a fact that made her feel sick. She needed to learn discretion and guile, not necessarily a given with a woman from Brympton.

By the time she had pursued those lines of thought to their logical conclusion, she was convinced that her time with Tomas had been quite lovely but that was it. It was unlikely to go further.

She flung herself down on the bed and buried her face in the pillow.

Please, please, she prayed, don't let it be that Tomas was using me. Or, not entirely.

The not terribly pleasant smell of the soap with which the household linen was laundered was all pervasive and she grabbed the T-shirt she had worn with Tomas. To her starved senses, it smelt of sun, of sex, of pines and of… him.

She rolled over and stared at the ceiling. At the back of her mind lurked a warning. However hurt and ragged she had been left by Rob, it was nothing to the tumult that awaited her.

Twisting a lock of her hair between her fingers, she looked up at the window. How puzzling life could be – and how she loved it.

The apartment was stifling, especially at night.

Eva was a cause of increasing concern. Since her stomach bug, she had become more reclusive, keeping to her bedroom for long periods. On a couple of occasions when Laure asked her for instructions, she told Laure it was up to her, which made her uneasy and more than a little apprehensive.

'Are you sure you wish me to make these decisions?' she asked, determined that matters were clear cut.

Eva's reply was slurred. 'Haven't I said?'

It became clear that the children were suffering from their mother's lack of interest. Maria cried for no obvious reason and Jan was noticeably truculent. Concerned about them, Laure decided to tackle Petr.

She chose her moment after the evening meal. Eva and the children had gone to bed and she asked Petr if she could have a word. 'Sure,' he said and carried his tankard of beer into the room favoured by the family for sitting in.

Petr put down the beer, flung wide the window and leant out, seemingly absorbed by the vista through which featured old roofs and church spires. Laure wondered if she had misunderstood and made a move to go.

'Stay,' he said, without looking round.

'I'm interrupting your evening.'

'A little. But you need to discuss something.'

In the daytime, the room was also used by the children and their things were stacked at one end of the room. Like the rest of the apartment, the room had beautiful proportions with a Bohemian glass chandelier hanging from an elaborately plastered ceiling. The pity was, as with most places she had been into, the paintwork was in its last stages and the furnishings, which included plastic chairs and a sofa from which the innards were spilling, were minimal.

Laure addressed his back. 'I wanted to ask.' She cleared her throat and went to the point. 'Is your wife getting worse? It's not

257

my business.' *No, it bloody isn't. Yes, it is.* She ploughed on. 'I think she might be.'

Petr turned around from his contemplation of the city. As usual, he was well dressed and groomed but he looked bone tired. 'Have you talked about this with the children?'

She approved of his instinctive reaction to protect them.

'No. I thought if there was something wrong, it would need careful thought.'

He nodded. 'Thank you. You're both tactful and sensitive.'

Petr sat down on the ailing sofa and indicated that she should take a chair. 'I should have consulted you earlier. My wife has been diagnosed with a serious illness.' He didn't specify what. 'The doctors are organising treatment.' He hesitated. 'We were hoping to resume treatment in Paris but, as things have turned out, we will remain here for the next year. It was one of the reasons we asked you to stay with us.' He lit a cigarette. 'Does that clear things up?'

It took a few seconds for Laure to appreciate what Petr was saying. 'You wanted Mrs Kobes to have treatment *in Paris*?'

He looked away. 'It was important.'

'Oh God,' said Laure. 'I mean, I'm so sorry.'

Petr sighed. 'We'll see how we go. We may still get to Paris for the treatment. It depends on a lot of things. The authorities would have to give permission and I'm talking to them about it.'

Eva's illness and treatment were not the topics with which to score a political point, but the ironies were certainly not lost on Laure. 'It does clear things up.' She glanced at her hands in her lap. 'The children sense something is wrong. Perhaps it *would* be a good idea to talk to them?'

'They miss Paris, which is to be expected.'

'It's deeper than that.'

'Are you sure?' But she could see he was nonplussed.

This apparent crack in Petr's customary assurance fuelled the courage to speak. 'They sense that their mother has withdrawn. Now you've told me the reason, I understand you don't want to alarm them, but I wonder if you should try and explain.' She added, 'As soon as possible. Children need reassurance.'

He made a face. 'I won't take that as a criticism.'

'It isn't a criticism, Mr Kobes.'

He looked at her. 'We are friends, are we not? We are beginning to know each other quite well. You must call us Eva and Petr.'

'Petr. The children are unsettled and it's my duty to tell you.'

He seemed pleased with her intervention. 'I'll make it my business to spend more time with them. I could come on one of your afternoon outings.'

Laure didn't hesitate. 'They'd like that.'

'That's wonderful to hear. I'm so glad you brought the subject up.'

She made for the door. Petr picked up his beer. 'It's such a relief having you to talk to,' he said. 'A relief. No, it's more than that, a pleasure.'

She knew that he was willing her back into the room, there to stay to talk and drink a beer with him. He was holding her gaze. *Please.*

'I'm glad I can help,' she said, desperate to be alone in order to think about Tomas. 'Goodnight.'

The children lit up like Christmas trees when, the following afternoon, their father announced that he would accompany them to Kampa Park and vied to hold his hand as they plunged into the afternoon heat.

The park was on a false island adjacent to the Charles Bridge and sufficiently large for the children to run around. Crucially, said Petr, there would be shade.

In the sun, the river looked flat and burnished. Beyond it, the city shone, its greyness transmuted into pale pastel shades. At the entrance to the park, Petr said, 'You go ahead, I'll join you in a moment.'

Laure looked over her shoulder to see he was talking to a balding man in a navy-blue suit. 'Apologies,' he said when he re-joined them. 'A colleague.' She noticed, however, he was frowning.

'I hope you don't have a crisis at work,' she said, more from politeness than anything else.

Petr frowned. 'What would you know about it?'

Taken aback, she stammered, 'I don't.'

'Sorry,' he said. 'I didn't mean to be so sharp. But no questions, yes?'

'Of course.'

If the watchers worried that they were also watched, did that not constitute paranoia? Laure wondered. Whatever the explanation, the goodwill between them had dissipated.

They found a place to sit under the trees. Despite the heat, Jan kicked a ball around. Because it had been so hot, many of the trees had been shedding leaves prematurely and Maria jumped like a puppy in and out of the rustling heaps.

Petr made himself extra agreeable and asked her questions about home and her family. Laure thawed at his obvious efforts and answered in some detail. Every so often, the children called out to their father and to those calls he responded wholeheartedly. 'They're so fond of you,' she said impulsively.

'Thank you. Do you think they'll settle?'

'They miss Paris. Naturally.' She waited for a moment. 'They will forget. In part.'

'Let's hope so.' He lit a French cigarette, not a Czech one, which she now recognized as a sign of privilege. 'I'm hoping I might be able to take Eva back in the autumn.'

'Excellent.'

'Her illness is a strange one. The doctors can't predict exactly what will happen.' He undid his cuffs and rolled up his shirtsleeves.

Greatly daring, she said, 'You must be envied for your travelling.'

'What makes you say that?'

She was provoked by his sharp response into replying, 'I've met some people who can't travel.'

'Ah, the guys from Anatomie?'

Too late to bite back the words. 'Actually, I'm not sure. The language problem… I don't always understand what's being said.'

He said in kindly way, 'Conversation must be a little difficult. What do you manage to talk about?'

'Not much,' she said.

His eyebrow flew up but he appeared to take her wriggle at face value. 'You know that women will hate you for being so friendly with them.'

She tried to not to reveal her elation. 'But how do you get to travel to France or Italy from here?'

Again, the whiplash reaction. 'Why?' Petr ground out his cigarette carefully on the dry ground. 'Are any of your friends thinking of taking a trip?'

'I don't think so.'

She focused on the river, reflecting that it, at least, was free to flow unhindered. 'It's seems so strange not to be able to visit Italy, say. Or Germany. Or Austria. That's all.'

'Austria…' he echoed, and Laure had no idea of what he was thinking. Maria chose this moment to fling herself against her father's knees. Petr ran his fingers through his daughter's sweaty hair. 'You must tell your friends that, if they are planning a trip, they must go through the proper channels.'

Thoroughly rattled, she replied, 'They're just musicians who like to sleep late. Musicians do.'

'Perhaps, but I should warn you that Anatomie are thought to support Parallel Polis.'

Her alarm deepened. 'I've no idea what that is.'

'It's a document written by a so-called philosopher. A Catholic.' There was a hint of nostalgia in the way he pronounced 'Catholic'. 'He argues that everyone should ignore State institutions and form alternative, parallel structures. He approves of the musical underground. Anatomie is part of the musical underground.'

'I don't know anything about it.'

'But you do. By association.'

'Just because I see some friends doesn't mean I agree with their views.'

'This is Czechoslovakia, Laure.'

She recollected the man in the navy-blue suit to whom Petr had been talking earlier. Sure enough, when she looked around she spotted him loitering by the entrance to the Kampa, his jacket hooked onto a finger hanging down his back.

He looked bored and hot.

'Do any of your friends talk about these subjects?' Petr was persisting.

Jan was teasing Maria by throwing handfuls of leaves into her face. Maria wasn't sure how to react. Petr called to Jan, 'Be careful.' He turned back to Laure. 'I'm only asking because I'm curious. Having been away so long, I'm in danger of losing touch with what is going on in my own country.'

Laure was now doubly sure she must keep her mouth shut. 'I don't know. As I said, I don't understand much.'

He turned towards her and, to her surprise, took her hand. Embarrassed and not a little alarmed, her instinct was to snatch it away. Finely shaped and well-manicured, it was a nice hand – but she didn't wish it on hers.

'I think you're terrific.' His voice was warm and reassuring. 'Clever and thoughtful. What more could my children want?'

She felt herself going red and cast around. 'Your friend is still here. Over by the entrance.'

He released her at once but his fingers left an impression on her flesh. Gesturing to the children, he said, 'Don't worry, you're quite safe with me. I'm not going to take advantage of you.'

She didn't answer but felt enormous relief.

'But *your* friends must take care of themselves. They know what they are doing.' He hesitated. 'You should be aware, Laure, that they're probably running big risks.'

Petr began to talk about the children. In the last few weeks, Maria had taken to goading her brother who displayed remarkable patience with the provocation. Laure offered her own insights, gained from having been with them these last weeks. Petr listened, questioned and seemed appreciative of Laure's point of view.

'You know them better than we do,' he joked.

That's right, she thought. 'I don't think so, Petr.'

'Jan is a good boy,' he said. 'Before you came, he was a little difficult. You have settled him.'

The compliment was unexpected and pleased Laure. 'I love them both.'

'You're part of the family.'

That made her uneasy. Yet, it also intrigued her. The trying-on-the-future-for-size kind of intrigue.

He turned towards her. She was tempted to edge away but he

made no further move. 'I've confided in you that Eva is ill. We think you're perfect for the children and we are fond of you. But I wanted to tell you that we admire you for the way you have handled your own family situation. I mean, the death of your father.'

Jan chose that moment to abandon his new-found chivalry and to push over his sister. Laure leapt to her feet to deal with the carnage. Maria howled and Laure sat down on the grass. Gathering up the little body in her arms, she whispered comforting words and rocked her gently. 'Don't let him make you cry.'

Maria quietened. Laure stroked her curly head and dropped kisses on the top of her head. Glancing up, she intercepted a dazed, bewildered look on Petr's face as he gazed on the tableau. It was as if he had been punched in the stomach and was struggling to work out what had happened.

When she returned the dirt-streaked, subdued Maria to her father, the conversation turned to other things.

From then on, Petr made a point of accompanying Laure and the children every so often on afternoon outings which pleased the children and their behaviour improved.

He was careful not to interfere, to listen to her opinions on the children and procured treats. A cake. A packet of biscuits… which they shared companionably between them in the hot afternoons.

Not infrequently, too, he requested Laure to join him after the evening meal when Eva was in bed and he talked about Paris and his childhood in Prague. He was curious about Laure's childhood and upbringing and pressed her for details. But the conversation of Kampa Park was never repeated. If they did touch on politics, Petr would say something such as: 'Let's just keep to the big narrative', and Laure was hyper-careful to appear ignorant about all matters Czechoslovakian.

CHAPTER 20

Berlin, 1996

$\mathcal{P}$ETR RECKONED THAT, ON BALANCE, THE BRITISH WERE probably not seriously interested in his presence in the city. However, having built up to hysterical proportions since the Second World War, the paranoia over Russia and the Eastern European countries would take time to subside and his known past contact with Laure would probably bump him up the list of persons of marginal interest. She would be reporting back.

The ironies were not lost on him.

He was at the Natalya Hotel, waiting for Laure to join him for dinner. Not entirely unexpectedly, she had rung to arrange dinner and suggested the Natalya. 'It's famous for its *kartoffelpuffer* and *schnitzel*,' she told him.

Reception was crowded by a large party which had filed in from a coach. Porters bustled across the foyer with luggage trolleys.

As a general rule of thumb, the Russians wore shiny suits and favoured savage haircuts. The Germans were more casually dressed and the men wore signet rings as wedding bands. The Italians had silk ties and the Poles liked leather.

The exchanges were polyglot, there was whiff of a woman's

265

perfume, not very nice, it had to said, but the cigars smelt good. Out of the blue, there was a spat. One of the Germans at an adjacent table raised his voice. 'Just fucking market the properties,' he hissed at his companion. 'That's your job.'

Petr noted the instruction 'to market'. Here was proof the ex-Stasi were in real estate, marketing and insurance, jobs that had not existed in the former GDR. But they all required administrative skills and powers of persuasion in which the Stasi had specialized.

The spat continued. 'You *Wessis* come in here with the fancy-pancy clothes and cars and expect us to do what you wish. Think again.'

Petr caught the eye of the Russian standing next to him. 'Tribal tensions,' he murmured in German.

The anonymity of the hotel always loosened tongues.

'I understand,' replied the Russian, sighing. 'At heart, we Russians are imperialists. We want to keep a grip on Eastern Europe like the West does on the West. It is how it is.'

The Natalya was a rare example of a surviving nineteenth-century building. It was not in the best of shape but most of its features – stone carvings and elaborate corbels – were intact.

The foyer was paved with marble slabs, some of which were cracked. Isolated circles of chairs and sofas, whose upholstery had seen better days, had been arranged in groups and a couple of potted figs struggled to survive. A fug of tobacco smoke rose from the bar area. The drinkers, mostly dressed in the same make and colour of raincoat, swarmed around the barman.

The scene reminded him of similar venues in Prague before the Party was ousted, when efforts to make anywhere smart and worldly failed through lack of funds and a terror of being seen to ape the West.

He chose a spot in the lobby with two chairs and sat down to wait. Not for long. A car drew up at the hotel entrance and deposited its passenger. His hand resting lightly on his knee clenched.

Laure walked into the foyer and divested herself of her coat at the cloakroom. She searched the foyer, singled him out and headed over, leaving him free to admire the way she appeared not to notice the attention that she was stirring. She wore nothing to shock or impress. In fact, her grey dress was badly cut and achieved something he would not have thought possible, which was to make her elegant body look awkward. Yet, the way she held herself, and her mass of shining hair, could not fail to draw the eye.

He got to his feet and held out his hand. 'You survived the journey?'

'Believe it or not.' She ignored his hand. 'We are warned that East Berlin is still bandit country at night.' The hostility was back. 'David, my boss, who you met the other night, was particularly concerned. A bit of a fusser. I promised him that you're a player.'

'Did you now.'

She did not miss a beat. 'I didn't think a small detail like regime change and being in a foreign city would prevent you from arranging things to suit you. Am I right?'

Laure was conveying messages. One, the meeting had been vetted. Two, they would be keeping an eye on her during it. Probably the driver of the car.

'I've booked the table,' he said, by way of reply. 'Since there is only one sitting, we should go in.'

The dining room was large, taken up at one end by a dance floor and liberally arranged with potted plants. They ended up at a table by the window which overlooked the concrete office block opposite. A dim light burnt in its doorway, which partially revealed the stained concrete and defective windows.

There was a silence, as if they were settling on how to deal with each other. Good-naturedly, he hoped.

'Petr,' she said gently. 'You should lose the habit of staring at people.'

He was startled. 'Do I stare?'

'You assess them. You watch them. You're a European capitalist now.'

He ducked his head. 'Old habits, eh?'

'You look in good shape.' She put her head on one side. 'It always amazed me how well you dressed. Considering.' A smile emerged. 'You haven't changed.'

He glanced down at his jacket, which, it was true, he had bought in Paris.

'And I always reckoned your shoes were handmade.'

'I wouldn't have gone that far.' He grinned. 'Could I?'

It pleased him that her lips gave a small twitch in response. 'No.' She allowed her napkin to be settled onto her lap by the waiter while Petr ordered goulash and cabbage for both and endeavoured to wrestle a bottle of wine out of the waiter. 'I'm afraid it will have to be beer,' he said, having failed to do so.

'It'll go with the goulash and cabbage.' She sat back in the chair. 'You can't spend Tuzex crowns here.'

'Stop it,' he said gently.

Laure was needling him. In the latter years of the regime, those favoured by the Party, including the Kobes, had access to the Tuzex stores, which sold unimaginable luxury – jeans, Lego, almonds, sneakers, Milka chocolate and the odd Hershey bar.

'Didn't it bother you that it was the biggest, baddest form of black market going,' she asked, 'and controlled by thugs? A gateway to organized crime? I used to ask myself why the authorities allowed it until I realized that's precisely what they wanted to happen.'

'The government needed hard currency,' he pointed out. 'There's an East German equivalent. I'm sure there's a French and British one.'

'And why did they need hard currency?' she asked, lightly. Ironically.

If he had had any doubts, which he didn't, this was not the Laure of old.

He watched the band assemble at the other end of the room. They looked weary and underfed and their first notes were discordant.

Laure leant forward in her seat. 'On the twenty-eighth of November 1989, the Czechoslovakian Communist Party announced it would dismantle the one-party state. Barbed wire and other obstructions were removed from the borders with Germany and Austria. On the tenth of December, a largely non-communist government was appointed and, in 1990, the government agreed to liberalize prices.'

'As a result of which, unemployment went up and benefits had to be introduced,' he intervened drily.

'What I'm trying to say is that life must have changed for you, Petr. Frighteningly? Yes? You were no longer in power. Did you hang on to the apartment in the Malá Strana?'

'For a while.'

For many reasons, he shied away from thinking about the apartment but, from time to time, its memories became almost unbearable.

Eva getting out of bed, making her way down into the courtyard and into the street. Making for the river.

269

The waiter had appeared with plates piled high and Laure waited until he had settled them in front of them. 'Did you get married again?'

'No.' He tested a mouthful and grimaced.

She watched him. 'Have you heard from the children?'

'I've spoken to them and they're intrigued that we have met up. Maria says that if you are ever in Paris, she will come and see you.'

Laure put down her fork. 'Can I ask you something? It's been bothering me.' She looked down at her plate. 'Eva's death? Was it straightforward? The way you told me suggested it wasn't.'

'I'm not going to answer.'

'You can't or won't.'

'I can't.' He cast around to change the subject. 'About your earlier comment about my clothes, there's no logical reason while you shouldn't like fine things and still be a communist.'

Laure shuffled a piece of gristle to the edge of her plate. 'A communist may look at a king and copy the outfits?'

'Did you come here to make me angry?'

'Perhaps.' Her smile was reflective. 'It's tempting.' There was a pause. 'So, you stayed at Potio Pharma but as CEO instead of international sales manager?'

'The board—'

'The *board*...?' she interjected. 'I love it.'

'The board,' he repeated with an emphasis, 'considered that I was the safe pair of hands required to oversee its transition from a state-owned company to a shareholder one.'

After the goulash, they were served with a slice of robust cheese and dense bread, both of which were surprisingly good. This was followed by a slab of greyish-looking cake with a dab of jam. They regarded this culinary triumph thoughtfully.

'It did say *torte* on the menu,' said Laure, in a way that reminded him of the easily amused girl he had once known.

Petr took an experimental bite. 'Call it what you will, it's terrible.' He pushed the plate to one side. 'Is your German as good as your French?'

'Almost. I took my degree in it, with French of course and some Italian.'

He wiped his mouth with his napkin. 'Didn't you want to read politics at university? What made you change your mind?'

'Believe it or not, I wanted a rest from politics.' The irony was marked. 'Anyway, if I wanted to work in the Foreign Office, I needed languages.' She toyed with her unused dessert fork. 'It's a strange coincidence that we've met again. But it happens. That's what makes life interesting.' She turned a pair of large eyes onto him. 'What are you really doing in Berlin, Petr?'

'As I told you. I'm a CEO now. Of a large company. We have to get it onto the European map.'

'And when you saw me at the reception?'

He thought about their last meeting and of what had taken place.

'It was a moment. I admit that. I wanted to know if...'

'If?'

'You still hated me.'

There was no hesitation. 'I did.' He had an image of her gathering up the sharp shards of that hatred. 'I do, Petr.'

He placed his napkin on the table. 'Like everything in this world, hatred ages. It begins hot, strong and sometimes violent. It ends up musty and brittle. Wouldn't you agree?'

'Or you grow to rely on it.'

Coffee arrived. It was thin, ersatz stuff but it almost burnt the tongue. They lit cigarettes and drank it slowly.

271

The band was playing a slow, smoochy number and the dance floor was becoming crowded.

He glanced at her over the coffee cup. 'Dance?'

She got to her feet. 'Is there any risk in you seeing me?'

Petr shook his head. 'Why would there be? We have a history that is bona fide. The Czechoslovakia you knew no longer exists. The Berlin Wall is a pile of rubble. East and West are climbing into bed. I'm a widower with no ties. Being seen with you is not a political problem any longer.'

'Or a social one?'

A group of men were becoming raucous. One of them tried to climb onto a table and was hauled down by his companions.

She slid into his arms. Petr closed his eyes for an ineffable second.

'Is it easy dealing with the West?' she asked. 'There must be so much distrust on either side?'

'Would you believe we manage, despite the fact we are Neanderthals?' He gestured to the adjacent table where a group of bulky men in grey suits were necking vodka. 'Which particular sin did you have in mind? Bribery? Extortion? Smuggling? But the short answer is yes. There are plenty of opportunities to distrust.'

Her fingers tapped a rhythm on his shoulder. 'I think you Czechs are both smart and emotional people. So are the Russians. The East Germans and British are different. But everyone likes being rich. Or richer.'

'So?'

He held her lightly, tactfully – the girl who had danced to a rock group, her cheeks flushed with sunburn. But the girl he had also seen beaten up and half naked in a cell. A sight that had driven everything from his head except the desire to protect.

'Are you trying to get information out of me, Laure?' The muscles in her back stiffened a little. 'If you are, it's quite funny, isn't it? A turnaround for the books, as you might say.'

The Laure of now was far too well schooled to give anything away. Looking up into his face, she said softly, 'Tell me the truth about Eva.'

His hand tightened on her waist. Taking comfort in its slenderness and warmth. 'You're right,' he said. He looked over her shoulder to the band. 'Eva killed herself.'

'Oh God.' She shook her head as if she had been hit physically. 'I'm sorry. I'm sorry. So sorry.' After a second or two she added, 'I feel for the children. For you. For Eva.' She looked up into his face. 'When I sat with her those times, she talked about you. So often.'

'Did she?' The intimacy of this exchange was making him clumsy and he almost lost his footing.

After a moment, she said, 'Eva loved you very much. She told me. She always worried about your happiness.'

'Eva was a very good and wonderful person,' he said. 'I was lucky to have her as a wife. It was just… things got too much.'

Was he imagining it but had Laure moved a little closer? Her cheek was almost resting against his.

Together, they danced on and Petr felt happiness brush over him, as light as gossamer.

'I'm sorry,' she repeated. 'Life can be cruel.'

He pulled her up against him.

She smelt of flowers. Her body was warm and yielding – as if it belonged under his hand. What he felt for her was so strong, so immutable, that it took his breath away.

Without warning, she came to a halt. 'Shall we sit down?'

They sat down and ordered more coffee. 'Let's not talk about Eva any more,' he said and she nodded.

The evening was coming to an end and he waited for the *coup de grâce* which would be the reason Laure asked to meet him.

It came.

The folds of her unsuccessful dress had ridden up a little, exposing the long legs that had been barely hidden by the short cotton dresses during that summer of 1986. At the sight, a rush of longing swept over him. And tenderness.

She folded her hands in her lap. 'Petr, I know you know what happened to Tomas. When we first met in Berlin, you suggested it. Why won't you tell me?'

He remembered the wind blowing smoke and grit between him and the waiting Laure at that station just over the Czechoslovakian border. 'I realized it's best to leave things as they are.'

'You were having me on. I should have known.' She paused before continuing. 'You insist that it wasn't you who betrayed Tomas,' she said collectedly enough but her knuckles had turned white. 'That's not the whole truth, is it?'

All those years of tormented introspection. He didn't like to tally what they had cost him. Or her. 'As I said,' he countered. 'My family was at risk.'

'What will it take, Petr?'

He was well versed in the tiny shifts in power play between people.

He looked into her eyes. *What will it take?*

Hers widened.

'Hallo, you two,' said a voice behind Petr.

'We were just passing,' said a female voice that Petr vaguely recognized. 'And here you are.'

'David. Sonia,' said Laure who did not seem as surprised as she should. 'You remember Petr Kobes from the party? I worked for him in Prague. Petr, you will remember my boss David Brotton and his wife, Sonia. Would you like to join us for a nightcap?'

Navy blue dress with white seams. The woman at the party.

As suspected, Laure had run this meeting through the embassy machinery which indicated a careful turn of mind and fastidious observance of protocol. He signalled to the waiter.

Sonia Brotton was drunk again. Not soddenly so, but well on the way. Petr wondered how the liability was tolerated and whether she had damaged her husband's career. She plonked herself down next to Petr and said, 'Laure has told me a little of her time with you in Prague. About the puppets and visits to the country.'

Petr sneaked a look at Laure. 'The Czechs love to pretend they are country dwellers, particularly the...' he searched for the word, '... the townees. At weekends, the cities empty and everyone makes for their *chata*. In summer, it's possible to live outside for much of the time. The forests and woods are very popular. So many of our stories and folk tales are set in the forest.'

He spared a smidgeon of compassion for Sonia. Her lipstick had smudged, the hand holding her glass was unsteady and she was drinking in this anodyne stuff with embarrassing enthusiasm.

'I remember the barbecues,' said Laure. 'They gave off such a smoky smell. The children loved it. I remember the sound of the trees as you lay in bed with the windows open.'

Sonia slumped back against her chair. 'I'm tired.'

David Brotton glanced at his watch. 'The car will be here any minute.' He turned to Petr. 'I gather you know Paris very well.'

'Yes. I enjoyed living there.'

David helped himself to some ice which had arrived in a glass with the drinks. 'It's the paradox. If you're sent abroad you should make the most of it. At the same time, it's unwise to become overfond of somewhere.'

Petr's English was good, but not as good as his French, but he had an excellent comprehension and not a bad grasp of idiom. 'Don't the British call it going bush?'

'That's it.' Sonia was beginning to slur. 'Some of those boys take to wearing grass skirts and flowers behind their ears. Head office try frantically to think up penalties but what can you do? If the sunset's got to you and the girls are willing.'

'Shut up, darling,' said David.

Petr reflected that a woman like Sonia did not the know the half of it and would scream blue murder if she did. In his neck of the woods, there were things that could be done to those who had gone bush. And were.

The lessons in surveillance tutored on how to spot the signs and there had been quite a trade in hauling people in. If cooperation was unforthcoming, there was always scopolamine, the truth drug. In the worst case, execution and a subsequent dumping of human ashes on the road outside Prague.

During his danger years, his fondness for the West had gone on record and he knew that he had eaten into his luck. On the other hand, he had delivered results.

He looked around the lobby. Anyone observing them would imagine four friends, who represented the new European order, were enjoying an evening together. He glanced over to Laure who was talking at Sonia who was, by now, almost speechless and had resorted to humming the dance tunes.

David Brotton maintained his focus on Petr. The initial impression of a harassed, well-meaning man with a liability for a wife and who was never going to make the high grades was misleading. 'I'm impressed by the number of eminent chemists working for you at Potio Pharma.' Brotton had done his homework. 'The work on anti-virals is going to change modern medicine.'

His admiration was genuine. Petr smiled, 'The Czech Republic is very proud of Dr Holý and the others.'

'Dr Holý leads the world in combating AIDS, smallpox, hepatitis B and shingles. Not a bad tally. But in the past...' Brotton was being careful, 'public health was compromised, I think.'

He was referring to the time when the concentration of toxic sulphur dioxide in the air over Northern Bohemia had been ten times higher than the legal limit.

'As you say, it's in the past.'

'If Potio Pharma is planning to expand, I would love to know more about your work on anti-virals.'

Would you now, thought Petr. When the federation of European Communist Countries had been forbidden to trade with the West (with a result there was no hard currency), production had been difficult. Now, they were powering ahead.

'Of course.' He sketched out a reasonably comprehensive overview of a programme that was being rolled out by the company but left out details that might be useful to the British. If the British wanted parity in the partnership, they would have to pay for it.

Brotton understood perfectly. Glancing at Sonia, he said, 'I think it's time for bed.' He stood up. 'Next time you're in Berlin, do get in touch.'

Goodbyes were said and the Brottons moved on. Laure prepared to follow them. 'Petr?'

He looked at her and thought of her as she had been in Prague. Then, she had been waiting for her future to reveal itself, and that joyful, inquisitive look that she often wore had touched him deeply.

He liked, too, her ability to see the funny side of things and he had watched her grief for her father mutate into a relish for life. She conveyed the sense that she was poised on the edge of discovery. And, with her love affair, came radiance.

He had envied it, lusted over it, yearned for it.

'You must tell me about Tomas. You have to tell me.'

It was after midnight when Petr got back to the hotel and ordered his taxi for the airport for early the next morning.

Brotton had done a good job of grilling him without appearing to do so, and he had returned the compliment. No doubt the other man was as exhausted as he was.

Laure was not stupid. She was right when she said the Czechs were an interesting people. They would be scenting opportunities to make political and financial capital out of their new systems, even if they were still feeling their way. Certainly, the West would be interested in their emergence.

Making for the lift in the lobby, he noticed a woman in a mauve rayon dress nursing a drink in the corner, doing her best to convince Petr that she was not focusing on him. She was middle-aged and almost beautiful but her long hair twisted up into a bun had been dyed too heavily. A watcher? It would no longer be the Party but possibly the new Czech state, anxious that its industrial secrets remained intact. It could be the British, but almost certainly not. A rival pharmaceutical company?

Or, maybe, his habit of keeping watch for the watchers was engrained?

If she was a watcher she wasn't very good at it because she was easy to spot. Pressing the lift button, he nodded in her direction.

She started and colour crept into her cheeks. He toyed with the idea of asking her up to his room but decided against it. If she was on his case, it might result in her being taken off it and that would be a shame as he could identify her so easily.

Sinking down onto the bed in his room, he placed a hand either side of him and pressed down onto the mattress. One of these days, both sides would give up the pretence and just admit they wanted to grab as much information about the other as they could. Then there could be big hugs and declarations of love all round.

He pulled back the sheets, got in and lay down.

He thought about his wife.

Thanks to her care at the Sainte-Anne Hospital in Paris, Eva had been under control.

When they returned to Prague from Paris, she was not. The downs were worse. The ups resulted in frequent hallucinations and a refusal to eat or to sleep. The dark seam of psychosis sewed into her family history and, which he now learnt, went back a long way had surfaced after Maria was born.

'I'm so sorry,' she would say after an episode. 'I'm so sorry, Petr.' Forgive me.

He remembered the promises they made. To respect each other. To love each other. To make a good marriage. To be honest.

'I hate you for not telling me,' he said on one occasion as she shook like a wounded animal. 'Think of the risk we've taken in having Jan and Maria.'

'Please,' she begged. 'Don't say that.'

He thought of her when they first met. So fresh and golden and, like him, longing for sex, for happiness in a partnership and willing to take on a younger man.

Unlike Paris, in Prague it was difficult to get hold of the right medication at the time it was most needed. This meant Eva was increasingly confined to their bedroom and the employment of Laure even more necessary.

It had been hot, hot, hot that summer.

Most nights, Eva crashed around the apartment kitchen in the attempt to produce a meal. She drank heavily. 'For the love of Marx…' 'Marx' was pronounced with ultra sarcasm. '…Let me have some relief.' She went early to bed leaving him, as often as not, with Laure.

Those had been moments of calm interspersed between the bitter episodes of mania and depression where Eva tried to make it work and apologized for what she had become. Those times, he found it unbearable to listen as she struggled to explain what it felt like to battle with inner disintegration.

'It is as if there is nothing of me. Nothing in me.'

'I've let you down.'

'I'm afraid.'

He was always frightened the children would hear and did his utmost to shield them. The return to Prague had been particularly dreadful. Prague's golem had taken Eva by the throat and the gains that had been made in Paris were wiped out.

'I should die.'

She said that quite often when she came round from the bad patches.

That time – that particular time – they had been in the bathroom getting ready for bed.

'Don't, Eva.'

Her eyes slid this way and that and he knew something was threatening. Every instinct told him to get her out of there. Too late, Eva took up his razor from the shelf and was out the door.

Hoping to God the children were asleep, he chased her back into the bedroom. She was standing by the window, her right hand holding the razor poised over her left wrist. At his entrance, she turned. Her face was as white as the sheets, the circles under her eyes violet, the body under the nightdress thickened by the drug regimes.

'I hate myself.'

'If you don't care about me, think of Jan and Maria.'

Eva wasn't listening to him. Nor had she for a long time. Or to anyone else. Whatever was in her – the demon – had kidnapped her thoughts, her mind, her feelings.

He tensed. Ready.

She sprang towards the door. He lunged at her, wrestled her onto the bed and held her down.

Eve cried out, 'Stop!'

He gripped her wrists and she writhed and beat her heels into the mattress. Her hands were slippery but so were his and he failed to get a sustained grip. The hand holding the razor slid from his. She raised it, bringing it slicing down onto his forearm.

The pain was startling. It was quickly followed by a line of red that turned into a stream. His anger erupted giving him additional strength. He bore down on her and succeeded in mastering her flailing arms and holding them in his grasp.

In that position, she quietened, hunched over onto her side, her nightdress blotched and stained and asked the wall, 'How long?'

He was breathing hard. He got up and opened a drawer. He dropped the razor into it and grabbed a handkerchief, which he tied awkwardly around his arm.

'Oh God,' he said, calling on a deity that he did not believe in.

Eva was breathing heavily but motionless, the fight gone out of her.

He bent over to kiss her shoulder, a kiss of peace which said: we've got through this one. Raising his eyes, he saw that Laure had been watching from the doorway.

She was transfixed. With horror? Fear? Disbelief?

All three.

Why had Laure got so thoroughly under his skin that summer in Prague? He worshipped his children, his job was demanding and left little time for anything else. He had worshipped Eva too. In his way. He was a man who had done his best to sort out his position – moral, philosophical, practical – and had been faithful to his commitments.

All the same and looking back, he had failed to understand the contradictions within himself.

Dropping his head into his hands, Petr did something he had not done for a long time. Not since he held the photograph of the children and himself taken in front of the Eiffel Tower that Eva had left for him.

He wept.

CHAPTER 21

*H*E RETURNED TO BERLIN IN THE LATE SPRING.

He had been busy. Back home, there had been an economic crisis, the infant Czech stock market had wobbled, national growth had gone into the minus and he was required at the helm of Potio Pharma to steer it through.

After Easter, the situation eased and he considered himself at liberty. A priority was to visit Maria in Paris who had made it clear that she loved France and wasn't coming home any time soon. *Plus ça change.*

Maria now wore carefully contrived student clothing, adopted Parisian slang, and dragged him to *boites* that 'only the true Parisienne knew about', which deepened his affinity with his daughter.

Over an espresso in the cafe by Pont des Arts, she asked him what had hit him when he first came to Paris. Petr found himself describing the chestnut blossom in public parks, the startling colour palette of women's clothes after the greyness of home, individually wrapped bonbons, litter, perfume: all varieties, floral and musky and dangerous.

'And the dentists,' he added. 'Don't forget the good dentists.'

'I want live in Paris,' she told him. 'Any objection?'

'Yes. Jan and I won't see you. But if you wish to, then you must.'

She lit up a Gitane. 'I'll come and go.'

From Paris, he contacted the British Embassy in Berlin and asked to be put through to Laure. It took several handovers and there were plenty of clicks on the line, which suggested the call was being monitored.

'Hallo,' Laure said eventually.

'It's Petr.'

'Petr. Are you well?'

She sounded detached, as if he was written off in her mental address book. As if, perhaps, she had given up on her questions.

'I'm coming to Berlin tomorrow for a couple of nights,' he said. 'Can we meet for dinner? We might be able to work something out.'

At her end, there was a sharp intake of breath. 'Come to my flat at seven-thirty,' she said.

In the Charlottenburg, a district in the former Western sector, trees were shaking out blossom and new foliage. An elusive fragrance drifted down from the most advanced. Holding a bouquet of eye-wateringly expensive orange roses in one hand and a bulky package in another, Petr got out of the taxi and looked up at the building where Laure lived.

What was he going to say? He had not, as yet, made up his mind. For someone who took business decisions crisply, his indecision was unusual and unsettling.

Laure's apartment was on the third floor of a mansion block leased by the British for their people. The lobby inside was cool and his feet echoed on the stone stairs.

Outside Number 7, he smoothed down the collar of an expensive overcoat – a coat his mother would have condemned as an expression of his shameful bourgeois cravings. He, on the other hand, considered it essential to survive.

Laure opened the door. She was dressed in figure-hugging black trousers and a blue loose-fitting sweater and looked nervous.

He held out the flowers. 'A little obvious,' he said, 'but I thought they had a certain something. The petals feel like soft cotton.'

'Obvious or not, they're lovely.'

'I was hoping they could be tied up in some smart ribbon but there wasn't any to be had. Only string.'

'No ribbon necessary.' She ushered him into the sitting area and disappeared to fetch a vase.

He looked around the room and was struck by how spartan it was, as if she did not expect to live in it. The furniture was utilitarian, the drapes at the windows were cheap ones and there was little to suggest that Laure was interested in stamping her personality on it. The only personal clutter were some objects on the table, intriguingly arranged as if they were a collection behind glass.

'It's like a shrine.'

Laure reappeared. 'I like making a relationship between objects.'

He picked up a small hand mirror with shells on the handle, of the sort he had seen sold in Prague markets. It was, to put it kindly, garish, as was the plastic flag in the Czech colours which he recognized from innumerable Party conventions. Beside them was a stone, which he was pretty sure was the one he had picked up at Tunnel 15.

Who knew what connections Laure made between these things?

The roses placed on the side table, Laure took two glasses out of the cupboard and a bottle of whisky. 'Your favourite, if I remember?'

He nodded. Nursing the whisky, he gestured at the room. 'You seem to be comfortable.'

'I am. I'm lucky and grateful.'

'I never asked you when we last met about your family.'

'My mother's in Paris. My brother's all over the place.' Her eyes sparked with humour. 'We've turned into nomads. Brympton can't get over it.'

He gestured to a briefcase parked by the table. 'It's no coincidence that you've ended up in the foreign office? They helped you get out of Prague and, no doubt, you were grateful. Is it a good job?'

'Berlin isn't exactly a barrel of laughs at the moment. But that'll change,' she said, 'and, yes, it's a good job.'

'I suppose the lure of gathering intelligence got to you.'

He was testing the water.

A faintly surprised expression crossed her face. 'I'm a cultural attaché. Nothing more. Nothing less.'

'But you have access to information.' He was thinking of the document she had produced in the car.

'Every embassy keeps files. It's the business,' she said, cool and matter-of-fact.

Nevertheless, an undercurrent flowed strongly, even ominously, through the comfortless room. He felt it. She would too. Petr went over to the window, which looked down at a small square, edged by young lime trees.

She came and stood beside him but kept a distance. 'Do you remember the time you came with me and the children to the park in Prague?'

'Very well.'

'You kept looking at me. I remember being frightened. Not quite understanding.'

'What exactly?'

He needed those few extra seconds to marshal his thoughts.

'That you...' she squared up to Petr, 'that you wanted me. Or

286

rather, not so much me, but my youth. Am I wrong?' She added, 'It's an old story, Petr. Father of the house fancying the au pair.'

He didn't care for the way she had summarized his torment at the time and defended himself. 'Laure, protest away if you like, but you did understand. You were having an affair, yourself. You knew exactly what goes on between men and women. But, yes, you're not wrong.'

'That's honest,' she said gently.

'I was very careful not to take advantage.'

'I was a young twenty-year-old and your employee, and you had promised my mother to take care of me. In those days, I believed what people told me.' She moved away, picked up the stone on the table and hefted it from one hand to the other. 'Before I grew up.'

Laure was protesting too much but it was probably calculated. 'I honoured that promise. I may have been a communist but not a predator.'

'True. I owe you that honesty.'

Laure's mother had sent him a letter, via the French employment agency, explaining that, because Laure was grieving for the unexpected death of her father, her daughter was postponing taking her degree to give her a chance to recover. 'I would ask that, as a responsible family man, you and your wife take care of her.'

'All the same, knowing your employer fancies you is grim and frightening.'

As yet, he had not worked out what she was driving at.

'It didn't stop your affair with Tomas.'

'Tomas wasn't grim and he wasn't frightening.'

Petr winced. 'In my defence, nor was I.'

At that Laure grinned. 'Tomas wasn't old and wrinkled.'

'You wretch.'

287

It was the first time she had referred to that past with any humour and the atmosphere eased.

She disappeared and reappeared with a bowl of olives. 'These are gold dust.' She placed them on the table, along with a plate of sliced German sausage. Petr tossed an olive into his mouth and bit into it. The taste was bracing and astringent on the tongue.

She sat down opposite him. 'There's something that haunts me. I need to know if I ever told you… stuff. Inadvertently? You know when we talked after Eva had gone to bed? Or when we took the children out?'

He found it difficult to recollect those moments: what he had perceived as a growing intimacy, the fact of her physical presence.

He remembered her suppressed excitement on the evenings she went out. Her radiance on returning from Anatomie's *chata*. Any fool would have deduced there had been discussions. Sex and politics were a combustible mix, and it didn't take much to work out their content. 'A hint here and there.' Laure bit her lip and sprang upright. 'Anatomie were known to be dissidents. You were from the West.' Drink in hand, he gestured towards her. 'And, in the end, you didn't trust me to help you get out of Czechoslovakia.'

'Of course not.' Laure topped up their glasses and screwed the top back onto the whisky so hard that the bottles rattled on the tray. 'You had warned me that you wouldn't. Remember?'

He watched the movement of her mouth – today the lipstick was dusty pink – which so intrigued him. Employing Laure had resulted in his carefully constructed life tipping into jeopardy and it had been very nearly disastrous.

By now, the lighting had come on in the street and he seized on it as diversion. 'I can never get over how bright the lights are in the West. The West should be careful and not waste resources.

We did better.'

'What rubbish you talk.' Laure sounded astonished. 'The old days were awful. The Party was awful. Life was awful...' A red-tipped finger was jabbed in his direction. 'Could I point out you were clever enough to escape to Paris.'

'And now, with the changes, I'm becoming a rich man. How's that for irony?'

'Nice.' She swished the whisky around her glass.

'I didn't mean to become rich, but it's happened.'

'Do *you* enjoy it?'

'I do.'

She looked thoughtful. 'Maybe it was always going to happen. You loved living in the West.'

He wasn't about to deny it.

'What are you going to do with your new riches?'

The sausage was a pinky-red and fresh-looking. He helped himself. 'I'll find something.'

'Establish a fund to find out what happened to people?'

She spoke without malice – but the implications stung.

'I'm going to defend myself,' he said. 'In my work, I did my best to bring badly needed know-how back home. The West shouldn't have a monopoly on knowledge. The Second World War brought terror, destruction, the collapse of order, and left the results for us to deal with. We wanted – needed – a system to heal our sore psyches, our dented political systems, our social myopias. Communism promised us that we were all in it together.'

'"Sore psyches, dented political systems, social myopias"... Good God.' Laure was laughing at him. 'And don't you mean the Russians?'

He looked across to the face that had, for so many reasons, haunted him. 'Are you taping this conversation?'

There was a hint of smile as she replied, 'Actually, no. But, if I'm doing the work you accuse me of, I could have been. Don't worry. Your coming here has been OK-ed. You're not considered a threat.'

He appreciated the information. 'I could take offence.'

'See if the Brits care.'

'Not cultural attaché speak, I think.'

Laure gave a proper smile.

Cradling the glass, he leant back against the sofa feeling that he could stay here for ever, swapping anecdotes, sharing a past.

And, yes, they could sit in a neutral, perhaps satisfactory, silence.

Laure broke it and the unexpected accord. 'Petr, I must know who betrayed us. Was it you?' She gulped her whisky down as if it was a rescue remedy. 'I know Lucia and Milos wouldn't have done. But, maybe, one of the others. I *need* to know. As you would do if something almost ruined your life. Perhaps did so? I know that I can put my life together again and what happened to me is nothing compared to what happened to Tomas. It was ten years ago…' Ten difficult years, he thought. 'And we are all learning to love one another.' Her voice dropped a note. 'Here's the chance to tell me the truth. A good thing to do?'

He knew this would be coming. 'Not necessarily.'

'Lucia had had a bad time, I know that much,' she cut across him. 'Her parents had been threatened. Like many, she lived on the edge. But she was a fanatic for the cause. I admired that in her. She was brave.'

'Perhaps.' He closed his eyes for a micro-second and made a decision. He would tell her something. 'But she informed on you, Laure.'

'*What?*' She sat bolt upright, eyes wide. 'Lucia?'

After the fall of the regime, he had made it his business to find out what the State had on him. The letter had been in his file in the archives. He quoted verbatim from it. "'Petr Kobes is employing a person who is spreading anti-communist sentiments and corrupting young children.'"

'I can't believe Lucia would…' She bunched a hand into a fist. '*Lucia!*'

'Motives *are* complicated,' he said, with more than a touch of irony. 'I learnt that, rather late but I have learnt it. Think of this. Lucia would want you out of the way because you attracted too much attention from the authorities. Better you vanished. It wasn't personal.'

'How did the police know about the meeting at the theatre?'

'Who knows?' he replied after a pause. 'It's possible we will never know the ins and outs.'

Was Laure craving retribution or absolution?

'Did *you* ever try to find out what happened to Tomas?' he asked.

'I did and got nowhere.'

'And he didn't contact you?'

'No,' she said pitifully. 'No.' Again, she sprang to her feet. 'That last day… when I left you.' She swivelled around to face him. 'Turning a blind eye is a national sport in Czechoslovakia. Why couldn't you have done the same?' She stood directly in front of Petr. '*Why?*'

He wanted to say: but I did for you.

'Tomas wasn't that important,' she went on. 'He wasn't a politician. He didn't matter.'

'If you are worshipped by the young, you do matter.' He sent Laure a wintry smile. 'Even Eva lusted after him.'

She was checked. 'I'd forgotten that. Poor Eva.'

Because he couldn't think of what else to do, Petr helped himself to a second slice of sausage.

'Am I prying if I asked what happened? I was fond of her and I would like to know.'

'Why didn't you tell me,' he demanded of Eva when the situation became intolerable. 'Because I wanted to be married,' she replied.

'Eva and I married within months of having met each other. She didn't let on about the illness in her family. It was possible she could have been perfectly healthy all her life. The doctors told me that two difficult births probably triggered it.'

'And?'

'She was being treated at Sainte-Anne in Paris when you arrived. After I was called back to Prague, the treatment was different. The doctors wanted to give her ECT and Eva refused.'

Taking about it gave relief. Even more so when – unexpectedly – Laure reached over and took Petr's hand. It was light, noncommittal, but it had been a long time since Petr had been touched in that way.

He looked down at Laure's hand around his and remembered the time he had held hers in Kampa Park and began to talk. 'She said she was living in a prison. One night she let herself out of the flat. I don't know if anyone saw her. But she walked down to the river and threw herself from a bridge.' Laure pressed his fingers. 'She left behind a photograph of the three of us. It was the one taken in Paris by the Eiffel Tower. There was a message written on the back. She wrote she wanted to give us peace, and to forgive her that she had failed us.'

'To say I'm sorry is inadequate. But I am sorry.'

'Laure…?' A tiny vein pulsed at his temple. She took her hand away, leaving its imprint, and he logged a rush of exhilaration through his body. 'People don't die until you forget them. Even if you are looking at a heap of their bones.'

She gave him a fierce, hard stare. 'Then you *know*.'

292

This was the moment he had planned. 'There's a reason I've made contact. I have something for you.' He got up and fetched the package and held it out.

She made no move to take it. 'A present?'

'In a way.'

'Why?'

'I thought it might build a bridge.'

'I don't want to take anything from you, Petr. Ever.'

Although it was not unexpected, the rebuke stung. 'Think of it, then, as being from the theatre company.'

'The company?' She was startled. 'This is from *the* company?'

He handed Laure a package. It was wrapped in stained brown paper and secured with string and he watched her tackle the knot. The wrapping peeled back to expose a flat, shallow box. She lifted the lid to expose an inner wrapping of yellowed newspaper. Dust sifted from it as she pulled it aside.

She glanced up at Petr with a question mark. 'Go on,' he said.

With a cry, Laure eased a female marionette puppet out of the box. 'Is it?'

'Have a look,' he said, with a cast-iron certainty that he had walked a path to the edge of a precipice from which there was no return.

The marionette's strings were neatly knotted down the back and the control bar tied up with ribbon. 'That's Milos's work,' she said tenderly. 'He was meticulous about putting the marionettes away properly. Always. Always. His life's work.' She touched a wooden hand. 'You know they're carved out of lime wood and some of them are very valuable?' Her voice trembled. 'It's Marenka. I *know* her. I would know her anywhere.'

CHAPTER 22

'*I*T IS MARENKA,' HE SAID.

Laure gave a cry and, lifting the marionette onto her lap, she cradled her as if she was a child. 'I've dreamt of her all these years. Of them. Of that time.'

He watched as she struggled for calm.

'After I met you here, I knew you should have her. The company was disbanded and their stuff confiscated. I got hold of her and she's been in my storeroom ever since.'

Laure stroked the wooden head. 'Did you wait patiently to get your life back, Marenka? Or did you howl in your agony but nobody heard?'

'Stop it,' said Petr. 'Please.'

'They have a soul, you know. Marionettes, I mean. They have life, too. They grieve.'

This was a side to Laure he had not seen.

'No,' he contradicted. '*We* grieve. Not them.'

She shook her head. 'Marenka, the Prince, Pierrot and the others are alive. Perhaps you don't see it.' She smiled at him, politely, as if she was sounding out a new acquaintance. 'A good puppeteer knows they live in a parallel existence to us. If they are to connect, then he or she must love them.'

This Marenka had a scarlet mouth, heavily lashed eyes, one blue, one green, and a crack running up her right ear. Laure traced the crack with her thumb. 'She was damaged when Lucia dropped her. We were having an argument and I always think it was deliberate.' She searched in the box. 'I wonder if… yes.' She exhumed a square of folded material which, unfolded, became a bride's veil. 'It's still here. Lucia made it from an old family heirloom. She showed me.' She stroked the lace with a fingertip and placed it over Marenka's head. 'I was horrified.'

Laure's romanticism touched him. 'They're certainly part of our culture,' he said.

She glanced up. 'I didn't understand then. The power they have, I mean.' She unwound the ribbon around the control bar. 'I can see Milos tying this,' and checked over the frayed strings. 'Marionette strings should be attached to the head, the back, the hands and just above the knee.' She looked up. 'The lessons are not forgotten.'

Holding the control bar taut, she lowered Marenka down until the wooden feet touched the floor and manipulated her, ineptly, along the length of the sofa.

'The different eyes were meant as a message,' said Petr.

'Were they?'

'There's no need to pretend any more, Laure. It was so easy to spot.'

'Well then, you know how effective it was.' Marenka shuffled to a halt. 'You and…' her voice hardened, 'your colleagues might well have interpreted the special meanings in the performances. But so did others who took so much more from them than you possibly could. Comfort and laughter. Truths that couldn't be spoken out aloud. The company was brilliant at that,' she said. 'Did you ever watch the Pierrot when you were snooping?'

He suppressed a flash of anger. 'I did.'

Her eyes had grown huge. 'It always made me weep. But it was a miracle. A marionette is technically dead but also alive in a way we cannot explain. The Pierrot suffers and we with him. He was the most tragic, most *wonderful* thing. You will never see the like. He refuses to be manipulated by the master. He knows the worst. He showed us that we could make choices and we could accept death.' Tears now spilled over. 'Because he was always about love, and loving life so much that he refuses to accept the compromise.' She wiped her cheeks with her sleeve. 'That's why he plucked out his own strings.' She added in a low voice, 'I don't expect you to understand.'

He thought of Jan and Maria batting through the leaves at the Kampa Park that summer's day and of Eva stealing out of the apartment and hastening to her death. He thought, too, of the moments after the man from the Party in the pork-pie hat had taken away his freedom.

'What happened to Milos and Lucia?'

Petr knew, sooner or later, Laure would ask him. Using his contacts, he had arranged for the relevant records to be opened up. 'It's an old Czech custom to gang up on public enemies,' he said. 'You probably know. Everyone feels safer. Lucia and Milos were associated with Tomas and Anatomie and, once Anatomie were arrested, they were known as public enemies.' He brushed some dust from the newspaper off his sleeve. 'It calmed down in the end. Things weren't as bad as the sixties. If it had been then, undoubtedly, they would have disappeared. They are probably living quietly somewhere out of Prague.'

'Aha...' Marenka's wooden limbs clicked and clacked as Laure eased her upright.

It was a sound to summon the past. On his ninth birthday, his mother took him to the marionette theatre where a demon chased a capitalist across the stage. Strings taut, teeth chattering, painted face as white as chalk. Afterwards, his mother complained that he had crushed her hand in fright.

'I'm out of practice,' said Laure.

Petr laughed.

Laure adjusted the strings and fanned out the bars and Marenka rose quivering to her full height, the veil modestly covering her face. Beneath it, a brown plait hung down her back.

'It's coming back to me.' With a twitch of the bars, Laure turned the marionette to face Petr. 'Like riding a bicycle. She's asking questions, Petr. Such as, why are you giving me to this woman?'

He didn't reply.

'I think you do know why,' Laure said. 'Guilt.' She busied herself with the strings. 'I've learnt one thing. If you're guilty about something you don't want to let it go. That's what I found. You like to prod it.' She corrected herself. 'You *need* to prod it. I did.'

It was a debate so painful that he could not enter into it. 'I felt you should have her.'

She looked up. 'You always were generous.' She tugged at the strings and Marenka tottered drunkenly towards Petr. 'The other question, the big question, she's asking is, "Where's my Prince? Where did he go?"'

A reply was necessary. 'Not a good, or sensible, question.'

'What will I do with you, Marenka?' Laure laid the puppet down on the sofa and stowed the bars in a way that Milos had taught her. 'She ought to be in a Czech museum, particularly as she was in Prague at the end of it all, the end of an era.' She touched a wooden hand. 'She has historic value.'

'Will you thank me?'

She faced him directly. 'Thank you.' She said it so simply that his heart turned over. 'Now, please. About Tomas.'

He looked at her. 'Always Tomas.'

'Yes, but this is about you too,' she said. 'Look on it as your salvation?'

Their eyes met.

A clumsy realigning of morality, grief and political observance? Of deep-boned desires? Of regret?

A bargain negotiated?

She took an audible breath – as if she was readying herself to dive off a high board. Reaching over, she undid Petr's tie. 'French, I think,' she said, then glanced at the label. 'How did I guess?'

Dropping it onto the floor, she took his hand and led him towards the bedroom.

Within seconds, he realized how skilled she was in dissimulation. What Laure felt for him was far removed from what he felt for her. Indeed, he sensed beneath the compliant body a deep contempt.

Sliding her arms up over his bare torso, she shivered. Putting his arms around her, he bent over and pressed his mouth against her shoulder as he had done so often to Eva.

'This has been a long time in the making,' he said.

She tensed. 'It wasn't yours to have.'

He cupped her head in his hands and bent to kiss her, long and tenderly. But, just as she was beginning to respond, she broke away. 'Don't do that.'

'Why not?'

She closed her eyes. 'It's too intimate.'

She waited until she had lowered herself on top of him before she said, 'Tell me about Tomas.' The beautiful skin had flushed over the cheekbones and, for a few seconds, he wondered if, despite herself, she was enjoying the encounter just a little. 'Is he… dead?'

The dead were easy to cherish, he thought. Tomas could never be said to be unfaithful, or that he had failed to live up to expectation.

She moved a fraction and additional pleasure shot through him. 'Petr, what happened to Eva was terrible but you *do* know what happened to her. But that is what makes it possible to live with.'

The sensations were overpowering. Petr closed his eyes and willed the moment to be sweet, valedictory, tender – to be a moment when the barriers dissolved. He reached up and touched her cheek. Was it possible that what he felt for Laure would ever confer the inner peace, the richness, that he craved? 'I don't know,' he lied. 'I don't know what happened to Tomas.'

Her movements stilled. 'Then we are in my bed under false pretences.' Abruptly, she moved off him and sat on the edge of the bed.

In some discomfort, he cursed silently. 'Come back.'

She stood up and reached for the robe hanging on the back of the door. 'You knew what I was asking.'

He lay back and put his arm across his eyes, aware that he would have a ferocious ball ache for the rest of the evening. 'Laure, if you think aborting this is a punishment, you're wrong.'

The truth was: it came close. His passion, his history, put him at a gross disadvantage, not least because he was fighting the strongest, most durable of entities: the ghost. 'You're no good to anyone if you're obsessed with a vanished man,' he said.

'That's my problem.'

The spots flashing behind his closed lids made him a touch nauseated. Throwing back the sheets, he levered himself upright, and made for the bathroom, slamming the door shut. Inside, he placed his hands on the basin rim and struggled to master his anger and intense disappointment.

He wanted to kill Laure. He wanted to hurt her. He wanted to make her shut up. Aghast, he looked up into the bathroom and saw the reflection of a man whom he did not recognize.

Eventually, he took down a clean towel from a stack on the shelf and wrapped it around himself. She was sitting on the bed but had put on her robe. He stood over her and said, 'Laure, you took a bloody stupid risk. Women get beaten up. For less. *I* could have beaten you up.'

'Maybe.' She looked up at him. 'But I don't think you are that kind of man.'

Lust still coursed through him and made him additionally savage. 'It's bloody foolish and you're not a fool.'

How many violent emotions was it possible to feel in a few hours? Many, as it turned out, and he was exhausted by them. Looking into Laure's face, he read in it triumph and, also, shame.

'I'm sorry,' he said. 'For how changed you are.'

She stood up and her hair fell over her shoulders. 'I'm sorry too, Petr. But you did something to me all those years ago that makes it possible for me to behave… well,' she shrugged, 'as I have just done.'

'So be it.' He reached into his jacket pocket for a cigarette and thought the better of it. He shoved the cigarettes back into the jacket pocket. 'For what it's worth, Tomas made it to the railway station where he was arrested and put into solitary.'

She was on him like a shot. 'Which prison?'

'On the Bartolomějská. It used to be a convent.' He settled himself against the bedhead. 'The nuns' cells turned out to be fit for purpose.' He frowned. 'And the church was used as a shooting gallery.'

'And you weren't going to tell me even that?'

'No.'

'Why?'

'Because it will haunt you.'

'Like it must haunt you? Or, should do.'

'Have some pity.'

To his surprise, she nodded. 'How can I find out? The StB must have kept records. Like the Nazis and the Stasi.'

'Good luck looking.'

'*You* will look for me, Petr. To right the wrong, to be peaceful … *you* find the information.' She twisted up her hair into a knot. 'You destroyed a future. Think of it as reparation.'

He had read somewhere that love was heightened and deepened by pain. But there was a limit and he was close to snapping point. 'Laure, did you ever really consider Tomas was probably using you?'

She had gone white. 'You've used that method before, Petr. Wasn't it called the contamination method? Maybe you still use it?' She refused to look at him and wrenched open the door. 'Tomas was a man who dared to take you all on and who never compromised. Who was brave. Who I loved. Who loved…' She stopped. 'Get out,' she said. 'Get out.'

He put on his shirt and began buttoning it up. She picked up her scattered clothes and placed them on the chair. 'Let yourself out.'

She moved off into the other room.

He sat down heavily on the edge of the bed. The old wild lusts and griefs swirled around his head along with the whisky, which he doubted he would ever drink again.

Laure moved around in the next room. He heard the clink of glasses and a shuffle of furniture. A silence fell.

He went over to the door and stepped through, only to bump into Laure coming back into the room. They faced each other.

'I'm sorry,' she spoke first. 'But you hurt me.'

'I'm sorry too.'

How eagerly love made do with the slivers that were offered.

Various expressions registered in the green eyes, none of which he could quite read. 'I honour my bargains.'

'I *know* Tomas loved me...' There was just a hint of uncertainty.

So that was it, he thought. The doubt he had planted had rooted. It had taken time but it was there.

Love went with pity? Power went with love? Cheating and short-changing too.

He swallowed. 'If I tell you what I know, you must promise to forget it and to live your life?' Her eyes were now so vexed and troubled that he was being dragged into their shadows. 'For your sanity.'

She allowed herself to be sat back down on the bed.

The new Czech Republic was not a cheap territory in which to operate and he had paid well for the information that he was about to pass on to Laure. In one sense, he had bought his own discomfort. To live with what he had unearthed was to be faced with the crimes and misdemeanours of the regime he had supported.

'Tomas was on the watchlist. He was a known dissident. You know he was frequently picked up and questioned. And beaten up. It was thought he and the group were trying to get information out to the West. He was arrested as he boarded a train to Vienna and taken to the Bartolomějská.'

She uttered a small sound of distress.

'Prisoners there were divided into three categories. Minor offenders, repeat offenders and serious offenders, which usually included the political prisoners. It was not a good category to be in.'

He was not about to give the details. In the past, political prisoners were assigned to the uranium mines, which were poisoned, brutal hells, run by thugs and killers. But Laure did not need to know the half of it. *That* he could do for her.

She folded her arms across her stomach.

'Do you wish me to continue?'

She looked this way and that. 'Yes.'

'Tomas was in the serious offender category. He was interrogated for three days at the end of which he was admitted to the prison hospital. The records show that he had broken arms, a broken leg and a serious head wound.'

'And who knows what else.' Laure dropped her face into her hands. Greatly daring, Petr stroked her hair. 'He was due to be transported to a prison outside Prague.'

'Oh God.' Pale with emotion, she lifted her face from her hands. 'Was there anything else?'

He hesitated, and she repeated the question impatiently.

'There's no record of him leaving the hospital, which could mean he died or someone was negligent. The records aren't infallible and many have been destroyed.'

She seemed to have got herself under control. 'OK. He could have died there. But we don't know for certain.' Her voice shook. 'Could he have got out from the Bartolomějská?'

Her accent had not improved. In fact, it was terrible, but it was one of the many attractive things about Laure. 'In his state, he would have had to have had powerful friends. I think you must accept that Tomas probably did not survive.'

Laure wasn't listening. 'Then it's possible he was sprung from the hospital and made it to... somewhere? Hungary?'

'Even if he did, it would be tough living on the run. Very. No papers. No money.'

'You're saying he was tortured?'

'If he wasn't talking, almost certainly.'

'Tomas wouldn't have talked.'

'Sweet Laure. He was being beaten up.'

'No,' she contradicted. 'Tomas had armed himself. Prepared. Mentally, I mean because he knew what might happen.'

'We both know that we don't know what someone would do in those circumstances,' he said, and Laure gave a sharp intake of breath. 'The ones you expect to hold out, don't. But the meek and flavourless sometimes do. They dig something out of themselves. Or they tell themselves that this is their last chance to make a mark on life, whether it's witnessed or not.'

'Well, you would be the expert.' Her hand resting on her thigh balled into a fist. 'I knew it, really. I felt it. I felt his suffering.'

'Listen to me: Tomas is almost certainly dead.'

She was silent. Then, she shook her head. 'Until I know for certain, I will leave the door open. But I can't forgive you for betraying him.'

'Are you quite sure that's true?' He flashed back at Laure.

She went as white as paper. 'It's a common reaction for the guilty to off-load guilt onto others.'

He spoke more gently. 'It's a function of human psychology to hide unpleasant truths behind so-called memory loss.'

'You lie,' she said. 'You always lied.'

'And you were careless with your words. Did you ever think about that?'

There was a long pause, and he saw her picking her way down the memories. 'I was frightened.'

'And angry with Tomas?'

She shook her head.

'Laure,' he said, 'you're older now. You must see the love affair in a different light. It was a thing of youth. Not real.'

Again, she shook her head. More than a little contemptuous. Impatient.

After a moment, he said: 'I had a family, a sick wife. Tell me, what would you do in the circumstances?'

'I calculated that, because you were fond of me, you would say nothing.'

The featureless bedroom, the rumpled bed, Laure's anguish, the harsh and unpalatable truths that were being aired… he knew he would never forget this encounter.

What if he took her by the arm and pulled her down onto the bed to take his fill of the pearly skin, of the tumble of hair, the sweep from shoulder to hip? He would murmur her name and tell her that all would be well between them and there would be peace, and ideology would lie down with ideology. He would tell her that he loved her and had done so for a long time and carrying that love through his life had scraped him raw and, yet, had been his greatest delight. It had been, he would add, a contorted, tainted love but, in its strange way, a true one.

Was it her grief or, because of her own, a heightened sensitivity to Petr's distress? Perhaps she prided herself on being someone who kept to their bargain? Laure turned to Petr and put her arms around his neck.

His surprise was intense, but he kissed her. She tasted of olives and the recent cigarette. He drew her down and moved his body so it lay against hers. Running his hand up from her thigh, he traced the waist and the softness of a breast collapsed against her torso.

As so often, the reality was different to the imagined one of surrender and hungry encounter. Laure tensed as he ran his hand up and down her body and stroked a nipple. 'Shall I stop?'

'No.'

It was cool enough in the room to cause her skin to gooseflesh and tiny fine hairs on her arms stood upright. He felt behind him for a sheet to draw over them but only succeeded in getting his hand tangled up in its folds. He fought free and tried to touch her between her legs. She moved away from under him.

'Let's not draw it out,' she said.

Halfway through, he opened his eyes. Laure looked contained, slightly indifferent, almost maternal. Nothing like the passionate, responsive woman that he had wished for. But this was the best he was going to get. He closed his eyes and allowed the hot, hard impulses to take him over.

Towards the end, she reached up, drew his face to hers and kissed him. For a few moments, that was good enough – until he realized that she was kissing a memory.

Getting dressed, he examined his face in the bathroom mirror and noted it was wiped clean of anything much. He brushed back his hair and knotted the French tie and stepped into the sitting room.

Laure was in her dressing gown, crouched down beside Marenka.

'This is goodbye,' he said. 'In another life, it might have been different.' She did not look up. 'Laure, please think about yours. Do you intend to spend it snooping and hanging around in the shadows at the behest of your embassy? Yes? All the things you rejected when you were in Prague.' Her shoulders tensed. 'Don't do it. I've had my life and made the mistakes. But I wouldn't want you to do the same.'

She shook back her hair as if to brush away unwelcome knowledge. 'I hope your life is how you wish it. And successful.' She stood upright and faced him and he ached to kiss her one final time. 'You're a good man, but a divided one, I think. You love your children. You were generous to me but your politics took you in other directions.'

He considered pleading for them both to begin again, to make something out of the disaster – and dismissed the idea.

'Do you remember the Pierrot piece I was talking about?' Laure stood up. 'The marionette who plucked his own strings out? I used to be frightened that it was Tomas. But, I think after all, it was you. You once said that Tomas would be the broken man but it's you who's broken.'

'And you,' he said.

There was a long silence.

'You and I are done,' she said. 'Done.'

He got back to his hotel room and stood for a long time with his back to the door, unable to put one foot in front of the other.

Not even after the death of Eva had he felt like this. Scorched inside and as if the roots tethering him to his life had been pulled up, one by one. Whether he could ever atone for the things that had been done, he did not know.

The contradictions of his history were savage but – not forgetting Czech humour – also funny. What would have happened if the Prince in the folk story had ended up helpless and out of control as he now was? What would have happened if the Prince had hacked through the defensive hedge of thorns only to find that Sleeping Beauty was not only not waiting for him, but hostile?

He ran a shower as hot as he could take it and stood under it for a long time. He dried himself, put on the hotel dressing gown and mixed himself a drink from the mini-bar and took it to bed.

Since the fall of the Wall, the hotel management had made efforts to compete with its Western counterparts, but the bed was far from comfortable and the sheets were cheap and slippery. He did not expect to get much sleep. Nor did he.

The following day, he attended the meeting. Afterwards, he ordered a taxi and drove to the airport where he got on a plane and flew out of the once divided city back to his life in Prague.

CHAPTER 23

Paris, today

*T*HE CELEBRATION LUNCH AT THE MAISON DE GRASSE WAS every bit as sybaritic and sophisticated as May wanted. Observing her reactions Laure was reminded that to take a delight in the luxurious was sane and pleasurable.

'It's so beautiful,' said May, on viewing the room where the lunch was to be held. 'So beautiful… that it hurts.'

The flowers – lilies, orange blossom and hydrangeas – had been flown in from the south of France. An arch of them had been constructed over the entrance to the dining room. Elsewhere, they were massed on the tables and in every nook and cranny. The effect was extraordinary and their scent intoxicating.

The tables were exquisite, each one a dream in white lawn, silver and flowers. Beside each setting was a bottle of Maison de Grasse's most expensive perfume and a nosegay of herbs, including rosemary. 'For remembrance,' Laure informed May.

'Well, that's what you're about, isn't it?' she replied.

Laure's audience, as she got to her feet after a lunch of wild salmon and red-currant Vacherin, was inclined to be kind. It was the kindness that stemmed from fabulous dining, champagne and the magic of white Burgundy.

'This is a very important occasion,' she began. 'In fact, it is quite a day when two sides of our culture come together. The one that does and makes...' she made a graceful obeisance to the Maison de Grasse top table, 'and the one that preserves.' She gestured towards the table around which were seated Nic, May, Simon, the lawyers and the trustees.

She was used to public speaking and generally it held no perils. But this was a moment for which she had plotted and worked, and she was close to betraying her emotions. 'Like many of you, I suspect, museums exert a fascination. As a child, I set up a button museum. Buttons being the only things which I could lay my hands on. I charged my long-suffering family sixpence to visit it. I learnt then that people love looking at objects, especially if the guiding curation behind their display gives an explanation and a coherence and connection. Who could fail to respond, one way or another, to the paintings on a cake tin that show the yearnings of a trapped housewife? Or, the picture of the grave up a Spanish mountainside which bears the inscription: "You promised not to take any risks". What is special to the Museum of Broken Promises is the explanations. In most museums it is the experts that supply the information. In ours, it is *you*, the public, who do so. Our museum gives a voice to the people in a way that few other institutions provide.'

Across the flowers, Nic smiled encouragingly. He knew how the speech would go.

'Every culture must have its museums and a country without them is a country that either deliberately, or unwittingly, destroys its past. That is always a danger signal.' She paused for a long moment.

'You could argue, therefore, that museums are as much political entities as cultural ones...'

Experience had taught her that she had only a couple more minutes to keep the audience's attention.

'Why a museum devoted to broken promises?' She looked directly at one of the smarter women with expensively slicked-back hair and minimal make-up. 'Which one of us has not experienced a broken promise in our lives? Either we made it and broke it. Or, someone made one to us and failed to keep it. The consequences can be funny, tragic, fleeting or life-long. However small, however large, those broken promises matter.' She gathered up the finale. 'There is, too, the possibility that a promise you considered to be broken was, in fact, not broken. But it takes time to see it. Who knows? The reflections on, and the interpretation of, an event can be many and, as we mature, the perspectives shift. That is one of the reasons that the turnover of objects in the museum is a constant one.'

May shot a look at Nic.

The scent of the lilies sifted through the room. Someone coughed.

'What is true, I think, is that we find it hard to accept that everything must end: joy, pain and life itself. But while we are here, observing a ritual, or making a formal gesture, offers comfort and the prospect of coherence. Donating to the Museum of Broken Promises, where the objects are treated with care, reverence and a little humour, can open up the healing process. The stories we tell about ourselves are not always completely truthful. Or, we fail to see clearly what we have done. The museum offers the chance for it to settle and for...' she slowed, 'the truth to become clearer.'

She paused, assaulted suddenly by the memory of snarling panic and fear. Of running. The pain of her injured hand. Weeping.

The exhaustion of having broken her heart.

'I say all this because I know…' Her old, troubled history was marshalled into words, 'I know from personal experience what it is to break a promise.'

She sat down to enthusiastic applause.

That evening after work, Laure ordered the taxi to drop her at the Canal Saint-Martin. After the luxury, she needed to ground herself in the streets where life was ordinary and harder. Dropping in at Chez Prune, she ordered a double espresso and drank it down gratefully. It was a trifle bitter but it did her just fine.

Chez Prune was full and she exchanged one or two greetings before leaving. She was in no hurry to get back home and lingered on the bridge over the canal and concluded that the water seemed clearer, less rubbish-strewn.

Every day the cluster of tents lining the banks grew more numerous. The fall-outs and victims from capitalism. The irony was not lost on Laure.

She turned north and took the long way around, past peeling plane trees, the tabac, the grocery, the old tannery on the corner with its rusting ironwork and the medieval *hôpital*.

As she rounded a corner, she almost collided with a young couple. She was in shorts and he in cargo trousers. Both had rucksacks. 'I don't know where we are,' he was saying in English. 'We're lost.'

The girl did not bother to look around but dug into her pocket and produced her mobile. 'Google will tell us.' Together they peered at the small screen, oblivious to Laure pushing past them.

Paris is in my blood, she decided and it was a supremely satisfactory thought. I will grow old here.

Back in the apartment, Laure sank down onto the sofa. The

window was open. She had kept it so in the hope that Kočka just might return but it was growing chilly and, in a few minutes, she would shut it.

Her mobile rang a couple of times but each time she ignored it. Having earned it, she was going to indulge in the luxury of silence.

After a while, she got up and shut the window. Having been asked to work up her speech into a more substantial article for publication in an art journal, she sat down at the table and opened her laptop.

A hideous screeching from outside interrupted her and she leapt over to the window. In the courtyard outside, Madame Poirier was beating with a feather duster at a small form cowering under the bush with the white blossoms.

Within seconds, she was out the door and down the stairs. 'Madame, stop it. Stop it at once.'

Madame Poirier placed a hand on her hip. 'Excuse me?'

But Laure wasn't listening. She was on her hands and knees beside the object of Madame Poirier's brutality. 'Kočka,' she said, 'Oh Kočka, you've come back.'

The cat's tormented eyes locked onto Laure. By the look of her, she had been starving, possibly injured, and was too weak to do anything.

With a cry, Laure gathered her up. She stank of rubbish, and God knew what else, but Laure never been so grateful to see anyone, or anything. 'You've come. Even though you can barely move, you came back.'

'If you take that cat indoors, then I must file a complaint with the landlord,' said Madame Poirier.

Kočka's head was resting in the crook of Laure's arm. 'File away.'

'You will have to leave.'

'Then leave I will. But the cat is with me for tonight.'

Walking back into the apartment, Laure banged the door shut with a foot and carried Kočka over to the cushion that she had previously occupied and laid her gently down on it.

Kočka blinked, unfurled a trifle and settled. Laure fetched water and a few of the cat biscuits and fed them one by one to her. 'To the vet with you,' she said. 'Tomorrow.'

She sat back on her heels, understanding finally that a transition – and a transaction – had taken place. 'It looks as though you've become mine.'

There was a knock on the door.

It was May, clutching an expensively packaged bouquet. 'The Rottweiler masquerading as your concierge asked me to give you these. They were delivered earlier. At least, I think that's what she said. She seems angry.'

Laure inspected the bouquet. Orange roses… *orange roses?*

The colour was not her favourite. She found it unsettling.

'Nic gave me a translation of the speech,' said May. 'I could see you got them eating out of your hand. One of the women cried, the one with the cropped hair.'

'Thank you.' She made no move to invite May in but couldn't resist the tease. 'I think you enjoyed it?'

'It was so *smart*. Can't wait to tell the folks back home.'

'So you do talk to your mother?'

'Nope. Not Miss Melia.'

Laure was getting to know May and was pretty sure the chippiness in her last comment masked anger. She allowed the extravagant length of black-and-white ribbon that tied up the bouquet to slip through her fingers. 'It's not my business but, perhaps, you should. She *is* your mother.'

May appeared to be fascinated by the flowers. 'I've spent more time thinking about whether or not to cosy up to a mother who hates the sight of me than you would credit.'

'Is it hate?' interjected Laure.

'Well, surely to God, it's not indifference. And it's not love. So, it's hate. It stuck in the craw once, but not any longer. But…' May's face darkened. Then she grinned. 'Other people can listen to me. And they do.'

She continued to hover on the doorstep, metaphorically on tip toe and raring to go. 'I have questions. Big ones. Serious ones.'

Laure was damned if she did, damned if she didn't. 'Five minutes,' she said and stood aside. 'You sit down, you get up and you leave. No snooping.'

On entering the room, May gave a small cry. 'The cat's back. That's great.'

Laure placed the bouquet on the coffee table. She had a sense that something, long dug deep into her, was uprooting. Whether it was a natural, or unnatural, process she did not know, only that Kočka had been a trigger.

'Five minutes,' she reminded May.

May sat down, facing Laure. 'I'll come clean. I'm good at what I do and I can usually hack it. But, with you, I've only got so far. We dodge around the questions. That's my fault as much as yours but I like you very much, Laure.'

'You mean you like Nic,' Laure interposed gently.

'Yes. I like Nic.' She leant forward. 'Here's the thing. Why give up a promising career in your foreign office? No value judgements here, but it seems odd. Were you sacked?'

'Actually, no.'

Actually, Laure had sacked herself. Petr had been acute in his assessment – she would give him that. The quasi-undercover life of the embassy that she thought would make sense to her did nothing of the sort in the end, only added to the muddle of regret and recrimination that she carried around. It had been a miscalculation.

May pressed on. 'I know that you were probably in low-grade intelligence gathering in Berlin. Who wasn't?'

'You and I are done,' she had told Petr. 'Done.'

'When I was working in Berlin, Germany was pulling itself together. Information was being traded all over the place. Ordinary citizens, businessmen, retailers. There's nothing unusual about that. In a transition people will try and find out what they can. They have to.'

That meant she had reported back to David Brotton about Petr and his business activities. Such as she had uncovered.

'You had a bad time in Prague.'

'You have no basis for that assumption.' Laure's response was curt.

'Aha,' said May. 'You did.' She shifted in the seat. 'What do you think about this. You go to Prague, all shiny and new and innocent. Something happens there. Possibly a man? Or a political shock?'

'Czechoslovakia was a communist country. Of course it was different.'

'So two systems, communism and capitalism, are battling away in you.'

'May, you should be writing fiction.'

'Your time there leaves you unsettled or, perhaps horrified or disgusted, so you dip your toe into diplomatic waters. It's a bit half-hearted. You are still unsettled and something is nagging away at you. So you try something else...'

Laure's mobile shrilled. It was Simon who she had been trying, and failing, to contact for the past twenty-four hours. 'May, I have to take this.'

Simon's voice was in her ear. 'Your unknown sponsor will be pulling out. His or her reasons? He or she feels that the museum is now well established, and you will be obtaining funding from other sources with no difficulty.'

Laure eyed up the rooftops framed in the window. Things were changing. As always. Pleasingly, the thought of how she must absorb herself in new options for the museum, the many meetings to hack out a way forward and the preparation of myriad documents did not depress her. 'We're incredibly grateful. Is there any way we can thank him or her?'

He chuckled. 'Offer your body?'

'To her or him?'

'I'll see what I can do,' he said.

She finished the call. Placing her phone down on the table, her eye was caught by the orange roses and the coils of expensive ribbon.

My God. A memory struggled to the surface.

She was then tearing at the cellophane surrounding the roses to find the gift card.

May cut off her next question. 'Are you all right?'

Laure was rigid with shock. May reached over and prised the card gently from her. 'Is it bad news? Can I help? Do you need something?' She cast her eye around the room. 'Water?'

'No.'

'Is it anything to do with that photo that came? Nic said it had an effect on you.'

'No.'

Not quite true.

'Is it to do with the museum?'

Laure clasped both hands together. In her inner ear, voices from another world competed. Some of them ghosts? Despairing. Defiant. Funny. Scabrous.

But not the one she had longed over the years to hear.

'Laure?' May sounded anxious. 'Should I get someone?'

Laure leant over and placed the card on the table. 'Do you know what it says?' May shook her head and Laure translated from the French. '"I have paid my dues."'

'Sounds Old Testament,' said May.

She made herself draw in long, slow breaths to steady her stomach. May sat down beside her and put her arms around her shoulders. 'Here,' she said. 'You can lean on me.'

And Laure did so, finding a surprising comfort in May's thin, whippy arm.

'What's happened?' asked May. 'Something has.'

Laure struggled to answer. 'Nothing.'

'For God's sake, it isn't nothing. It can't be. You're the colour of the sheets in my grotty hotel and you're about to throw up. It's something.'

'I can't tell you,' said Laure.

'Yes, you can,' said May. She placed her hands on Laure's shoulders. 'You *can*.'

Laure looked into the blue-grey eyes and the complications that lay behind them. 'I can't trust you.'

May sent her a crooked grin. 'You can for a couple of hours.'

It was very late in the evening when May let herself out of the Laure's apartment.

Laure remained motionless in her chair. Drained. Purged?

She had told her story to the least likely person she could ever have imagined telling it to.

At the end May commented: 'It's not surprising you feel like you feel.'

How would you know? Laure almost asked but something in May's expression stopped up the words.

May read Laure's thoughts. 'Because I'm damaged, too.'

She had insisted on unearthing the half-bottle of brandy stowed in the cupboard and pouring out a healthy dollop for each of them.

Alcohol loosened her tongue and Laure heard herself confessing, 'When you've experienced something so... blazing... it's difficult afterwards, perhaps impossible, to settle. Or, for me, it was. Anyway, I didn't trust myself any more. I was married for a time, you know. And it didn't work for me. I regret that and what I failed to bring to it. But, with luck, you can find a substitute.' She spread her hands. 'And I did.'

May nodded and then asked: 'It's curious that you have never really pushed to find out what happened to them all. Why?'

'I did.'

May was sceptical. 'Especially now. There're so many ways to trace events, people, the truth. As your mystery sponsor obviously did. Perhaps...' she looked down at her empty glass. 'You didn't want to? Not really.'

Laure had no answer.

CHAPTER 24

Prague, 1986

*L*AURE PEERED OUT OF THE WINDOW THAT LOOKED DOWN into the courtyard of the Kobes' apartment.

A figure with brown hair and wearing a striped waistcoat loitered under it. Laure undid the catch and leaned out. 'Have you been throwing stones?'

Tomas grinned up at her. 'Whenever do I not?'

With her heart in her mouth, she smiled back. 'You think you're Romeo.'

He shaded his eyes. 'I do, and you're my beautiful Juliet and I've come to take you away from the house of discord.'

Laure glanced back over her shoulder. It was Saturday and Petr had taken the children out to an aunt who lived outside Prague and wouldn't be back until the evening. Eva had briefly emerged from her room earlier in the day but had returned to it and shut the door. 'Give me five minutes.'

When she emerged from the entrance, Tomas snatched at her hand. 'Today is a day to forget everything. Except us. But you'll have to hurry up.'

'How did you know I would be free?'

'I felt it,' he said with utmost seriousness and she burst out laughing.

Parked up in the courtyard were two bicycles in, more or less, reasonable condition. 'You can ride a bike?' Tomas was suddenly doubting and she laughed, too, at his expression. 'I thought we could cycle along the river and eat at a place I know outside the city.'

Tomas led them down to the tow path – Laure more unsteady than she cared to admit – and they headed south out of the city. Before long, the houses which flanked it had narrowed to a ribbon. As they skidded over the dry ripples, the bicycle wheels sent up plumes of dust and, having got her balance in, Laure picked up speed to match Tomas.

The river traffic thinned and the noise levels dropped and the sounds of summer took over. Water splashed, pigeons sounded, there was an occasional blast from a tinny-sounding transistor radio. Rising from clumps of honeysuckle was the hum of foraging honey bees. From the large, working farmyard came an aroma of dried mud, and a fainter one of horse.

The unused muscles in Laure's legs and buttocks made themselves felt. Sun beat down onto her hands and her back. Would she get freckles? She didn't care.

Tomas was in front of her, which granted Laure the luxury of watching him unimpeded and she registered each detail greedily. His left foot turned inward on the pedal. His forearms were burnt deep brown. His hair had been roughly cut at the nape.

From time to time, Tomas looked back to check she was OK, a gesture that gave her more pleasure than she could ever imagine.

'Fancy a swim?' he called over his shoulder as they approached a bridge. He wheeled right and led her alongside a tributary flowing into the main river.

They rode upstream for a mile or so. Here it was to venture into a landscape that had enchantment laid on it. Apart from the sky, river, trees and birds, there was nothing. No one. This was solitude that couldn't be far removed from the garden of Eden, she thought, awestruck by the silence, by its intrinsic other world-ness.

Poplars grew down to the water's edge, their roots creating a gradient that would make it possible to get in and out of the water. Tomas parked his bike and, with a groan, dismounted.

'Out of condition?' Teasing Tomas was a delight – because he didn't always like it.

For a second, he was disconcerted. Then he wasn't. He caught her by the wrist. 'You witch.'

The river sent ripples against its banks. In the field behind Laure, the bone-dry crops rattled and rustled against each other and birds on the watch for insects and grain dived earthwards and rose back into the air with piercing cries.

She wanted to lay her head on Tomas's hot body and to listen to his heartbeat. She wanted to kiss the purple bruise that had sprouted on his arm and to splash water over their hot feet.

How visceral her responses were these days, she reflected, amazed at the way her mind now operated. They were about sex, the flesh, sensation… and all about the other thing which had violently seized her. Love.

'Coming?' Tomas stripped off his shirt and stepped out of his trousers.

Her fingers were not quite steady as she unzipped her shorts and eased off her shirt.

'You look like an ice cream,' she said. 'All pale here…' She touched his groin, 'but so brown here.' She laid her hand flat against his chest, searching for the heartbeat.

He laughed. 'Same for you,' he said. 'Stand still.' Very slowly he ran his finger up Laure's body, staring at the knee. 'Lovely brown legs, haunches that the poet should write an ode to, shoulders and arms to match your legs. A face that has seen the sun but, somehow, is as luminous as the moon and a mouth for which men would gladly die.'

'Sounds like a song,' she said.

'In a way, it is.'

He took her hand and drew her down to the water's edge. 'Be careful of your feet.'

The ground was rock hard but turned to mud at the water's edge. Her toes sank into it and she tried not to imagine which insects or worms would scurry around her flesh. A root caught her around the ankle and she clung onto Tomas.

Thus entwined they waded into the river, sliding and slipping over the uneven river bed. At first tepid, the water was cooler in the middle of the river where the undertow was strong and the water deep. The colder water was silk on her heated body.

It took her two seconds to recognize that Tomas was not a good swimmer. But she was and easily negotiated the current as she swam upstream.

She raised her hands and let herself sink below the surface.

Bubbles drifted surface-wards, her hair streamed behind her, the outlines of her flesh wavered and refracted and, on the river bed, ribbons of weed flowed towards the mother river.

For one second, she asked herself if it would be better if she never resurfaced and broke the perfection of it. She imagined the struggle as her lungs filled and how she would search for the comfort and sweetness of Tomas's image as the darkness took over.

Gasping, she rose to the surface and swam back to him. 'Do you know the legend of Rusalka?' he asked.

Weightless, she hung onto him. 'Tell me.'

'She is an unquiet, dangerous being who lives in the river. She lures men to their deaths.'

Laure found a foothold and stood up. 'Have I lured you?

He wrapped his arms around her. They smelt of heat and river water, of underwater things. 'Not to my death, Laure. But you have cast a spell.'

He drew her towards the riverbank.

At that moment, she was washed clean of doubt and worry and sensed that Tomas was too. Here in this tree-fringed, water-lapped place with the birds making free with the sky, she groped towards an understanding... that her spirit had undergone a rebirth. That bones, flesh and spirit had realigned themselves into the Laure who whispered over and over again: *I love you.*

Yet, on the return journey, Laure felt inexplicably sad and Tomas was mostly silent.

The outlying houses of the city came into view. Without warning, Tomas put on his brakes and got off the bike. 'Stop.' Laure obeyed.

Grass-stained and grubby, they gripped each other, hard and a little frantic, the sun beating on his bent head and her raised face.

'I wanted to do this before it all begins again,' he said. 'Away from everything.'

'Do you know something?'

'No.' He snatched up a fistful of her hair and gently pulled her head back. 'I've learnt that every moment like this has to be felt. It vanishes, of course. But, also, it can be taken away before it vanishes.'

She wondered what was bothering him. What it was he might not be telling her?

Listening to the beat of his heart, Laure held him hard against her, not wishing to move, or to think and they remained like that for a long time.

Back in Prague, he made her dismount before they reached the Kobes' apartment. 'I'll take the bike and you go back. It's best that way.'

She watched him wheeling the bikes down the street until he was out of sight.

Sometimes Laure thought she *had* fetched up in a Czech surrealist story.

She could not prove it, but she was convinced that she was being followed, which had a superficial thrill attached to it. On the other hand, paranoia was infectious. Why would she, the girl from Brympton, be a target?

As the days went by, she found the situation less intriguing and more sinister. The encroachment got to her. Once, she was so incensed that she whirled round and sent whoever it was a V-sign with her fingers. It was a stupid thing to do but it offered a tiny release.

She warned Tomas. 'I think I've become an object of interest.'

'Any foreigner is. It's a condition of life here.'

'Petr was asking questions. Talking about the Parallel Polis.'

Tomas shrugged. 'Hardly a surprise. He's an informer and a stooge. A weak man. He doesn't know what's really going on.'

He spoke with a contempt that, curiously, Laure couldn't match. 'I'm not sure that's right. Petr has principles which make him strong.'

'Ask him where his principles are when he informs on someone.'

'You've got him wrong,' she explained. 'It's not people he's interested in, it's his work at Potio Pharma.'

He placed a finger on her lips. 'Did you know you're very sweet?'

She nipped at his fingertip with her teeth. 'And also right. Bear that in mind.'

'Maybe.'

That was one of the good things about being with Tomas that she was discovering. He listened to her and, as a result, she was developing the mental resources to help her interpret the experiences that were coming her way.

They were backstage in the marionette theatre. Tomas's arm was wrapped around Laure's waist. 'Did you tell him anything?'

'Not as far as I know.'

'It's the not knowing that's the problem.' He pulled her to him and his leg nudged between hers. Bending over he kissed her thoroughly and the sweet, sharp sensations took over. Resting his forehead against hers, he said, 'That was nice.'

Her hand was on his back and she splayed her fingers to feel the bumps of his vertebrae: *I love him.*

Tomas kissed her again and another thought flashed: *I would die for him.*

Laure followed him into the kitchen where Milos was drinking mint tea. He smiled at Laure and made a remark to Tomas in Czech. Manicki and Leo, plus Vaclav the electrician, also rolled in and a heated debate struck up which was, as far as she could tell, something to do with storing Anatomie's instruments at the theatre.

She was conscious that a pane of glass had inserted itself between them and her through which she was observing. They were like the men she knew back home and, yet, they weren't. They were smaller, paler, less nourished, more volatile. Tomas had his back to her but Vaclav, with whom she had struck up an infant friendship, smiled at her.

329

She knew they were discussing her. 'Tomas?'

He explained. 'They wanted to know about your employer and Manicki agrees with me that he works for the KSČ.' Laure frowned. 'The KSČ is the Communist Party.'

Manicki interrupted in broken English. 'And/or the Russians. It fits. They only let the most trusted ones work abroad. He's probably controlled by someone high up in the party.' He stepped up to Laure. 'You must say *nothing* ever. Ever.'

Manicki smelt, not entirely unpleasantly but significantly, of unwashed clothes, and she wondered if he was living on the run.

Laure thought rapidly. 'OK. I take the point.' Tomas made a rapid translation. 'I know you think I'm problem but remember that I could always relay information on him.'

Where on earth had *that* come from?

Milos gave a soft whistle and looked up at the ceiling. The others stared at Laure and she realized she had made an error.

Manicki said, 'We don't joke about those sorts of things.'

She wanted to protest that she wasn't joking but realized it was better to shut up. Everything was suspended – almost breathing – until Tomas dropped his hand on her shoulder and kissed her cheek. 'That was sweet of you, Laure, but… don't play. Please.'

Later, as she packed up for this session, her cheeks burned. She had been guilty of flippancy, of unprofessionalism, of treating something very serious as a game.

Returning to the Kobes' apartment, Laure stepped off the Charles Bridge. Instead of continuing straight ahead as she normally would have done, she turned right and followed the street running north for several metres and stopped in front of a shop with the sign 'Truhlář Marionety'. Displayed in its window were a couple of marionettes: Pinocchio and a jester with a cap and bells.

Close up, she could see that the carving of this pair was sinuous, but the paintwork crude. She gazed long and hard at their white faces. *We are aware,* they were telling her, *that we only have life when you say so. Yet we have souls too. We feel pain and suffer. We offer you the ecstatic and the surreal. We can be angry and malicious.*

She lingered at the window, which, as she was also known to be working with marionettes, was legitimate. However, she was using the reflection in the shop window to track the movement of the man (today dressed in beige trousers and a white shirt) who had been following her. Cornered by her manoeuvre, he was loitering by the entrance to the bridge. He had flat features, a small mouth and looked tough.

She leant forward, ostensibly to obtain a better look at the jester marionette. Being followed had got to her and her bravado was replaced by the worry that she didn't know how to cope.

By the time she moved off and continued on her indirect route back to the Kobes' apartment, she had pulled herself together. Why should goons win the mind-game battle?

A couple of nights later, Anatomie were performing at a theatre off Wenceslas Square and the group were all there.

Laure was at the marionette theatre where the evening perform-ance of *The Bartered Bride* was in jeopardy. The lighting was in melt-down and, with much cursing, the company gathered around to sort it. Unable to contribute, and with Lucia cold-eyeing her, Laure gathered up the used mugs and carried them into the kitchen.

They required intensive scrubbing and there was no such thing as a Brillo pad to be had.

Milos came in for a drink of water and she stood aside so he could run the tap. He drank thirstily and said in his fractured English, 'Tomas tells me your employer has been asking questions.'

Laure nodded.

Milos rinsed the glass. 'Never answer questions,' he said. 'Or ask them. Never.'

'But how do you find anything out if you don't ask?'

'You don't.' He replaced the glass on the shelf. 'Nobody knows anything. It's the rule.'

Hand on hip, she regarded him. 'This country is like a maze. Never ask questions. Never answer them. Just blissful ignorance?'

Milos approved. 'You've got it. Our greatest novel, *The Good Soldier Schweik,* is about a man who fights militarism and bureaucracies and wins but, I think, always by mistake because the good soldier is also very stupid.'

'You never know what's forbidden?'

He grinned in his good-natured way but his eyes were bleak. 'And you do in your country?' He saluted with a clenched fist to the forehead. 'This is Comrade Milos, Grade Three, Marionette Pioneers, first battalion, based in The Milos Marionette Theatre, in the People's Republic of… Czechoslovakia.'

Milos always made her laugh.

The lighting problem solved, the customary pre-performance frenzy erupted into which she was pitchforked. A tiny gingerbread figure was missing. Could Laure look for it?

It was lurking in one of the boxes in the kitchen. Milos snatched it from her and disappeared. Laure was left to tidy up and to ready the back-up marionettes in case there was a disaster during a performance.

She lifted a marionette called Marenka and pulled gently at her strings. 'Good evening, dear Marenka,' she said.

Marenka did duty as Sleeping Beauty and Cinderella, or any ingenue part.

'Marenka is the young, innocent one who finds herself in puzzling situations but wins through because her innocence has the power to resolve,' Milos had told her. 'And this Marenka is a messenger. Look at the eyes.' Marenka had one blue eye, one green. His voice was full of mischief. 'See. It means there are different ways of seeing. But,' he tapped his lips, 'you must *never* say anything.'

'Your life is a busy one, it seems,' she told Marenka and could have sworn that the marionette's mismatched eyes and full red mouth moved in response. Laure touched the painted cheek.

Marenka sighed and settled back onto her perch.

The marionettes' clothing was stacked beside them, ready for quick deployment, including the Prince's red-checked shirt for his peasant persona and his Pierrot costume. The Sleeping Beauty's nightgown and the diminutive lace bridal veil used for wedding finales were folded alongside.

Enchanted, Laure held the veil up to the window. No expert, she could see that the lace itself was of the highest quality and so was the skill that had made it possible to include one of the smaller lace flowers at its centre.

'Do you wish to see where it came from?' asked a voice.

Laure turned to see Lucia in the doorway. She seemed out of sorts and spoiling for a confrontation.

'It's beautiful,' said Laure. 'And looks antique.' Lucia frowned. 'Old, I mean,' Laure added.

Lucia crossed over to the cupboard in the corner. Opening the cupboard precipitated a shower of paint flakes onto the floor, which was dotted with them.

Lucia took down a box from the shelf. 'Are you ready?'

The contents were shrouded in yellowing tissue paper, which Lucia peeled back. 'My mother wore this, her mother before her, and her mother before that. If I marry, I will wear it. It's old. Nobody knows how old.' She took a piece of rag from the pile in the corner, dusted the table and lifted out the veil out for inspection.

A waterfall of lace flowed over the table. There was a square missing from it in one corner but, otherwise, its colour was still pure and the silk netting, with a border of lace flowers, intact.

Lucia watched Laure's reaction. 'It's different in your country? Yes?'

Laure touched the lace which felt like honeycomb on silk. 'A bride often wears a veil but not many would have one as beautiful as this.'

'You don't like what I did. Cutting it?'

Laure spoke before thinking. 'No,' and hastily amended, 'but it's none of my business.'

Laure frowned. 'Of course, you would not understand. How could you? In your country, you can keep things, I think, even if they are old. But not here. We have to sacrifice precious things for the greater good.'

'I see.' Laure did not ask where on the spectrum of the 'greater good' the desecration of beautiful lace figured. Then, she felt ashamed at her failure to understand.

Lovingly, reverently, Lucia traced the shape of one of the flowers. 'You don't see because you're a stranger. The marionettes mean a lot to our culture. More so than you could ever know.'

Lucia was being insulting but Laure decided to let it ride.

Lucia picked up the veil and pulled it over her head. 'The veil doesn't mind if it is cut. What we do here is more important.' It sounded as if Lucia was warming up to a battle speech. 'If we don't have our stories, then we're finished. This theatre is important.'

'The marionettes send messages?'

The silken shroud masked Lucia's features but could not disguise her eyes glittering with hostility. Or the touch of fear. 'Why do you want to know?'

'I'm curious.'

'You shouldn't ask those questions.' The words were so viscously articulated that Laure took a step back. 'Don't you know that you should never ask questions here.' Laure shook her head. 'It's only ignorant, stupid foreigners who do.'

'For St Nicholas's sake, we need help.' Milos appeared and vanished.

'Why don't you go back to England? It would be better for everyone. You are… how do you say? A nuisance.'

'My employers wish me to stay.'

'Ah. And you will, I think.' Lucia was stopped in her tracks. 'Don't imagine that you will have Tomas.'

'Isn't that for him to decide?'

'You know,' said Lucia, 'you're nothing special. Any man here who can gets himself a girlfriend from the West. It's the thing to do.'

A cold feeling enveloped Laure. 'And?'

Lucia pulled off the veil, folded it and laid it in its box. She seemed to be deciding what to say, or to do. 'Next year, I'll wear this.'

'You're getting married?'

'Yes, and yes.' Lucia stuck her face into Laure's and enunciated slowly. 'We'll be getting married. With a big ceremony and all the family.'

There was a sick feeling in her stomach. 'We? Do you mean Tomas?'

Lucia didn't say yes. She didn't say no.

'It'll happen,' said Lucia, slotting the box back into the cupboard. 'You'll go. Soon, I hope. Gone like the snow. You are no use here, only a problem.' The cupboard door was warped and required pressure to shut it and she exclaimed angrily. 'God help us, we have no furniture, no locks, no fucking future.'

CHAPTER 25

*A*RE YOU ENGAGED TO LUCIA? ARE YOU MARRYING HER?
Have you decided to marry Lucia?

There were so many ways to pose the question which – with
choking intensity – trembled on her tongue. Thinking about which
one to choose, and how and when to broach it, made her faint.
And, also, angry.

But no need to be gormless, lass. Her father's sayings didn't help
much either, except to remind Laure that she did have another
existence and that she could choose to return to it. The fall-back
position didn't help. Laure wished to be where she was. Here. Now.
In the thick of it, entangled in the sticky strands of politics and
passion.

It was late on Sunday afternoon and Tomas was taking her
for a beer in a dive by the river, run by one of his friends. His
telephone still didn't work – no surprises there – and he had
taken to leaving messages at the marionette theatre when he
wanted to make contact.

As usual, they chose to walk through the hidden alleys and
passages. Being acquainted with their intimacies, often rubbish-
strewn and with broken cobbles, almost persuaded Laure that she
had become an insider. They were part of the enigma of the city,

and these out-of-sight routes had become one of her pleasures. But not today.

Tomas led the way and she watched his slight figure with a hunger that grew sharper each day. She tried to put herself in the other woman's shoes. Any woman – Lucia – must love the hunch of his shoulder, the thin hands, the thick brown hair in the passionate, ravenous way that she, Laure, did. Any woman – Lucia – would feel the combination of exquisite joy and pain as she did.

Perhaps, in return, Tomas would see a softness in her (the half-French girl) that Lucia, who had been (of necessity) toughened by anger and suspicion, no longer possessed.

Could he see instead in Laure someone in whom he could place his trust and imagine a bright, certain future?

Tomas waited for her to catch up. 'You do take care when you're on your own?'

Her lips were suddenly dry. 'You do mind about me?'

He looked at Laure. 'What do you think?' He seemed impatient with the question.

Her senses swam, and she was electric with longing. 'I hope you...'

He cut through. 'Laure, I have fallen in love with you. Very deep. Very intense. That you should know.'

He had succeeded in taking her breath away. And the shock of it crackled through every cell. 'I love you, too,' she faltered, the words strange and new to voice aloud.

Tomas shot a hand heavenwards. 'My God, she loves me,' he cried. 'What more can I ask of life?'

'Even if I am a useful girlfriend from the West?'

He shot her a look. '*Especially* if you're a girlfriend from the West.'

The poisoned blister festering in her heart was punctured. What did it matter if she was the useful girlfriend from the West? It was a risk she would take. What was love but risk?

Tomas added, 'Listen, don't worry about being followed. It gives you protection. There're plenty of drunks and bandits around who would consider it their life's work to rob a girl like you. Or worse. They won't if there's a goon around.'

They had emerged by the river over which were sliding the reflections from the setting sun. Tomas steered them into a street flanked by walls behind which were tall-ish buildings. Where two walls met, they opened into a garden furnished with tables and chairs. The place was run by Radek, an old friend of Tomas's who, in return for Anatomie's occasional appearance there, ensured that Tomas got his favourite beer.

'What do you mean "a girl like me"?' she asked when they were seated on the grass down by the river and the beer had been served.

He raised an eyebrow. 'You don't get it, my loved Laure, do you? Then, I must tell you.' He leant over and rubbed a lock of her hair between his fingers. 'Beautiful and well cared for. Shiny. The product of a good hairdresser and years of using a good shampoo.'

This was the most tender and seductive of love letters and she closed her eyes to listen.

Tomas's fingers rested on her cheek. 'Your skin is full of life. It tells me that you have been well fed. It tells me that you have eaten fruit and vegetables and good meat all your life.' He took up one of her hands. 'Look at your strong nails and soft skin.'

Enraptured, she smiled.

'These little details tell the clever observer that you are worth robbing. They're trained to spot the details.'

Her smile faded.

'Let's forget about them.' He wrapped his arms around her. 'Is it too hot for this?'

It was true that his body against hers felt like a radiator but she didn't care.

'I want to relish each moment,' he said in her ear. 'When you live with systems as they are here, it's a requirement. Every cold beer, the sun on your back, every bar of music. Every mouthful of good food. The smell of summer.' He nuzzled her ear and the increasingly familiar sensations smartly awoke. 'And sex. Especially sex.'

A beer later, she got up the courage to pose the question: 'Is… was Lucia your girlfriend?'

Tomas was not at all put out. 'She was once.'

To Laure's distress, her hand holding the glass began to shake. 'Oh.'

He rescued the glass and its contents and wedged it down into the grass. 'I thought it was only films that were black and white,' he said, and she recognized a reproof. 'Lucia and I have a long history. We grew up in the same area of the city. Both sets of parents have suffered. We owe each other a lot and, unless our dear leaders decide to shut us up in prison, we will know each other for the rest of our lives.'

'Did she believe Tomas? She all but told me that you were getting married next year and I should bugger off. She looked like she meant it.' Laure's tooth probed at her bottom lip. 'She looked like she still wanted you.'

'Did she now?' He was amused. 'Lucia has other plans.' He took up a lock of hair, bent over and kissed it. 'But you must remember you will go.'

'Christ,' she said, a word that never passed her lips but, in her agony, it arrived.

He peered into Laure's face and what he saw checked him. 'Laure, Laure, don't look like that. What did you expect?'

'I don't know.'

'It's impossible,' he pointed out. 'You can't stay here.'

She could see the situation from Tomas's point of view. From all points of view. A well-nourished English girl parachutes into a country that has been struggling with deprivation and lives under a tyranny that is slyly dressed up as paradise. A rock musician fancies her. Maybe something more? But she, on the other hand, is poleaxed by her feelings. Everyone knows, and she reluctantly and late to the party, that her love affair is only a summer's lease. They know, as she knows, that when she leaves, it will be as though she had slipped into the river and the waters had closed over her head.

They will forget. She won't.

She felt herself flush. 'Tomas, I'm the outsider. Of course. But it doesn't make you and me any less important. You must see that. Understand. Deep down understand.'

She tried to scramble upright but he pressed her back onto the grass.

'It hurts me too,' he said. 'Very much.'

'If you say you feel… strongly about me, if you say you love me.'

'You'll be in my songs. That I promise.' He took one of her hands in his and stroked it. 'Don't spoil it, Laure. We have too much sadness in this country. Accept what we have for what it is. I love you very much. You are, remember, a woman from the dreams. A lioness from the African plains.'

'From Yorkshire, actually.'

He grinned. 'From Yorkshire, and you're clever and funny and brave and I want every bit of you.'

Stupidly, she asked, 'Would you go back to Lucia?'

'Stop it.'

Puzzled, she tried to pick her way through the raw, angry places that this conversation had exposed to find the flaw in his argument. 'But that's to be how the State wants you. Acquiescent. I thought rebellion took place in the heart, not just the streets. If you want me, you must do something.'

'I'm tempted to say that you don't know what you're talking about. But, then, you do.'

He continued to stroke her hand, taking care over every joint, exploring the lines running down her palm.

She could disagree. She could be angry. She could beg... but, in a revelatory flash, she saw a way through, using politics. 'You're on record as saying you want a new Czechoslovakia, the rule of law, an independent judiciary, free elections, a market economy, social justice... and, as a result, you could be arrested at any moment?'

'True,' he seemed indifferent. 'Although things are happening, the movement is gathering, it'll be years before the system cracks.'

'Are you in danger?'

After a moment, he nodded reluctantly. 'Probably. The warning about the telephone was a clue.'

A flicker of cramp went through the big toe of her right foot as she scrunched it down. 'Then you must get out. I'll help you.'

He flung himself back on the grass and slotted his arm across his eyes. Destabilized by the impact, dust sifted towards the river. 'How do you say in English? Don't go there?'

'You can. You can fight ideology and isms by escaping.' Her confidence stuttered into life and the way forward seemed clear. 'You know the right people who forge papers?'

'I do. Not easy and people have been caught. And what happens when I get out?'

She heard her own voice: warm, cajoling, determined. 'You marry me and then you can get British citizenship.'

He shifted his arm and squinted up at her. 'I'm doing what I'm doing here. I'm not a deserter.'

'True desertion is to give up on your country. Whether you are here or there.' Love had sharpened her insight into him. He would be doubting himself, his future. 'You're thinking that, if you came over, no one would know who you are. A rock star with no audience. A nobody. That's hard after being a somebody here.'

A boat with a lantern at its prow glided across the water, barely breaching the surface, and Laure caught her breath at the sight. 'But you can, and would be, somebody elsewhere.'

The accumulated warmth from the day sifted up from the grass sward. She lit a cigarette and smoked reflectively and recollected a conversation at the *chata* where Leo had explained that at the election the previous May, 99.39 per cent had turned out to vote and 99.94 per cent of them had voted for the carefully selected government candidates. Then she thought about the marionettes back at the theatre, hanging on their pegs waiting for their call to life, subversive or not. Fighting for a cause could be addictive. . . and she was beginning to see this picture.

'You think a revolution is going to happen? In the future? Never?'

'Difficult questions. But revolution certainly won't happen if people like me leave.'

The boat was joined by two others and the trio sat serenely on the water in the evening sun, casting starbursts of light.

She felt him drawing away into a place where she was not welcome.

'You said yourself there were cracks. You've told me about the opposition to Soviet troops in the country when they invaded in 1977, and you've talked about the resistance going on now. But you also said getting rid of the regime is a long way off. You have a life. Shouldn't you give yourself the best chance to lead it?'

'Keep your voice down,' Tomas said, sharper than normal.

'Are we quarrelling?'

'Don't be silly.'

Carefully, she ground out her cigarette, wrapped it in a scrap of paper and handed it to Tomas. He glanced down at the pathetically small package. 'We've made a Czech in you, Laure.'

'*Of* you.'

'Of course, of you.' He was silent for a moment. 'Why are you trying to teach me English?'

'Why do you think?'

He laughed. 'Shall we go back to where I live?'

Tomas had never invited her to his place before. 'Yes.'

'It's not comfortable. Will you mind?'

They walked back up from the river, turned into the street that ran parallel to it and headed for the bridge. A couple of cars came up behind and they stood back to allow them to pass. Suddenly, Tomas gripped Laure's arm so hard that she almost cried out.

'Do you see that white building ahead? Get there and turn into the courtyard and wait for me. Do as I say,' he hissed into her ear. 'Don't ask questions.'

With that, he turned and walked back the other way. Obeying his instructions, she walked briskly towards the white building, one of the older ones by the river, and did not look back even when she heard a screech of tyres and inhaled a whiff of burning rubber. Car doors slammed.

Fear almost made it impossible to move. What if Tomas was picked up? What if she was?

Turning into the entrance, she found herself in a courtyard, similar to the one the Kobes occupied, surrounded by three-storeyed apartments with ironwork balconies. It was an unexpectedly peaceful place filled with plants.

Not that Laure paid much attention. Struggling to bring herself under control, she perched on the edge of a stone trough and smoked another cigarette. How did Czechoslovakians manage to exist in this way? With such continual anxieties?

A few minutes later, Tomas walked in through the courtyard entrance. Pale, sweaty and clutching at his shoulder. She uttered a cry of distress and ran over to him. 'They've hurt you.'

He flinched at her approach. 'The goons were after someone who probably got away. That puts them in a bad mood and I didn't want to give them the pleasure of spotting me. But they did and decided to give me a beating up to prove how much love they feel.'

'Lean on me.'

His features were drained from the shock. And pain? 'It's not too bad. Probably only bruising. I sent you in the other direction because I didn't want you involved.'

Relief gave her daring. She reached up and pulled his head down to hers and kissed him passionately. 'You taste of tobacco,' he said.

'And you of beer.'

They stood apart. Of the two, it was Laure was trembling with the shock of it. 'They beat you up for no reason?'

Above, a window banged shut and a trickle of mortar slid down the wall.

'Do you want to sit down?'

He shook his head. 'Let's get out of here' He put his good arm around her shoulder and they walked into the street, Tomas stumbling ever now and again.

'I'm going to give you some advice, Laure. If you're taken, be prepared. They know the answers before they put the questions. It's an old trick.'

'And?'

He was talking more to himself than to her. Rehearsing what lay ahead of him, she realized with a new terror.

'I would be asked what I believe in and I would reply that I believe in peace and equality and whoever is questioning me will almost certainly laugh. And you can see why. Their isms are not mine. The trouble is they reserve the right to make you agree with theirs.'

Apart from a woman with a bulging string bag, the street was empty.

'They will ask me about the songs and I'll reply that I'm not prepared to answer as I do not consider the questioner to be a representative of an enterprise that creates my sort of music. They will also put it to me that the music creates anti-social agitation and I will again reply that I have nothing to do with agitation as I find it repellent.'

'I think I understand.'

He glanced down at her. 'I've been arrested more than once. Each time it's trickier, but I am also wilier. But it's a risk.'

'Then what are you doing with Anatomie?' she asked. 'Why?'

'Proving to myself that, despite your sly insinuation, I'm not inert, which was what Jan Palach accused us Czechs of.' Laure didn't know what he was talking about. '1969. A bad year,' he said.

'Palach?'

'Palach was a student and set himself alight in Wenceslas Square, which was his protest at our failure to resist. By burning himself to a shrieking cinder, he was pointing out that taking refuge in cartoons, opera and depression, which the Czech people do, was not good enough.' He sounded strained. 'So help us, Palach was right.' He reflected for a moment. 'Leo and Manicki feel the same as me, though we don't talk about it.' After another pause, he said, 'It's both a good and a terrible story.'

Pain. Smell. Dying in a violent, excruciating way for a cause. She found it too terrible to say anything.

'He left us a challenge to prove we are not inert.' He pulled Laure to a halt and, leaning against the wall, kissed her again. Eventually, he drew back and said, 'And you're not.' His teased her bottom lip. 'Inert, I mean.'

The vision of Palach routed (for the time being), Laure sighed with relief and happiness.

'But, really, what *are* you doing?' she repeated later as they slowly made their way across the Charles Bridge towards the house in the Mŭstek quarter where Tomas lived with a bunch of musicians, which included Manicki.

'I'm a rock soldier making war on the system.'

A couple of girls in frayed cotton trousers passed them on the bridge and stared and one of them sent a filthy look at Laure.

'A rock god, you mean,' said Laure.

Where Tomas lived had once been expensive and desirable but was now rundown and, he told Laure, its basement so damp only a duck could survive.

'Careful,' said Tomas as they entered the front door and pointed to the stone corbels flanking it. 'Mrs Pigeon is bringing up a large family.'

Sure enough there were guano splashes on the stone floor and a mighty susurration of young, hungry birds sounding from a nest on the ledge.

The facilities were shared, including a cracked lavatory that did not look as though it had long for this world. 'Sorry, sorry,' said Tomas as he pointed it out.

'I don't care,' said Laure.

His hand on her back propelled her up the stairs to the first floor where Tomas had his room. 'When the snow comes, I share it with Manicki because the roof leaks. But today it's all mine.'

There was a bedstead, minus its mattress which was on the floor. The reason was obvious as the bedstead lacked a workable leg. There were piles of clothing, Anatomie posters tacked up on the wall, an ancient-looking washstand with a blue-and-white bowl that looked antique and valuable, and Tomas's guitar stacked in a corner.

Tomas crossed over to a cardboard box in the corner. 'Are you there?'

Laure was startled. 'Who?'

Tomas reached into the box and lifted up a tabby cat. 'This is my true beloved. His name is Kočka, which means cat. He and I share the same spirit. He's an old man now and not so well. But we talk to each other.' He cradled the purring animal in the crook of his arm and ran a finger down Kočka's spine. 'He's been my companion, I tell him things, he criticizes my songs, and I do everything I can to make him happy and comfortable. But he's getting old. Very old, and there's nothing I can do to stop it.'

'Don't look so sad,' she cried, almost jealous.

'I don't care what happens to me, but I care what happens to Kočka. I ask all my friends to remember if anything happens, Kočka must be safe.'

'Safe?'

'Taken to a vet. I've hidden money to ensure that he can be put down painlessly. When I took him on that was the promise I made. I would give him the best death and the best life I could. In return, he has loved me without a cloud. And…' he dropped a kiss on Kočka's head, 'I have loved him.'

Feeling inadequate to deal with the coming calamity and, possibly, the rivalry, she watched Tomas ease Kočka back into his nest. He glanced at Laure. 'OK?'

She nodded.

He stripped off his shirt, revealing his slight, sweaty torso which was covered with red marks and bruises. The largest bruise was forming on his back above his right kidney and she exclaimed over it.

'No need to fuss,' he said gently. He turned her to face him and his accent grew more marked. 'I'm serious now. You ask me my reasons for staying. This is it. It's from a banned publication. "No philosophical, political, scientific view or artistic activity that departs even by the merest fraction of official ideology or aesthetics is allowed…" Let me try to remember the exact words. "No open criticism is permitted, there is no right to a public defence, and the Ministry of the Interior busies itself monitoring the lives of its own citizens, tracking their movements, tapping their phones and apartments and arresting them without charge in the street."'

Half-mazed with lust, she digested the implications. 'Then you are telling me there's no choice.'

'I am.'

'But you put your life on the line, it could become so difficult that it'll be a sort of death.'

'Who was it who said there're many kinds of death? Giving in is one. Jan Palach chose his way. We must find another.'

Despite the heat, she shivered. 'I can't bear it.'

'Is there a choice but to breathe?' He backed her over to the mattress.

'But how?'

'There's music. There's the marionettes who mock ghosts and ghouls to make them bearable. There's pricking goons like your employer but so cleverly they don't realize it.'

But they do, she wanted to cry out.

Wincing, he made her raise her arms and peeled off her T-shirt. Like his, her skin was slick with sweat. He leant over and licked her shoulder. 'Salty. Lovely.' He drew her down onto the mattress.

'If my life is in danger,' he said, placing his hand on her breast, 'I will remember this. And you.' He gazed into her eyes and she read in their expression a glow of love, melancholy and lust. 'The danger makes it all the sharper. You'll find that.'

She had a terrible intimation that he was half in love with martyrdom. Or that it beckoned from a flower-strewn field. She reached down and cupped his head between her hands. 'But your duty, your absolute duty, is to survive.'

Eva was not getting any better. 'It's the heat,' she maintained. 'It never agreed with me.'

The heat could be blamed. Over the last few days, its quality had changed. It was heavier, more pervasive. Stickier. It pressed down, soaking clothes and burning exposed skin.

The high temperatures were a challenge but, with Eva, more was at play. Anyone with half an eye could spot the bags under her eyes, her waxy skin and her struggle with any form of exertion. On a couple of occasions in the past few weeks, she had disappeared into hospital overnight and returned with bruised arms and a needle mark at her elbow.

At those times, Eva was forced to stay in bed and, if Petr was out, Laure sat with her after the children were asleep. The two women didn't talk much apart from some exchanges about the children and Laure was far too occupied thinking and dreaming to be worried by the silences.

On this evening, she went to check on Eva who was lying flat on her back in the main bedroom, both arms flung out as if she was being crucified. Laure was touched to see that she was wearing one of her Parisian nightdresses, a confection of ivory silk and lace, over which Laure had laboured with the iron.

Laure sat down. The room was very tidy and, when she considered the effort that must have been made, she admired Eva's determination. Neatly arranged on the bedside table were Eva's medications and a pile of books, the top one being – from what she could gather – a political tract.

Eva opened her eyes and requested a glass of water. Laure poured it out and propped Eva up. She sat back down again while Eva sipped at it.

Her gaze drifted to the window and her thoughts to Tomas.

'What does he tell you?'

She snapped back to attention. 'I don't know who you're talking about.' She took Eva's glass and set it down on the bedside table.

'Let's not pretend, Laure.'

'If you mean Tomas, he doesn't say anything.'

'Really?'

'Really.'

Eva may have been ill but her mind was sharp enough. 'You have it bad, I think.'

'Bad?'

'Your love affair.'

'Oh.'

'He'll be using you.' There was a small note of malice. 'Whatever sweet things he says.' Laure frowned. 'You don't believe me, and I suppose that's right. But don't forget.' Having said her piece, Eva tired of the subject and concentrated on her discomfort. She shifted painfully in the bed. 'If I was in Paris…' The tone was wistful.

'Isn't it possible for you to get there?'

'It's *possible*. But Petr has to be very careful not to annoy the authorities while he is negotiating. All of us in the family have to be careful.' She shifted position and uttered a subdued groan. 'If I was in Paris, I'd be getting better.'

'You *are* getting better,' said Laure. 'The doctors say so. Petr says so. You must believe it.'

Eva laughed. 'I've spent my life believing.' She pointed to the framed photograph on the wall of Petr receiving a certificate of merit from President Gustáv Husák. 'Belief is an art.' She closed her eyes. 'Loyalty is an art.'

Her elegiac tone frightened Laure and she cast about for a diversion. 'Did you grow up in Prague?'

A hint of animation crept into the drained features. 'No, in the country. To the north of the city. A beautiful village. Or it was. The air was pure. Not like here where it's so awful. I'm frightened for the children breathing it. The Party should do something about it.'

'How did you meet Petr?'

'A delegation came to the village for a summer holiday. He was one of them,' said Eva. 'He was younger than me but I took one look and decided he was my future. It was as simple as that.'

Laure couldn't resist saying, 'That was some belief.'

Eva turned her head on the pillow. 'I suppose it was. A big one. In your lifetime, you choose one or two of those and it's important to stick with them, whatever your doubts. It took me a while to learn that. The sticking-with bit, I mean.'

Laure bent over to straighten the sheet, a thick linen one which must have been hot and propped Eva up on the bolster. 'You must concentrate on getting better.'

Eva sank back. 'Thank you.' She closed her eyes. 'Petr has promised me that I can be buried in the village.' She looked up at Laure. 'That's a comfort to know.'

'You're not going to die,' Laure said.

'You never know. It's as well to think about what happens if you do.'

As Laure left the bedroom, Eva said. 'Thank you for staying to help look after the children.' She paused. 'Petr appreciates it. Not just the children.'

Laure grasped the door handle tight.

'But,' continued Eva, 'I think you'll be happy to go home when the time comes. Don't you? Being far from home is not a good thing.' Eva was making a point. 'I will be frank with you. If Petr remains in Prague, then it's better to get a Czech woman to help out. Or...' This time the pause between the sentences seemed extra meaningful. 'Or, to marry. You're very nice and very good, but you're young and you don't know how things work.'

Astonished, Laure exclaimed, 'What are you thinking? I'm not going to *marry* your husband. Nobody is.'

Eva sent Laure a half smile. 'I've learnt not to be absolute about the future.'

It was as if Eva no longer considered herself to be part of the equation, which was almost as troubling as Eva's suggestions about Laure and Petr – which she took to be sick and weary fancies.

'Eva, I will help look after your children as long as I am here, and as best I can. But that's all.'

That night, Petr and Laure ate supper together as usual, working their way through boiled potatoes and beans which they ate under the chandelier. Petr was deploying his trick of making Laure feel that she was the only person on the planet, to which she responded half-heartedly.

He noticed. 'You seem preoccupied? Is there anything going on?'

'No,' she answered.

'It's very nice having you here,' he said, gesturing to the room. 'Otherwise, it would be very empty.'

He drank his beer and diverted her with questions about Brympton, squirrelling out details about local transport and the National Health Service. Laure described the train which ran cross-country between Leeds and York which she took on schooldays. 'It was the only way to get there.' She looked across the table, 'Do you really want to know all this stuff?'

'Trains are important. For example, it mattered to you that it arrived on time and was affordable.'

The meal over, Petr cleared his throat and said, 'I'm afraid I have to discuss something that can't be ignored.'

Something in the atmosphere shifted and she was unsure why. 'Is it Eva?'

'It's been reported that you made an obscene gesture in the street to an official.'

The walls of the room seemed to creep in. 'How do you know that?'

'Does it matter?'

'Well, yes. It does.'

'The Ministry of the Interior busies itself monitoring the lives of its own citizens.'

'We've had this conversation, if you remember. Foreign nationals are fair game.'

'Tell me, who don't you spy on?'

'Laure, did you make that gesture?'

She was damned if she was going to lie. 'I did.'

'I'm not going to ask why although, as the person responsible for you, I'm entitled do so. What I must ask is that you never do that again.'

She was tempted to say: *how dare you*?

He spoke slowly, as if to a child: 'It's clear you don't understand how to conduct yourself here. Or, how doing something like that affects our families.'

Why didn't she have more practice in this sort of thing? 'But you're one of them and protected. What does it matter what I do? Especially, if it's hardly worth noticing.'

'What do you mean?' Petr sounded icy.

She glanced up to the chandelier for inspiration. Its heavy glass drops were reflecting the evening sun and exuding pinpoints of light. A little less certainly, she said, 'You're close to the Party. You do things for them.' He got to his feet and came over to her and the normally kind eyes were anything but. Laure's attack faltered. 'Aren't you?'

'You don't know what you're talking about.' He picked up his cigarettes. 'The authorities have put you on a list as an "oppositional". They will refer to you as a "reactionary bourgeois" and when it comes to sorting out your visa there will be a black mark. Maybe sufficient to get you deported.'

She wondered if he was deliberately overdoing it. But why bother? She knew, and Petr knew, he would win this bout because the very thought of having to leave Tomas made her feel faint.

He grew cold and serious in a way that was new to Laure. 'You're thinking you could quit our employment and go and live with your lover. And I'm sure you accuse me of being the Party's stooge. Maybe that's true. Maybe it isn't. But what is true is, if you didn't have my protection, then you would be vulnerable. Very.'

Both knew he was speaking the truth.

'Don't you wish to say anything?'

Funnily enough, when push came to shove, she minded that Petr thought badly of her – and that was puzzling. Her relationship with him was, obviously, more complicated than she imagined.

'It won't happen again.'

CHAPTER 26

*L*AURE WOKE AT 6 A.M. THE CHILDREN WERE STILL ASLEEP and the interregnum between her waking and their waking was hers to possess.

Her nightshirt was bundled up around her hips. Shifting to adjust it, her hand brushed her stomach, which was satisfyingly flat. She let it rest on the bony part of her hip.

The days had come and gone, beads on a string, and each one she fancied as a colour. Red for her passion, blue to mark a second sun-drenched trip to the *chata* which Tomas so loved. Green, for the song Tomas wrote and composed while she lay naked in his bed and watched. Black, for the marionettes: the water spirits, the princes and princesses, the whack, slam and slap grotesques and their metamorphosis under her dazzled eyes into mysterious life.

The beads had been counted and the end of September was in sight. The nights were cooling and the sun less fierce.

Why did Tomas love her?

The question was always there, a pulse that beat along with that of the one at her wrist. A while ago, she had resolved it was a question that should not be asked, let alone answered but, like many such speculations, it was disobedient.

He loved Anatomie.

He loved his country.

'We have to bring back basic freedoms.'

'Artistic freedom is the right of every human being.'

She kept the best recollection to the last.

'You're different, Laure. Thank the deities.'

In the old days she might have shrugged that off as easy words but, in this country of writers and artists, she was beginning to look at words with a new respect. They were freighted and a source of power.

He loved her. And weren't words everything?

At least, Eva was no worse and the drop in the temperature brought some relief. The children were preparing to go to their chosen schools. 'Elite ones,' Petr explained, with no hint of irony. 'Otherwise, they have no chance of keeping up if we return to Paris.'

The new timetables indicated that Laure would not enjoy the same freedom to come and go as she had during the summer and she would have to renegotiate. She swung her legs out of bed. Nothing like the present.

In the late afternoon, dressed in jeans and a T-shirt, with a flower-patterned scarf tied around her head, she walked to the Újezd and caught a tram to the Kinsky Gardens.

The tram was crammed with workers going home. It gave her a slight cultural shock to realize that a couple of those who had space to read were absorbed by books of poetry.

More than one of the passengers was likely to be an informer and she wondered, if the regime ever fell, how were the informers and those informed on going to shake down together? She turned her head to look out of the window. Revenge? Vendetta? Spilt blood? Fear and loathing?

They were folded into everyone's luggage.

Alighting at the stop, she joined the stream of people, mostly young, some of whom were clasping flowers, who were making their way across the Kinsky Gardens towards the Štefánik Observatory and she was struck how quiet they were.

Laure cast a look over her shoulder. Who were the watchers here? The girl with the long red hair streaming down her back? The man with a raincoat over his shoulder and the ubiquitous pork-pie hat?

The now familiar rough-and-ready stage had been erected outside the Observatory, dominating a grassy arena over which the electricians scurried like beetles. Rising from the earth were the aromas of grass and dried plants, sweet-smelling, hot-smelling – and unmistakeable.

Her rucksack, which held a precautionary bottle of water, weighed a ton and she slung it over a shoulder and made her way towards the stage, which wasn't easy. People clung onto their vantage point and did not appreciate a foreigner shouldering past, muttering 'Excuse me' in bad Czech. Eventually, she reached the stage and exchanged a grin with Vaclav, the electrician. By and large, their relationship was wordless, but they got on fine. Reaching over a hand, he hauled Laure up.

A sea of bodies was building, lapping over the grass arena up to the shrubs and tall grasses which provided a natural boundary. The stage planking sounded hollow as she trod over it and jumped down at the back.

In a makeshift tent just behind the stage, Tomas was in a huddle with Manicki and Leo. He looked up as she entered. 'About time.' His smile was for her alone – and, for the hundredth time, she thought she might die of love.

He reached over for her. 'Good day, bad day?'

Their manager was hovering, shouting in Czech and pointing at his watch.

Aware that the authorities had only given permission to hold the event provided the time limits were adhered to, she kissed him and said, 'Go, go, they're waiting.'

By the time the first chords were struck, the audience had worked itself up – shouts, snatches of singing, a fisticuff – but quietened as the opening numbers were played.

These had been commissioned for this gig: the lyrics written by a poet banned from publishing his work and the music was Tomas's. Many of the numbers had animal titles. 'Midnight Bears', 'Snake in the Grass', 'Dead Fish'.

Laure wormed her way to the side of the stage where she could better analyse what was going on. Tomas's music had undergone a subtle change. Into the out-and-out Western Europe rock-and-pop influence, into the defiant blare and gangbuster kidnap of the senses, had crept the rhythms of the Slavonic dance, a tiny hint of the Bohemian bagpipe and a glorious riff on Smetana's *Vltava*.

The evening deepened. The audience grew bolder and yelled, stamped, waved their hands. The lights bathed Anatomie in the chiaroscuro she had seen in paintings and lit the passage of thousands of insects winging in to feast.

She yelled and waved with the best of them.

It wasn't just the powerful music to which those massed bodies were responding. In the dusk, they were giving in to forbidden yearnings and loyalties. Tasting resistance like wine on the tongue.

Laure feasted on the figure of her lover, waistcoat hanging loose, a suggestion of sweat-streaked torso under it, dominating his guitar and the microphone. 'Czechoslovakia resistance is cultural,' he said, 'very special.' Watching it, hearing it, *feeling* it, was to draw its subversions into her veins.

Why hadn't she paid more attention to history at school? Then she might have had a better idea of how regimes eventually die. *If* they died. There were so many layers to unpeel. So many cross-currents to master.

But what she *could* see, and experience, was the wasteland of lives and dreams it generated. A catalogue of unnecessary deaths and the destruction of talent and opportunity. An ingrained habit of being fearful. A population who had the morality beaten out of them by repression that the authorities pretended was love.

Tomas shifted. His gaze caught hers and they exchanged a look, complicit, lustful, tender, and Laure forgot about anything else except her own desires.

Too soon, far too soon, Leo struck up the penultimate number. 'Tunnelling' was a story of mice working their way through harvested grain in a silo, thereby creating underground highways and hidden passages.

'Make of it what you will,' said Tomas when Laure had been puzzling over its lyrics. 'Remember, mice are good at infiltration. Nobody notices them.'

There was a pause. Tomas held up his hand and, as the crowd roared, he swung into the final number, 'Kočka.'

'If a cat wants

To kill the mouse

He must first catch it'

Halfway through, with an ecstatic audience shifting and swaying, the lights on the stage were cut with a crack of electricity and plunged into darkness. More than one person screamed. Looking towards the sound, Laure saw the outer edge of the crowd shift and crack. Immediately, in a Pavlovian response, a percentage peeled away and hastened into the dusk. *They know the form,* she thought. Some, trapped at the centre, tried to fight their way out. Others held their ground. An impasse threatened.

Their boots trampling the grass, holding torches chest height, dozens of green uniformed state police emerged into the light and, in a perfectly drilled manoeuvre, ringed the audience. Precise. Stealthy. Taking up a position by the stage, their commander issued orders through a loud hailer which Laure did not understand.

Anatomie continued to play, the music ringing through the dark. Brave, wonderful Tomas…

A detachment of the police now formed a tunnel and directed the audience down it to the exit. Several of the bulkier ones jumped up onto the stage and wrested the instruments from the men.

From the side of the stage, Laure watched as Tomas battled to prevent his guitar being taken by one of the police. But when it was in danger of being damaged, he yielded it up with a shrug.

She knew enough by now to know it was vital that she kept out of sight and made for the tent to pick up her rucksack and to head out.

Too late. Leo, Manicki and Tomas were ushered into the tent, followed by the police commander and his sidekick, both with the powerful torches.

Manicki fiddled with his hair, pulling strands this way and that. Leo stared through the tent entrance when the tail end of the audience could be seen dispersing. Tomas buttoned his waistcoat deliberately and slowly.

He did not look at Laure. She did not look at him – and that was the hardest thing.

Eventually, the police commander issued another order and the three men were escorted out of the tent. His sidekick turned to Laure and levelled an order at her. She shook her head. He repeated whatever it was. Louder. Again, she shook her head and spread her hands in a gesture indicating that she did not understand.

Exclaiming irritably, he seized her by the arm and pushed her out of the tent and escorted her to the exit.

On the abandoned stage, the electricians were performing a frantic demolition job. Flex dangling from one hand, Vaclav sent her a look from under his lids and tapped a finger to his lips. *Say nothing.*

Say nothing.

Laure repeated Vaclav's admonition to herself with a sense of growing astonishment that she was where she was. It would be touch and go if she could ever make anyone in Brympton believe her. *Bloody drama queen,* Jane would say.

She was in a windowless room devoid of furniture except for two cheap plastic chairs adorned with cigarette burns and a black Bakelite telephone at the centre of the table. Its flex was slotted through a hole bored through the table top and ran over to the connection box in the wall. A mad arrangement, she thought. If you didn't remember it was there, it might trip people up. Maybe that was the point?

How long had she been here? Three hours? Four? The goons were nasty. It had only been only with the greatest difficulty that she had persuaded the young bully of a guard to give her a drink of water and allow her to use the lavatory. She wasn't frightened so much as angry and desperate to know where Tomas and the others might be.

Aware that she should be more alarmed for herself and it was stupid to downplay the situation, she could not help being fascinated by the tin-pot quality of the set-up. Plastic chairs and an awkwardly hooked-up phone were not, in her book, props for the ultra-threatening.

For the nth time she checked her watch. The big hand was on its path to ten o'clock. On the dot the door opened to admit a man in neat grey trousers and a pressed shirt whom she vaguely recognized.

'Good evening, I'm Major Hasík,' he said in formal English, placing a briefcase on the floor. 'We have met before with your friend Tomas Josip. I'm going to ask you a few questions and then I very much hope you can return to your place of employment.' He sat down in the chair opposite her. 'Are you thirsty?'

She shook her head. 'Why am I here?'

He peered at her. 'I have a feeling you think you're being harassed. Is that correct?' Laure did not reply. 'Just to show that is not the case we have telephoned your employer and asked him to come in. You will be more comfortable with him on the premises.'

'How thoughtful.'

'He'll be bringing in your passport which will allow us to verify that you are who you say you are.'

Laure had been asked to cite her name, nationality and occupation at least five times. 'That will be a relief.'

'You shouldn't make fun of this process.' He was mild, ingratiating even. 'It is very necessary, you know.'

She caught a flash of ruthlessness and cunning. She shifted in her seat.

He glanced down at the file he had brought in with him. 'Your boyfriend is a member of Anatomie. How long have you known him?'

'Four months.'

'How often do you meet?'

'Twice, three times a week. Whenever it's possible.'

'Do you sleep with him?'

She licked her lips which had gone dry. 'Is that relevant?'

He looked at her. 'You do, then.' He got up and came and stood behind her chair. 'And what is your pillow talk, Miss Carlyle?'

'Is that your business?'

He bent down and put his mouth close to her ear. 'If it involves ideas that are forbidden, it is.' He returned to his seat. 'What are your boyfriend's politics?'

Her dry lips were giving her trouble and her heart was thumping. 'I have no idea.'

'That's a stupid answer. If you are involved with someone you will know.'

'He's a musician and that's what occupies him. He hasn't time for politics.'

Don't say too much.

'Does he approve of how the State handles the economy?' He reached down, opened the briefcase at his feet and took out a Hershey bar. He placed it beside the telephone on the table. 'Do you know this is forbidden capitalist chocolate? It was found in the rucksack you were carrying.'

She glanced at it. 'It's not mine.'

He shook his head gently. 'Best not to contradict. Where did you get it from?' Laure was silent. 'I think it was given to you by your boyfriend who obtained it illegally from the Tuzex store.'

'Do you mean those shops that only the elite can shop in?'

He did not blink. 'There's no point in being rude, Miss Carlyle. Or childish.'

365

'I'm sorry.' She forced herself to think clearly. 'Anyone can walk into a Tuzex then?'

'Indeed. All are welcome. But not everyone is entitled to Tuzex crowns with which to shop in them, and certainly not your boyfriend, which means he must have obtained the money on the black market. Engaging with the black market is considered an imprisonable offence.' Laure widened her eyes and fought for calm but, the experienced bully that he was, he detected her growing unease. 'If you think about it, it's just. The average wage is 3,000 crowns a month. Some of these black marketeers are making anything up to 250,000 crowns a month.'

'I can't comment on that,' she answered. 'But the chocolate isn't mine and he didn't give it to me.'

He folded his hands and looked benignly at her over them. 'Oh dear.'

By now, the room's lack of ventilation was telling on her and she found herself hoping desperately for Petr Kobes to arrive. 'Are you going to interrogate me for having a bar of chocolate?'

'My dear girl, is this an interrogation? I'm just asking some questions, that's all.'

Cleverly done. The chocolate had been planted and she might be able to argue them around to accepting that it was not hers. However, having admitted she only saw him two or three times a week, she knew she could not prove that Tomas had not bought black-market 'bony' in order to spend it at the Tuzex.

Wasn't there a protocol on which she could call? She wondered if she could demand for someone to come from the British Consulate. Was there a British Consulate in Prague?

At that moment, the telephone rang. A blaring, discordant intrusion into the near silence and it made Laure jump out of her skin. Major Hasík picked up the receiver, said his name and listened. 'I understand,' he said and put down the phone. 'I'm afraid your employer has been detained, which means we'll have to keep you until he is able to come.' He managed to look regretful.

She shot to her feet. 'Keep me where?'

He looked even more regretful. 'Here.'

She said desperately, 'I would like to contact someone from the British Consulate or Embassy. This can't be legal.'

Major Hasík smiled. 'My dear girl, the British will have all gone home for the night. And you are subject to Czechoslovakian law if you are living in Prague. We are offering you the highest justice.'

She blinked. 'Did I hear that correctly? The highest justice? You can stuff that.'

Major Hasík sat quietly with his hands folded neatly on the table top.

'But I'm a British national. They will come.'

'The British like their nine to five. So, I don't think so.'

'But you can't lock people up because of a bar of chocolate. It's ridiculous.'

'Did I say that was the case?' Major Hasík placed the chocolate bar, which was in danger of melting, back in his briefcase. 'No, we are keeping you here for another reason.'

'But *what* then?

He stood up and loomed above her. 'How remiss of me not to mention it. You and your friends have been arrested for the crime of an organized disturbance of the peace.' Again, he smiled. 'That's quite a separate matter. And a serious one.'

There were no spare cells available and, she was informed in sign language by the bully blond guard, she was to remain in the room. After a while, she fetched the second chair and managed to stretch out.

Her eyes were heavy with exhaustion and her head ached. If she was truthful, she was terrified and longed for sleep. She had just managed to fall into a doze when the telephone shrieked. The shock of it almost knocked her off her chair.

It went silent.

But not for long.

Throughout that long, foetid night, as she struggled to sleep, it rang. Every hour or so, shrilling for seven or so rings before falling silent.

. She had never hated anything as much before, and doubted she would hate anything as much in future, as the sound of that telephone.

Towards 5 a.m., nauseous and dizzy with anxiety, she hauled herself upright. If they were doing this to her, what were they doing to the others?

The door opened. She shut her eyes and grasped the side of the chair with her hands, willing herself to be calm and clever about what was coming next.

She opened her eyes. The bully blond guard stood over her. He reached over and twisted a lock of her hair between finger and thumb and said something in Czech. Hauling Laure to her feet, he inserted his hands under her T-shirt and ripped it apart. A grin spread over his face – greedy, intent and frightening.

'Stop it, please.'

Encircling her body with one arm, he reached with the other hand for his trouser belt and unbuckled it.

Laure screamed and dug her elbow hard into his torso. He released his grip and bent over which gave her an opening to whip around the other side of the table. His trousers sagged around his knees, revealing his engorged penis.

Again she screamed, which succeeded in enraging him. Grabbing his trousers, he charged at Laure.

She was slammed against the wall, her head hitting it with a crack. He pinioned her with a leg between hers and wrenched open her jeans and hauled them and her knickers down to her knees.

His fingers scrabbled between her legs, jabbing and poking. She felt his finger forcing its way up and the pull and tear of her resisting flesh.

She gasped, seized his hair and yanked as hard as she could. In response, he pushed her legs wider and threw her to the floor. Straddling her, he dragged her jeans and knickers off and slammed his body between her legs.

It would only take a couple more seconds and he would get what he wanted. His penis was rammed against her thigh. A hand grasped her chin and forced her head painfully to one side. He got ready by raising himself onto his elbows – and thrust into her.

The pain. The disgust. The terror.

She heard herself moan aloud.

With a superhuman effort, she threw herself onto her side, pulled at the telephone cord hanging down from the table and brought the telephone crashing down.

It landed a blow on his shoulder. For a second he was stilled – and she thought she might have a won a reprieve. Then he roared out something incomprehensible but the import was plain enough. Grabbing the telephone, he brought it down hard on her head.

A shower of neon-yellow sparks fountained across her vision. A crack sounded in her ears, it was followed by a floating sensation and, somewhere far away, pain. In the background, she heard Petr issue the command. 'Stop.'

Laure rolled over onto her stomach, jarring every bone in her body. Sighed. Then, everything was black.

In his room in the Můstek house, Tomas was cradling her softly and tenderly. They were lying on the mattress and Kočka was perched on the ledge where the sun came through the window.

'And?' he said.

The side of her head was badly bruised, and her body ached from head to foot,

It was still an effort to talk. 'Petr Kobes arrived as the guard hit me and got me out. He stopped ...' she struggled not to cry. 'Stopped him. Finishing... He never...' she looked at him. 'You know.'

Petr insisted that she was examined by a doctor who had pronounced her injured but not seriously. 'I am so sorry. I am so sorry,' he repeated more than once, every line of his body conveying his extreme shame and distress.

Petr could have said: *I warned you*, a temptation that he avoided, for which Laure was grateful. But he did dissuade her from contacting the British Consul close by in the Thunovská. 'I know you're angry, Laure, but it would be best, and kind of you, if you don't stir up trouble.'

In the circumstances, the word 'kind' was odd, but she took it to mean that it would be easier for her, as well as the Kobes, if everything was kept quiet. He stood in the doorway of her bedroom. 'That's my advice,' he said. 'I've sorted things out with the powers that be.'

He had taken a step into the room. Instinctively, Laure brought the sheet up to her chin and he came no further. 'Eva and I are so sorry and apologize for what has happened to you.' He was genuinely upset. 'We can deal with the children and you must spend the day in bed.' He turned to leave the room. 'One thing. This time I managed to protect you. The next time I won't. Do you understand?'

'Won't be able to? Or, don't wish to?'

'I leave you to work that out.'

Laure stirred in Tomas's embrace. 'And where were you in the prison?'

'Down the corridor. I heard your scream and me and the boys set up such a row, they had to do something. Kobes did the rest and they let us go with the warning that there would be no more concerts and they would be watching.' He looked down at Laure. Her shock and fright had overpowered her and the tears rolled non-stop down her cheeks. 'Tell me more.'

'It's difficult...' Every time she opened her mouth, her brain froze.

'It's good to talk about it.' He used his thumb to wipe away a tear. 'Believe me. I know. It's the way to survive.' He was whispering to her, willing the trauma to subside. Or, at least, to become something she could live with.

She closed her eyes. 'You told me once that to survive is our duty. Remember?'

Her nose was running.

'Good girl. My loved Laure. Now, tell me and it will leave your chest.'

'Get it off my chest, you mean.'

It was a small room, furnished with a table and two chairs facing each other.

There is no window in the shot. A black Bakelite phone, the squat old-fashioned type with a cumbersome dial and plaited cording occupies centre table. The cheap plastic chairs are embossed with cigarette burns, and the floor is of rough planking. There are no indications as to where the room might be.

'He smelt. He hurt me… he really hurt me and I don't know if I can let anyone touch me again.'

She tried not to concentrate on the physical details. She must not remember the crack of her head on the wall, his finger brazenly, disgustingly inside her. Or the tear of her flesh. She must tell herself, over and over, that it could have been worse and she was here, with Tomas.

She roused herself sufficiently to ask, 'Which prison was it?'

'The Bartolomějská.' He slid her arm under her body and shifted her gently, carefully, into a more comfortable position. 'It used to be a convent until the nuns were booted out. Think of that, my lioness.'

'God,' she declared faintly, 'was not there.'

'I'll never forgive those fuckers,' said Tomas.

A little while later, he said. 'Now, you know, Laure. You *really* know.'

Her torpor lifted. 'Tomas. If this is what happens… your future… come with me. You could have a life.' She watched his expression and was dismayed to see a zealot's light in his eyes. 'A life,' she repeated. 'Is that not a good aim?'

'This is my life, Laure.'

She didn't care if she made him angry and tried again. 'You're frightened that you'll be a nobody.'

'That's probably true,' he admitted disarmingly. 'But whatever my motivation, good, bad or weak, here I stay.'

CHAPTER 27

$\mathcal{A}$ COUPLE OF WEEKS LATER, LAURE WALKED FROM THE
Kobes' apartment to the marionette theatre in time for the late
matinee. Her head ached and her skull still felt like eggshell but
the bruises across her legs and torso were fading from purple to
yellow.

Of course she was being tailed. A commonplace happening now
and part of her Prague life.

Carrying her rucksack, she picked her way across the square,
her thoughts a messy confusion.

Interrogation. Violence. Terror.

How did one process them?

Milos was on the door and prevented her from entering. 'You
need a permit.'

It had been a warm day and, at first, she wondered if the beer
he was necking had gone to his head. 'Is something happening?'

'We're on strike so no performance,' he said with a look that was
both conspiratorial and wary. 'Lucia was going to contact you to
tell you not to come.'

'Well, she didn't. So... dear Milos, let me in.' He produced a piece
of paper on which he wrote in purple ink: 'Permit to enter and exit'
in Czech and handed it to her.

She smiled at him and, as she knew he would, he sent her one of his cheeky grins back. 'What's going on?'

'People want to talk about ideas. The theatre is a useful place to gather. It's not wise but it's happening.'

Backstage was packed with unfamiliar faces, including a man standing guard to the Green Room in a combat jacket and his hair tied back in a ponytail.

In the passageway, the cracked mirror reflected a to-ing and fro-ing of figures holding sheaves of paper and clipboards. In the tiny dressing room, the normally neatly stacked masks and black clothing had been swept aside for ashtrays and beer bottles. The fug was appalling.

'What ideas?' she asked Milos who had followed her in.

'There are no ideas,' he replied. 'And you are not seeing anything. OK?' He wagged a finger at her, more serious than she had ever seen him.

'OK.' She agreed. 'I don't see anything.'

She spent the next hour tidying up from a previous performance and was stowing the marionettes on their pegs when Milos reappeared. He sat down at the table and took up a sheet of black paper and scissors. 'Stand still.'

'Why?' But she did as she was asked.

'Turn your face to the door.'

The scissors scrunched into the paper and he set about making one of his silhouettes. She had observed him at it before and knew that each minute adjustment in the way he directed the scissors would result in miraculous likenesses.

His English was fluent tonight. 'You have a good face for this.' He made a long cut. 'And a swan neck. And hair like a river.'

'A river.' Laure giggled with pleasure. 'Thank you. How long do

I have to stay like this?' She touched the sore place on her head.

'As long as it takes.'

It wasn't long. Within fifteen minutes Milos presented her silhouette. It was rather good. Better than rather good. 'Thank you.' She scrutinized it, curious to see if the changes she was aware had taken place in her were obvious. Same nose. Same-shaped head. Hair a little longer.

'You can't keep it,' he said. 'Someone else wants it.' He tapped his finger to his nose and Laure found herself grinning like a clown.

'Can I have the one you've done of the "someone" in exchange?'

'I'll stick it in your rucksack. It's one of my better ones. Take care of it.'

After a while, Laure's curiosity got the better of her and she let herself into the area behind the stage where the puppeteers stood for performances and peered over the backdrop.

People were filtering in ones and twos into the auditorium which had become an inferno of cigarette smoke, sweat and beer fumes. Several girls with headbands onto which had been stencilled the Czech word for 'Freedom' were sitting on the floor. A man in dirty jeans and a white T-shirt dictated into a machine. Another strummed a guitar and sang 'We Shall Overcome'. A heap of wilting flowers lay in one corner. Someone had tacked a poster depicting the cartoon of a large disembodied ear onto the wall.

Milos was at her elbow. 'You're not seeing anything at all, Laure.'

'No, I'm not seeing anything.' She congratulated herself that she understood the code. 'What does the banner which I am not seeing mean?' She pointed to the back of the auditorium where a sheet with a slogan painted onto it had been tacked up on the wall.

He took a little time to translate. 'Is 1986 the Year of the Truncheon? Don't Wait. Act to stop it.'

'And the ear?'

'It's meant to make fun of the state who listens. But in the wrong way. The person who drew it has been in hiding. It's his most famous bit of work.'

It was both funny and disgusting – the ear itself had bristly hairs growing out of it and the penmanship was savage. Powering its pen strokes was a bitter humour that suggested, to Laure at least, depression. 'So,' she said, 'if language is misused, the image is more powerful.'

'That's what we are about,' said Milos. 'The government lies with its false words. We reply in a different way.'

Looking fired up and dressed in her puppeteering subfusc, Lucia arrived. She shucked off her shoulder bag and let it fall with a thump to the floor.

Laure looked away. 'Tomas?'

'Lucia's forbidden him to come,' Milos answered. 'Everyone in Anatomie should lie low.'

'Do the authorities know about the meeting?'

Milos looked at her thoughtfully. 'Who knows, but it's happening.'

He put his hand on Laure's shoulder and she felt his breath on her cheek. Her heart thumped with solidarity, affection and excitement. 'Be careful, Milos.'

'But you too.'

Close to the tears that had dogged her since her beating up, she hugged him. He pressed her to him tightly. She winced but she didn't mind. Soldier and *campanero*. 'I can't do without you.'

After he had returned to the green room, she picked up her rucksack, slipped into the auditorium and settled herself at the back by the exit. Her head felt mushy. The virus that was fear pulsed through in her bloodstream.

376

Lucia came over and hunkered down beside Laure. 'Tomas told me about what happened.' She had outlined her eyes with kohl and looked both exotic and impressive. 'I warned you about getting involved.'

No one could fail to be impressed by Lucia, thought Laure. Even if one disliked her and she was not sure that she could dislike a woman who was a pretty good Joan of Arc.

'You must get out of this country. You're now a focus and it's not good for us.'

Laure touched her sore head. 'Even if I have the wounds?'

'Especially if you have the wounds.' She got to her feet. 'There's too much that you could compromise.'

Should she, asked the small voice in her head, *escape?*

Around eight-thirty, Tomas walked in, guitar in hand. He was recognized and there was a muttered cheer. Lucia looked aghast, grabbed him and gave him what for. Tomas grinned.

He walked over to Laure and slipped his hand inside the waistband of her trousers and pulled her to him. She leant against him, feeling every bone against hers. He nuzzled her neck and she inhaled his smell which she so loved. 'Is it safe?'

'No. And?'

Milos emerged from the green room bearing plates of sandwiches that had been shipped in from nearby cafes. These were handed around and the audience sat on the benches and floor to eat. Tomas settled on the floor and pulled Laure down beside him.

The lights dimmed. The yellow curtains whisked back.

'Oh,' said Laure.

The Pierrot prince and Lucia, his puppet master, faced the audience. Marionette and master were yoked together but, she now realised, she had been mistaken in assuming the puppet master

377

possessed the power. The centre of gravity belonged to the Pierrot and always had done.

The violin struck up, its sensuous, lustrous, grief-stricken notes paving the way. Pierrot stood up to confront his Gethsemane and began his journey to his death.

The wooden limbs were molten with feeling. He was an innocent and, yet, this Pierrot knew everything. He was telling of suffering, of oppression, of loving, martyrdom and of death-in-life. He was baring his soul.

He plucked out the first string. Look at me. To be a resistant you must first know despair.

Only inches behind him, his puppet master was forced to metamorphose from manipulator to impotence. If he, Pierrot, was to look down into the whistling abyss, so must Lucia.

'Don't cry,' said Tomas in her ear. 'It's a good thing. He refuses to give in to the master. He refuses to be mastered. He chooses annihilation. He chooses freedom even if it means death.'

She turned her face into his chest and wept uncontrollably. Tomas stroked her hair. 'But... remember the Pierrot comes back each time. He is us. He is us together.'

She spread out her hand and felt for the heartbeat under Tomas's pale skin and narrow ribcage.

The curtains shut and what remained of Pierrot vanished.

Speeches were being made. A tall, dark-haired girl was declaiming with emphatic gestures. She was followed by several others equally fervent. The speeches came to an end and Lucia unrolled a film screen in front of the stage.

'Listen to me,' said Tomas above Laure's bent head. 'The world will survive whoever is in power. But let's understand we don't need prophets. What we need is decency and honour. And work.'

A projector was switched on.

'Forbidden film,' Tomas explained.

The first fuzzed frames were projected onto the make-shift screen and included mug shots of a smiling Dubček, the politician who had tried to liberalize communism in 1968. Cheers went up. Tomas translated the commentary for Laure. The Russians piled on the pressure for Czechoslovakia to conform and tried to shoot his reforms to pieces before sending in the tanks. The shots from a later period showed Dubček looking haggard and tearful.

The sandwiches were circulating and disappearing fast. Laure reached out to snaffle one – and froze. 'Tomas,' she dug her finger into his thigh. 'Don't look but there's police in the doorway.'

A figure in the now familiar green uniform had taken up a stance in the doorway. Behind him stood several other uniformed figures who were propping up a sagging figure.

'How many?'

'Seven?'

Tomas did not miss a beat. 'Get out. Now. Climb over the railing into the next garden.'

Lucia tried to rip down the screen and fractured shots of the increasingly dejected Dubček played on. A policeman stepped forward and snapped off the projector.

The policemen dragged their captive into the auditorium. 'Oh my God,' said Laure. 'Leo.'

Leo raised his head. He had been beaten up and badly. The fair hair was dirty and matted with blood. A rogue stream of it ran down his cheeks. But he was alive. He raised his arms into the air and it became worse, far worse. A groan was forced from the onlookers close to him. His hands were a broken, bloody pulp.

A woman screamed.

For the first time since she had known him, Tomas's expression resembled Pierrot's staring into the abyss.

The lead policeman assessed the scene. His gaze lighted on Tomas and Laure and satisfaction spread over the flat features.

Tomas melted away as the policeman moved over to Laure. 'Name?' he asked in Czech.

She hesitated.

'Name?' he repeated.

She gave it. He produced a notebook and made her write it down and moved away.

'This is what the pigs have done,' cried Leo in English, the man of few words. 'They have taken everything from me.'

The policeman grasped Leo by the wrists and he called out in pain.

'You go,' hissed Tomas in her ear.

An unthinkable scenario flashed through Laure's mind. 'Not without you. They'll kill you this time.'

Leo was thrown down onto a bench, struggled to stay upright and slid to the floor. His blood splashed around him.

A chaotic, churning scene unleashed. Many of the gathering were now on their feet. The defiant ones shook their fists and shouted at the uniformed men. Some sidled for the door. Some slid down to the floor and refused to move.

Laure summoned every power she possessed and might ever possess. She grabbed her rucksack and pulled Tomas towards the door opening into the garden. 'If you don't come too I'll give myself up.'

For a spilt second, he was irresolute. Then, he took the decision and pushed Laure out of the garden door. 'Run.' She didn't need to be told twice. As she sped past the sundial, she smashed her hand on its rough stone. The impact made her fingers go numb.

Tomas hopped over the railing and helped Laure scramble after him.

Sirens blared, orders issued and booted feet sounded on the cobbles. Inside the theatre the mayhem was punctuated by shouts and screams.

Tomas knew the route which told Laure he must have thought about it. They snaked along the edge of the wall and scrambled in and out of a couple of gardens and made for a cast-iron gate at the end of a terrace. It opened into an alley. 'Put your arm around me,' he ordered, 'don't hurry.'

She gasped for breath. Extraordinarily, she felt exhilarated and defiant. Those bloody pigs would not get them.

Making a superhuman effort, she slung her arm around Tomas.

Tomas was pouring with sweat. So was she.

They sauntered down the alley, turned left at the bottom and then sharp right into Zelezná. Tomas dropped his arm and guided her into a covered alley which gave them some camouflage.

'Where are we going?'

'I don't know yet,' he said. 'But it's probably the end for you and me.' She cried out and he touched her cheek. 'You know that.' In the distance, the sirens were blaring.

In places, the shadows thrown by the arches were dense and the badly maintained cobbles impeded progress. *Secret Prague*. Hiding in it was no longer diverting or playful, but crucial.

They emerged into the Kožná. 'Go back to the Kobes,' said Tomas. 'Pretend you don't know anything.'

'The goon took my name and Petr will be told. He wants to get back to Paris and needs to keep in with the Party. He told me he wouldn't help out again.'

Tomas came to a halt. 'You must leave the country, then. Tomorrow. I can't help you, Laure. I wish, I wish I could.'

She had already worked that out. 'I'll go to the British Embassy.' She wrapped her uninjured hand around his damp neck and forced him to look at her. 'You *must* leave, too.' She peered at him. 'Yes? *Yes.*' He seemed to be listening. 'Leo is the warning. They'll smash you up too. But if you survive, you can return, Tomas. One day. Nothing lasts.' He frowned, and she whispered, 'Look at history.'

He drew her into the shadow of the wall. 'I love it when you're the expert.' He looked up at the evening sky and she watched him greedily while he came to a decision.

'Think,' she urged. 'Don't be a martyr. You're no use if you're dead.'

His eyes met hers and she saw the change in them. 'There *are* ways. Milos knows about them. He has them ready for any of us who need them.'

'He's told me about them.' Cradling her swelling hand, she took short breaths to alleviate the pain. 'So you *were* thinking about it.'

'We all think about it. It's a way of keeping sane. But it's the last, last resort.' He spoke with great tenderness. 'If I do this, I need to get the papers, which will take a few days. I'll have to hide. Milos will have told you about the train from Prague to Vienna on Tuesdays.' As he sometimes did, he used his thumb to smooth the frown from her forehead. 'The guard on the Tuesday train can be bribed. But you must do something for me.'

'Anything.'

'Kočka.' Tomas swallowed. 'Get word that...' There was desperate sadness. 'Get word that he should be taken to the vet. The money for it is in the clock on the wall. He's too old. He won't thrive without me. We've been through too much together.'

She smothered her own tears. 'I'll do it.'

'Listen.' Tomas was keeping a weather eye on who was in the street. 'Gmünd ... repeat the name.' She did so. 'Gmünd is the boundary station on the Austrian border and the most dangerous point. The station after Gmünd is where you should pick me up. Give me a day's grace just in case.'

She realized then that he *was* going to be with her.

'You must be so silent on this. Not a word.'

That was easy. 'Of course. Never.'

He looked over her shoulder. 'Things can be got out of you.'

She inhaled a shuddering breath.

'Don't listen to what anyone might say about me. Do you understand? Promise me?'

She laid her hand against his cheek, feeling the heat of his skin warm hers. 'Of course.'

A mother with a baby in her arms was plodding towards them. Her grey cotton skirt had a large wet stain on the lap area. The baby was crying, and she was preoccupied and weary. As she passed, she glanced at them before moving out of sight.

'I'll be there, waiting. Waiting for you. For as long as it takes.' Wincing, she scrabbled in her rucksack. 'Do you need money? Take this.' She thrust notes into his hand. 'Will you have the clothes, the right papers?'

'Milos knows the right seat to book, the right station, what to say.'

'I hope your name won't be Wilhelm.' She was snatching at a straw. 'I refuse to love a Wilhelm. It should be Viktor for Victory.'

There was both too much, and too little, to say.

In the distance, a church bell chimed and the sound of additional police sirens.

'My God. Every single policeman in Prague must be on this one.' He looked down at Laure. 'It was knowing you, Laure, that tipped the balance.'

To her shame, she felt a wild surge of joy.

'It was bad enough not being allowed to study at university, or to travel, or to join a library. But it was deal-able with. I knew the game and I played it. Like all of us. But when you came along, I understood what it was to be unfettered.' He kissed her. 'I'm paying you the best compliment when I say that you will not really know what I'm talking about.'

'Where will you go?' she asked, desperately staving off the goodbye.

'There's a safe house. I'll be there until the papers are done.' He sounded very wry. 'We think it's run by the British.'

'How will I know?'

'You won't. Whatever you do, don't say anything to anyone.'

Could the sun spool back on the sundial in the garden? That way miracles happened and the portion of time that contained the Tomas of this moment could be smoothed of its dangers and traps. Believe, she told herself. Believe – like those who built the city's ridiculously ornate churches believed – and Tomas would be safe.

She glanced over her shoulder. 'What else did you want?'

He hesitated. Eventually, he slid off his waistcoat, tore at the seam at the back and pulled out a document. 'It's a list of names that will be interesting to the West. Profiteers. Businessmen. Party members who could be turned. We've collected them over the years, often at some cost.'

She looked at the paper and a dreadful disappointment opened up. 'So you *were* using me.'

He grasped her chin and made her look at him. 'What do you think?'

Hungrily, she searched his face. Was he… did he? What could she believe?

He slid his hand under her T-shirt and cupped a breast. 'For memory,' he said. His hand rested on her hot flesh and the sirens shrieked.

He seemed slighter and thinner than ever. More vulnerable. More determined. Her rock god. 'If only you knew, Laure.' She lifted her hand to his face. 'Oh my God, your hand,' he said. 'I have to go,' and bending over he kissed her hard.

Then he was off, leaving Laure dizzy with the pain of goodbye and doubt.

Petr would be notified that a banned meeting had taken place at the marionette theatre and they would give her name to him.

Therefore, she had only a few hours.

Go carefully. Move as if she was someone who had responsibilities and purpose and was being brisk about it. But no faster.

Do not get stopped.

Laure's recently acquired tics went into overdrive. Check out the shadows. Use the alleyways. Double back if worried.

Her hand throbbed and burned, which was helpful as fighting it diverted her panic about the next move. Eva and the two children were having an early supper with a family friend and Petr had agreed to pick them up in the limousine at 6.30 p.m. and to bring them back.

In and out before they arrived back.

Reaching the Kobes' apartment without incident, she went straight to the family bathroom. It was in its usual state of untidiness.

Eva's medication was stacked carelessly on a shelf. Petr's shaving stuff beside it. The towels had not been hung up and the bath needed a clean. She did not give the mess a second thought but raided the first-aid cabinet. Aspirin to help her to think straight and the bandage, which Maria had used for a cut knee and still bore a faint bloodstain, to bind her hand.

It was ten past six, and the phone rang in the hall. She did not answer it.

In her room, she sank onto the bed.

Think.

Working clumsily, she positioned the document along the underside of her wrist and bandaged up her hand, making sure it was hidden, and safety-pinned it tight. The watery red smudge on it gave it verisimilitude.

She was light-headed. Again. Shocked. Again. She had fallen into a trap of false optimism. *And all manner of things should be well.* This was a city impregnated with spirits and demons and they played a tormenting game with ingenues.

How did one pray?

Pray she must – to those demons and spirits of Prague. Pray, too, that her faith was justified.

She sat on her bed and worked out the best options. First, pack the rucksack with the things she could not bear to abandon. The hand mirror. Milos's silhouette. To these she added basic clothing and what money she still possessed. Her passport, of course.

She would leave behind the photograph taken of her by Vaclav at a rock concert in Kinsky Gardens (too incriminating if she was hauled in) and, except for what she stood up in, her clothes, including the Parisian dress.

And she would leave behind the old Laure.

Rucksack packed, she was opening the front door when the family clattered in. Dropping the rucksack onto the floor, she kicked it into the corner. 'I heard you coming,' she said.

'I knew you'd be waiting,' said Jan.

The children twined their limbs around hers, and she hugged them both with her good arm. They smelt of a cheap pop drink, the residue of which stained Maria's mouth.

Eva had been crying but she said, 'We had such a good time.' The distant look was back, and she moved painfully slowly. 'But I must go to bed now.'

'How are you?' said Petr. 'Head OK?'

She told him she was fine.

'No, you're not. What have you done to your hand?' He lifted it up for inspection and she flinched and cried out. He parted her fingers to examine them. 'Can you move them? If you can't they might be broken.'

'I fell on them when I left the theatre. It's just bruising.'

He put his head on one side. 'You fell, you said?'

'Yes.'

'Must have been a nasty fall. Wait in the sitting room, I'll bring you something.'

She did as she was told and heard him shooing the children into their bedrooms with instructions to undress. She glanced down at her hand lying in her lap. Two of the exposed fingers were swollen to twice their size and a purple bruise mottled her thumb.

Petr entered with a glass of brandy. 'Drink.'

She did as she was told and took a grateful mouthful.

He sat down beside her. 'You'd better tell me.'

His proximity felt menacing. She closed her eyes and it flashed back.

The finger inside her… somehow so much worse than the penis. The pain of her hand. The terror and the disgust. The humiliation of her half-naked body.

The telephone rang. Petr raised a questioning eyebrow. 'Should I answer it?'

'Let's enjoy the brandy.'

It rang for half a minute. From her bedroom, Eva shouted, 'Stop it!'

'She doesn't like the noise,' said Petr.

The telephone went silent.

'Next time,' said Peter, 'and there will be a next time, I must answer it before it makes Eva feel worse.'

She arranged her hand on her thigh. 'I am going to leave,' she said. 'I'm sorry.'

It alarmed her that he didn't seem more surprised. 'Are you going back home? You must let me arrange your ticket back to England.'

Thumps could be heard in the other room. The children were playing tag.

'Yes. No, that's very kind but not necessary.'

'Where then? Have you got a new job?'

'Actually, I have.'

'You didn't think that I could be trusted to protect you?' That was the first admission that she had had from Petr of his influence behind the scenes. He spoke with authority and she wondered what it had taken to achieve that inner certainty. 'When a country reaches a certain maturity, it is prepared to tolerate some dissent. Rock concerts being among them. It's a question of how they are handled.'

She cradled her hand. 'I want to thank you and Eva. You've been very generous…'

How long before the telephone rang? Five minutes? Three?

'... I hope you feel that I was of use to you and the family.' She licked her lips which had gone dry. 'To Eva.'

Petr's stillness was alarming. 'I thought better of you,' he said eventually. 'It's no light thing to leave an employer in the lurch. Especially when they have been good to you.'

She knew she was blushing. 'I thought it would be best. I know I've caused you trouble. You made that clear after... you rescued me and I don't want to do that again.' Experimentally, she touched a swollen finger. 'You see, I'm not giving up my right to independent thought.'

'No,' he agreed, a shade contemptuously.

Petr Kobes: the weak party *apparatchik* that Tomas considered he was? The sword and shield of the system? A family man maintaining an impossible balancing act?

How would the tally read in the future?

'And your arrangements? The documents, etc.?'

'I imagine there are flights? Or I could take the train which would be easier.'

'A train. Where to? Paris? Belin? Vienna? And when?'

'As soon as you and I have agreed,' she improvised.

He shifted position, and she caught a whiff of superior power, of satisfaction at partial information capture, and thought: *why did I say that?* 'I can't let you go for at least a month. We need to find a replacement.'

Unwisely, she clenched her hand – and the responding intense pain drove everything else out of her mind. 'That's not possible. I said I'd be at my new position very soon.'

'I see.'

Having been sensitized and irradiated by her own recently discovered responses, she heard something deeper and disturbing in his tone.

Jealousy and disappointment.

'He was using you, Laure.' He allowed her a moment to digest what he was saying. 'There's evidence. I was going to spare you but...' He got up, went over to the bureau and extracted a folder.

'I *know* Tomas.'

He pushed a photograph in front of her. 'Did you know, then, about the American?' She glanced down. The image was blurred but it was of Tomas with his arm around a tall blonde standing on the riverbank. 'A nice girl. Beautiful girl. She had to be sent back home.' He shrugged. 'Same tactics.'

She turned her head away.

The paper scratching against her wrist was a reminder of how little she did know – and a lifetime of future doubt began its determined muster at the back of her mind.

Somehow, she must fight herself. 'Lie to me as much as you wish. It won't make a difference.'

'You must know that you would never be together,' he said. 'There have been plenty of other women and it's never happened.' His words were soft and sincere. 'He was playing you, Laure.'

She said desperately, 'We will be together.'

'Together? He'll be coming with you?'

'A slip of the tongue,' she said.

Petr a kept the photo plumb in front of her. 'When is the start date for your new job?'

Tomas was looking at the camera but she, the girl, was gazing at him.

Her vision misted. What? How? When?

'When did you say?' Petr persisted.

What? How? When? 'Early next week.' Petr nodded and her heart thumped in terror. She had given him a piece of valuable

390

information. He gestured that she should stand up and she obeyed.

'You must tell me where you're going. Otherwise…'

'Otherwise?'

'This.' He grabbed her wounded hand and brought a karate chop down onto the forearm. Laure writhed with pain. 'And this,' he said. Bending over he pressed kisses onto her neck and crushed her against him in a brutal grip.

It was then she truly understood that Petr desired her.

Wrenching herself free, she managed to get out, 'I knew you were capable of many dishonourable things but never that.'

She couldn't read his expression. Regret? Tenderness? Breathing hard, he stood back. 'I'm showing you what will happen if you don't cooperate. It won't be me who does those things to you. It will be those other men. They won't spare you. They will hurt you until you pray to die, and then hurt you more. Believe me.'

She was trembling uncontrollably and Petr drove home his advantage. Grabbing her hand, he twisted it hard. 'This is what will happen. You will come out brutalized and raped.'

The pain drove the breath out of her. Eyes streaming, she doubled over and threw up the brandy. 'Sorry,' she said, the vomit trickling over her chin and onto her T-shirt.

She eyed the door.

Mistake.

Petr placed himself between her and it. 'Do I give you up, or do you tell me what you know and let me deal with the situation?' He added, almost as an afterthought, 'No one polices the guards in those places, Laure. In a few minutes the phone will ring and I must have an answer. Where are you going?'

Laure gathered her wits. 'It's none of your business but I'm not staying in this country.'

391

'So you must have travel plans.'

He knew – precisely and with calculated strategy – how to draw out inferences from questions and answers.

The nausea returned and she clapped her hand over her mouth.

'Is he worth it, Laure?'

She looked away.

'I don't want to do this. But you force the issue.' Petr picked up the folder and held up a piece of paper in front of Laure. 'Do you know what this is?'

'I don't read Czech.'

'It's a certificate of marriage between Michelle Pitt and Tomas Josip, dated a year ago.'

Astonished, Laure stared at Petr. Despite her shock, she managed to say: 'You've been planning this.'

'I thought I should protect you.'

Strangely enough, Laure believed him. In his way, Petr did wish to protect her.

A succession of images sifted through her mind, as slow and luxurious as if she had all the time in the world. Brympton in the winter sunlight. Her arrival at Paris's Gare du Nord. The bedroom at the *chata*. Tomas half-naked and bruised, holding Kočka in his arms.

He had been lying.

This time, the pain which overwhelmed her was of a different order and it was one she didn't think she was capable of bearing. Or the revulsion that came with it.

Her brain shut down. Logic and reason vanished. In their place was jealousy of this unknown woman and a burning, vengeful anger.

Petr was observing her reactions. 'You're so young, Laure.' His

392

voice softened. 'When I saw you in that room in the Bartolomějská, I was agonized that all your sweetness and trust might have been beaten out of you.'

The world as she had perceived it had taken on a new shape. The certainties had gone. All she knew now was that she must flee this city of demons and repression and lies and pretence before she lost the ability to work out what was right or wrong, true or false. 'I've been offered a job in...' Her lips were too dry to articulate the words and she tried again. 'They want me to start as soon as...'

'Early next week,' intervened Petr, smoothly.

She struggled to make sense. 'I thought it best, after what happened after the concert. It's best for you and the family.'

'So, perhaps you are going to Paris by train?'

Silence.

'Berlin? I'm told you can look over the Wall in places from the West.'

He was assessing, weighing, measuring. Hints, probabilities, certainties, piecing them together with a mind trained to do so.

Silence.

'Vienna then?'

She dug a finger into her palm. It was only a tiny gesture but he noted it.

He pushed the paper under her nose.

Tomas is married?

Anguish and jealousy goaded her on into a dark place. 'Yes,' she said, after a moment.

Petr got to his feet. 'I'd better go and talk to my wife,' he said. 'Why don't you sit down again and finish the brandy?' He went out of the room.

Seconds later, he returned. 'Laure...' He looked almost grief-stricken. 'The marriage certificate was forged.' He shrugged. 'It's an old trick. I was taught it a long time ago.'

Mouth dry and tasting of vomit, she looked up at him. 'What...?'

'I'm sorry,' he said.

He disappeared.

She dashed for the wastepaper basket in the corner and was sick for the second time, regurgitating bitter, bitter guilt.

She had been duped and, idiot and unbeliever, she had fallen for it.

She heard the bedroom shut and their voices strike up behind it. Her hand holding the glass shook as she raised it to her lips and drained the lot which left her coughing and swimmy-eyed.

She put down the glass on the table, hoping it would not leave a mark. Stupid to be worrying about such things at this moment. Stupid to have been in the apartment when the family returned. Stupid to have been proved so shabby a spirit, so traitorous.

For the last time, her gaze slid over the room. The chandelier, the plastic chairs, the peeling paint. The beautiful proportions of the room. This was unreal. The sort of story that the marionettes would enact.

A girl is awakened by a handsome prince who carries her off and the wicked witches give chase.

The children had gone quiet. No doubt they were tired and had gone to their rooms. In the passage, Laure hovered outside their doors, wishing very much to kiss them goodbye.

Behind the close bedroom door, Eva cried out and began to sob.

In the hall, the phone rang.

Adrenalin blasted in and she picked up her rucksack.

Within a few seconds, she was down in the courtyard and heading out through the entrance. As she turned into the street, she glanced over her shoulder.

Petr was the window overlooking the courtyard, staring down into it.

She knew he knew she was there.

She couldn't be sure but, as she turned into the Malá Strana, she could have sworn he waved.

Her hand throbbed in time with her pounding feet.

If he loved her, he might give her a chance. *Them* a chance. He might hold what he knew.

What she had told him.

After a while, she slackened her pace. First stop: Tomas's apartment to see about Kočka.

Second stop: the British Embassy.

'Don't listen to what anyone might say about me.'

His voice was in her ear.

'Do you understand?'

'Promise me?'

But she had… listened …

CHAPTER 28

Paris, today

*T*HE MAISON DE GRASSE LUNCH HAD CREATED RIPPLES in the press and each party regarded the other with satisfaction.

It was all change for the museum: finances, positioning, the sponsorship.

'The requests for copies of your speech keep coming in,' Nic informed Laure when she walked into the office a couple of weeks later. 'And *what* have you got there?'

Laure set down the cat basket. 'A cat. No, *my* cat.'

'And?' said Nic.

'She's coming to live here. The vet thought it would be better. Not so confined as a flat. More room. When you've lived on the streets, you can't take being cramped.'

'At weekends?'

'She'll come home with me. I'll probably have to move unless I can strike a deal with the landlord.'

Nic peered into the basket at the scrawny, unglossy little form. 'She's no beauty.'

'Don't hurt her feelings. Her life has been bad enough.'

Nic watched as Laure unpacked various bits of equipment,

including a cushion. 'There's no room in here to… er… swing a cat, so where's that going?'

'On the ledge under the window where she can get the sun.'

'OK,' said Nic, unflappable to the last. He glanced at his screen. 'You have two interviews this morning. A man with a pink plastic violin and someone who refuses to give his name but swears he's not a murderer or a terrorist. Are you willing to take the risk?'

He sounded dispirited.

She leant back on her heels to look at him. 'You're missing May.'

As Laure had predicted, May had returned to the US to write up her pieces. Paris was expensive, she said, and she needed to earn her crust. She had been rueful and resigned and had not lingered over the goodbyes.

Laure had refrained from asking how things were left between her and Nic. Had he netted her in? His expression suggested not.

May had left an empty space. She had been nosy, mistaken, risky and fun, and her thin arms had been strangely comforting.

The nameless man turned out to be called John Irvins, a stocky, bearded youth. After the introductions, he placed a golf ball on the desk between him and Laure.

'Astic Company specializes in sourcing land for golf courses,' he began, an indignant flush visible around the facial hair. 'They bought up a swathe of land abutting our village, part of which was a bird sanctuary, and wanted to absorb the common land which had been left to the village in perpetuity. A big battle ensured.'

Laure had an idea of what was coming.

'The council was weak and cash-strapped. The villagers lost their fight and the golf course was built. However, we managed to extract the promise, which was put in writing, that no buildings would be built on the bird sanctuary. But as soon as the contract was signed off, the lorries arrives to put up a huge clubhouse on it.'

He spread out photos of wrecked nests, wrecked habitat and, worst of all, the bodies of fledglings whose parents had been killed during the development.

Irvins was sad and clearly angry at his and others' impotence in the matter. 'The common people had no rights. They were crushed and exploited by rich predators. This is capitalism at its worst, its most rapacious and most mendacious and there was nothing we could do about it. I would like to donate the golf ball to the museum...'

'Ah, capitalism,' said Laure, picking up the golf ball.

Later, when she was writing up her notes of the meeting, she heard Nic exclaim. 'What the—?'

Importing the almost visible wave of energy on which she customarily surfed into the room, May was poised in the doorway, holding out a tray of coffees. A trick of the light made the fair hair seem electric.

'What are you doing here?' If someone could frown and grin at the same time, Nic was that man.

May offered him the coffees. 'Anyone would think you weren't pleased to see me. However, I'm here on unfinished business.'

She turned to Laure. 'You asked me once what I would bring to the museum. Here's my answer.' She stood to one side and beckoned to someone outside the door.

'I deny absolutely that I come from a bourgeois background,' said a voice in thickly accented English.

A second figure was now framed in the doorway.

A tumult began in Laure's ears.

'But Spejbl...' she said trembling, her chair screeching over the floor. 'But Spejbl, your father was a well-known shop owner. You mustn't tell lies in front of visitors.'

Nic was staring at Laure as if she had gone mad.

The man was approximately Laure's age, dressed in a denim jacket and jeans. He had a set of white teeth, pepper-and-salt hair and a receding hairline that enlarged his forehead.

The teeth were very much in evidence as he smiled broadly. 'Don't you mean, don't tell lies in front of people you know. Visitors won't know if you are lying and, therefore, won't care.'

And she was there again, backstage at the marionette theatre, peering over the backdrop, on fire with lust, love and the joy of being part of a resistance.

Nic's face was a study as Laure steadied herself on the desk. 'Milos?' she asked. 'Milos, is it you?'

She put out her hands. He put out his and they clung together.

'A long time,' he said.

'Where? Where have you come from?'

'Prague. Your colleague here found me and ordered me to come. She doesn't understand the word "no".' He added, 'We can travel now, you know.'

'I know. I know.' To Nic's obvious consternation, Laure began to cry. Noisy, wrenching sobs.

May slid her arms around Laure and Nic said, 'I'm going to put the kettle on.'

Laure mastered herself sufficiently to ask, 'Are you well? Is your life OK?' She gestured to the chair. 'Please sit.'

They gazed at each other silently, mentally traversing the black holes and rocky terrain of their history.

'I am changed.' Milos spoke first. 'You not so much. Smarter and more beautiful. And you have this…'

'I have this,' she echoed. 'And you have?'

He was finding his feet in speaking English. 'A marionette theatre in Prague. I have a family. I married Lucia.'

Laure was dumbfounded. All she could think of to say was, 'I hope she wore the veil.'

'It was destroyed when the authorities shut down the theatre.'

'I want to know everything,' she said. '*Everything.*'

The noises of Paris could be heard through the open window. Cars, vans, the calls of the vegetable vendor.

'How did May find you?'

'Easy.' May laid a tentative hand on Nic's who snatched it up. 'After we talked, Laure, I flew to Prague – I do recommend it – and started with marionette theatres. Didn't take long. And here we are.' She paused. 'I owed you.'

'You didn't go home,' said Nic.

'No. Obv.' She placed a hand on her hip. 'Do I look as though I'm in New York?'

Good luck, Nic, thought Laure, with a lift of her heart. With the future. With the fact that May most definitely has the upper hand.

'I have something for you.' Milos reached down and placed a battered-looking package on the table. 'I have kept it for all these years. Just in case.'

She stared down at the package. Time did a backwards flip. She began to be aware of her skin, her breathing, her pulse.

Milos undid the parcel and the tissue paper parted like a bivalve to reveal a collapsed puppet, resembling nothing so much as a pile of bones in the ossuary.

The beat at Laure's temple intensified.

She registered a black cap, wooden outstretched hands, folded limbs, the face of a marionette, tangled sundered strings and uttered a cry. 'Pierrot.'

'Tomas instructed me that, if anything should happen to him, I was to get him to you,' said Milos. 'He was insistent about that. He said it would be the most important thing I could do.' He repeated, 'the most important thing…'

Laure was powerless to move.

'Tomas said you would know what he meant by sending him.'

Laure closed her eyes and hung onto the edge of the table.

Nic coughed. May stopped writing.

'He also said you were to promise to reattach the strings.'

As usual, Chez Prune was busy but Laure managed to get a table by the window and ordered a carafe of red wine.

It arrived with a plate of roasted nuts. Laure poured out the glasses and pushed one over to Milos. Together they raised them and drank a toast to Pierrot.

At first, they didn't talk much.

She clasped her hands on her lap. 'Tell me everything.'

Milos had already downed his wine and helped himself to a second glass.

After Laure fled, the theatre was closed down and everyone was scattered, he told her. Leo was eventually released from custody but his left hand had to be amputated. He was given a minor role in the new Czech republic. Manicki went to ground. Rumour had it he cut his hair and worked as a barber. Milos and Lucia got a bus south out of Prague and settled near Tabór where he set up a carpentry business and sat out the remaining days of the regime. He and Lucia had two children. After they had grown up, he and Lucia returned to Prague to set up the theatre.

'It's our one true love,' he said.

Laure held tightly onto her glass of wine. 'Did Lucia betray me?'

Milos detached her grip from the glass, set it down and took her hand. His was rough from years of labour but, as it had always done, felt safe in hers. She knew him of old and he knew her. It was enough.

'Yes. But she had her reasons. You must forgive her.'

'Is it Lucia asking for forgiveness?'

'No, I do. She's my wife.' The new teeth were disconcerting, but she was glad Milos had had them fixed. 'I am asking for her. Does she have it?'

She thought of her own Gethsemane. The dry earth of regret. The guilt. The punishment of never living through a bright, golden day without it.

Her grip tightened on his. 'Yes.'

'Then you must visit us in Prague and, maybe, we could sort out things between you two?' His smile faded. 'We could visit places and pay… our respects.'

'Yes,' said Laure. 'I would like that. Very much.'

Afterwards, they walked along the banks of the Canal Saint-Martin. It was now almost dark. The expensive boutiques were lit up. Someone had strung fairy lights across one of the iron-work bridges which only reached halfway across. The rough sleepers were cooking up meals where they could and securing their tents.

The water slapped companionably against the banks.

Laure stopped. 'And Tomas?' she asked, brittle with despair and dread.

Milos walked on a pace, turned and came back. 'Tomas is dead. They killed him, one way or another. You must know that.'

She was silent for a long time then she sighed.

'Always a tiny bit of me...' she said. 'Hoped. Prayed. That he had survived. I gave away the escape route because I was so angry. I'd been told that Tomas had married an American. I realised it was a lie but I couldn't unsay it.'

'Which American?' asked Milos. She told him and he shook his head. 'You're right. It was lies, Laure.'

'He warned me not to believe what they said about him. I failed.' She looked directly at Milos. 'In that crucial moment, I lost faith and it was enough.'

'But Lucia put the goons onto you,' said Milos, 'which resulted in the raid. Think about it. It was the system that exploited what we felt, what we did. A chain of small repressions, making a big one. Most people were guilty of tiny betrayals. It was the price of existing.' He spoke urgently. 'Laure, look at me. To survive, we have to believe that.'

'Can I forgive myself?'

'We have to.'

She thought about Tomas's last moments. In fear and, without doubt, in pain. She hoped he had kept his faith. *Please could he have kept his faith in his rightness.* Maybe, he summoned music to help him.

Maybe, maybe, towards the end he had thought of her once or twice?

Milos drew Laure's hand into the crook of his elbow and, together, they walked along the banks of the canal. 'I will string Pierrot for you,' he said. 'Before I leave.'

CHAPTER 29

*I*T IS EVENING AND THE TEMPERATURE IS PLUMMETING. ITS colours and vistas subtly altering, Paris is shedding its autumn coating.

Laure makes her rounds of the museum.

In her office, Kočka is ensconced on the ledge above the radiator and Laure puts out her food and cat litter tray for the night. Recently, Kočka has allowed Laure to kiss her and she drops one on Kočka's newly luxuriant fur.

Laure moves on, closing the shutters as she goes.

The rooms are still and quiet, the heating dying down for the night. In Room 7, Laure adjusts the frame containing the pillowcase and, in Room 3, brushes a coating of dust off a windowsill.

The lights are already switched off in Room 2 and all the objects, except for the bridal veil that glimmers faintly, are shrouded in the falling dusk.

She stands by the window. The lights pool across the rooftops and a couple of pigeons waddle across the roof tiles. A long time ago, she threw bread pellets at the Prague pigeons with Petr and she thinks of him now and of how he chose to pay his dues.

She is grateful.

'Go back to Alabama,' she urges May before she leaves with Nic for the evening. 'Go home soon and sort it out with your mother. You must not leave unfinished business unfinished.'

'Like you did,' May says.

'Like I did.'

This is her house. Her life.

The reverie is broken by a sound. She swings around.

Two stringed marionettes are hanging on the wall, close enough to be touching. The female marionette wears a veil and has a brown plait. The male has a black cap, a Pierrot costume and a freshly painted face.

Often, when the breeze filters in through the window, or an extra number of visitors go through the room, a draught is created and the marionettes sway and clack in response. Sometimes, it looks as though they are holding hands.

She stands in front of them and looks up into their faces. It's a constant source of astonishment how all-seeing their gaze, how tender and malicious their souls. To care for them is to cherish and to be cherished by them.

She raises a hand and places a finger on Pierrot's chest, searching for the heartbeat that is Tomas.

It's there.

So is forgiveness.

Her long path to consolation is traced.

Clack, I loved him.

Clack, he loved me.

ACKNOWLEDGEMENTS

$\mathcal{S}$OME YEARS AGO, OUR SON SENT US ON A LONG WEEKEND to Prague where we fetched up in the Museum of Communism. At that time, unlike its spanking and impressive home today, the artefacts were housed in a couple of rooms. But they left an indelible mark on me, including the black telephone in a small cell which rang when you stepped inside.

The novel is a direct result of that visit. However, I could not have written it without consulting many histories. I would like to single out Kevin McDermott's lucid and admirable *Communist Czechoslovakia, 1945–89* (Palgrave). Anyone wishing to get a handle on the complexities of that time could not do better than to read it. Also Ivan Klíma's *My Crazy Century, a Memoir* (Grove Press, UK), Timothy Garton Ash's *The Magic Lantern: The Revolution of '89 witnessed in Warsaw, Budapest, Berlin and Prague* (Vintage Books), *Under a Cruel Star: A life in Prague 1941–1968* by Heda Margolius Kovály (Granta) and the superb *Stasiland: Stories from Behind the Berlin Wall* by Anna Funder (Granta). I have taken facts, sentiments and scenarios from all of them. Any mistakes are mine.

I would like to thank my super-nova editor, Sara O'Keeffe, and the team at Corvus. Also my agent, Judith Murray, without whom none of this would be happening and Justine Taylor for her skilled, tactful and meticulous copy-editing. To my fellow novelists, Fanny Blake and Isabelle Grey, who have been on hand to mop the brow, I owe you much. Equally, the dear friends who visited on a regular basis, bearing medicaments and cheer, when shingles struck I will never forget. A big thank you to my sisters, Alison Souter and Rosie Hobhouse. To Jane Thynne, author of the bestselling Clara Vine novels set in Berlin, and Jim Mitchell, both experts on the city, who pointed me to the places to go I offer deep gratitude. If I have got anything wrong, I know you will let me know. However, I have invented a couple of extra streets around the Canal Saint Martin in Paris for the purposes of the novel. I hope I am forgiven.

I would also like to thank Barnaby of www.insidertour.com for his fascinating walk around Cold War Berlin. I was enraptured.

To Benjie, Adam and Lucinda, Eleanor and Henry, Alexia and Flora… you make everything worthwhile.